Karst Geomorphology

Karst Geomorphology

J.N. Jennings

Basil Blackwell

First published 1985

Basil Blackwell Ltd
108 Cowley Road, Oxford OX4 1JF, UK

Basil Blackwell Inc.
432 Park Avenue South, Suite 1505,
New York, NY 10016, USA

First edition, *Karst*, published 1971 by
Australian National University Press

British Library Cataloguing in Publication Data

Jennings, J.N.
   Karst geomorphology.—2nd ed.
   1. Karst
   I. Title
   551.4′47   GB600

   ISBN 0–631–14031–X
   ISBN 0–631–14032–8 Pbk

Library of Congress Cataloging in Publication Data

Jennings, J.N. (Joseph Newell)
   Karst geomorphology.

   Rev. ed. of: Karst. c1971.
   Bibliography: p.
   Includes index.
   1. Karst.   I. Jennings, J.N. (Joseph Newell).
Karst.   II. Title
GB600.J46 1985   551.4′47   84–21589
ISBN 0–631–14031–X
ISBN 0–631–14032–8 (pbk.)

Typeset by Katerprint Co. Ltd, Oxford
Printed in Great Britain by Bell and Bain Ltd, Glasgow

Contents

Contents

Professor J. N. Jennings
1916–1984

Joe Jennings completed this book just before he died of a heart attack while skiing. He was thus active to the end, both intellectually and physically. Born a Yorkshireman, he remained one all his life, even though he moved to Australia in 1952. From Yorkshire he gained his inimitable accent, his ebullience, pugnacity, generosity and humour, and also his appreciation of landscape. Although this book is devoted to karst landscapes his geomorphological interests went far wider, encompassing studies of the Norfolk Broads, sea-level change, dunes, lakes, glacial phenomena and many others. He produced over 200 papers and monographs, and researched into karst in the far corners of Antarctica, New Zealand, New Guinea and Malaysia, as well as in Europe, North America, the Caribbean and China. He attacked field work with relish, whether on the exposed surface of the Nullarbor or in the confines of the darkest caves.

He was a productive, meticulous, objective and catholic natural scientist who never sought, but frequently received, academic honours – a first class degree from Cambridge, the Back Grant and Victoria Medal from the Royal Geographical Society, a Professorial Fellowship at the Australian National University, the Presidency and Honorary Membership of the Institute of Australian Geographers, the W. B. Clarke Medal of the Royal Society of New South Wales, and numerous awards for his speleological endeavours, including Honorary Life Membership of the National Speleological Society of America.

Karstic studies will be the poorer for the passing of a man who combined amiability with a pronounced firmness of view, kindness with directness, and enthusiasm with scholarship. This book gives an insight into those qualities and demonstrates the breadth of his view and the internationalism of his commitment.

Peter Bull
Andrew Goudie

Publisher's Note

The publishers wish to express their gratitude to Professor Andrew Goudie and Dr Peter Bull for their invaluable assistance in preparing this book for publication and also to acknowledge the many offers of assistance and practical help received by them from the late J. N. Jennings's colleagues and fellow researchers.

Preface

Although my first edition of this book, published in 1971, was received kindly, advances in the last decade have been such that it has had to be rewritten, even though the scope and intended audience remain the same.

An introduction should be brief. Keeping within a modest frame required a more rigorous selection than before. I stand by my selection, but I must tell cavers, many of whom I hope will read this book, that this is not a physical speleology, and caves have had to assume their due place in a geomorphology of karst.

My intention is to interest the many rather than provide a treatise for the few. So as far as possible I have been content with proximate explanations in words and have avoided mathematical exposition and formulae, of which I should in any case make heavy weather. I have endeavoured to explain technical terms as they arise in the text, rather than refer the reader to a glossary. Also, I have tried to employ English terms to the maximum, though some of the foreign language equivalents in common use have been cited and a few used perforce.

A criticism of the previous edition was that the treatment of the uses of karst study in the final chapter said either too little or too much. Since then, practical and more comprehensible applications of both surface and underground karst have multiplied and diversified. The space needed for a satisfactory exposition of this applied side now seems too great for its inclusion, and I content myself with a blunt statement of its value here.

It is in relation to water supplies that karst study is most valuable – to the finding, storing and protecting of such supplies from pollution. This is most particularly the case where the need for water is greatest, as witness the efforts in this regard of Chinese karst scientists (Chinese Academy of Geological Sciences 1976; Yuan *et al.* 1979). The handling of water resources remains the prime economic spark for karst research today, as it was in the time of the French speleologist, Édouard Martel. Karst presents peculiar problems for engineers needing stable foundations for buildings, roads, railways, aerodromes and dams, in the last case as additional to the problem of reservoir leakage. Dam construction in the karst half of Yugoslavia has led to an amplification of investigatory techniques (Milanović 1979). The mining industry needs understanding of the functioning and evolution of karst with regard to both buried karst surfaces and palaeoaquifers, both likely sites for ore emplacement (Society of Economic Geologists 1971). In the present century caves have almost ceased to function as homes, working places and stores; instead, they have become major sites of tourism and recreation, as have spectacular surface features in karst. Management of karst for these purposes and for their scientific values is now a major task if it is to be done with due regard for conservation (Stitt 1977), and for that, management knowledge is the first requisite.

In the first edition of this book I explained that, because of the history of karst study, I had cited a much higher proportion of literature that was not Anglo-American in origin and language (140 items out of 341) than is usual for introductory works. If this time there are proportionately fewer citations from continental Europe, I trust my colleagues from those countries will understand the didactic reason for this. In the last decade British and North American speleologists have done quite a lot to repay what they owe.

My personal debt to friends, colleagues and assistants has also grown with the passing years. Too numerous to name all, it would be fairest to name none; however, a few I must. I am grateful to Paul Williams of Auckland University and Derek Ford of McMaster University in many ways but above all for their generous help in enabling me to join them in the field in karst areas in New Zealand and Canada respectively. In Canberra, Keith Fitchett and Jim Caldwell, with their support in field and laboratory, greatly helped me build up my personal experience, which I trust gives this book a reasonably firm basis. I thank them especially, but I do not forget all those with whom I have gone underground, for without such expeditions there can be no understanding of karst.

There is a difference of scale between Weathercote Cave in Yorkshire and Atea Kananda in New Guinea but it was precisely the same stunning effect of coming close to a waterfall underground and feeling acutely the power of natural forces that at the age of 11 started my interest in karst – or, for that matter, in geography. If that interest needed any renewal, perhaps nothing had as much effect as travelling in south China some years ago, when incredible Chinese paintings turned into the hardly more believable reality of tower karst, provoking images of giants in drunken reel transfixed into immobility.

Joe Jennings
Australian National University
Canberra

1   The Nature of Karst

Karst is terrain with distinctive landforms and drainage arising from greater rock solubility in natural waters than elsewhere. This is a simple definition, and what does and does not necessarily follow from it requires some discussion.[1]

Solution is not always the most prevalent process in karst, nor is it necessarily the dominant one, but it does play a more important role here than in other kinds of landscape. Its most critical effect lies in the enlargement of underground voids, causing increased permeability of the rock. This leads to the progressive replacement of surface by underground drainage. Nevertheless karst cannot be defined simply in terms of that replacement, because some kinds of karst – e.g. tower karst – have mainly surface drainage while other terrains, such as volcanic pumice country, may lack surface drainage from another cause and fail to develop further karst attributes.

As more water passes through the rock, the voids become large enough to become caves. Caves are bigger and more varied in karst than in any other terrain: yet neither is this a criterion for defining it, because some karst, such as the Chalk Downs of England, has no caves. Moreover, caves of quite different origin are important landforms in other domains such as young volcanic country.

In normal landscapes small streams in small valleys join to become large rivers in large valleys, taking water to the sea in an obviously integrated way. This harmonious pattern is broken up in karst by the development of small, centripetal drainage basins, and closed depressions take over the landscape to varying degrees. Superficially, it lacks organization and the drainage system has to be sought underground. Again, karst definition cannot rest on closed depressions since they can

---

[1] The word 'karst' is a recent introduction to English. There is no native word for it even though parts of England, such as Craven and Mendip, are karst features. The same is true of the United States. In Western Slovenia karst is elaborate and spectacular: this is where the word originates, coming into English usage via German. Western Slovenia was the classic region for the study of karst terrain during the nineteenth century when it was part of the Austro-Hungarian empire.

be rare, if not completely absent. Conversely, they are equally characteristic of altogether different kinds of relief. In arid lands, there may not be
enough water to form valley networks against the contrary effects of
earth movements and of wind. Wind builds as well as erodes closed
depressions. Indeed, it can be difficult to distinguish between karst
depressions and dune hollows where calcareous sand has been blown
inland from beaches over limestones and then converted to limestone
itself, as in the south-east of South Australia.

Greater solubility of a substance is accompanied by a greater liability
to come out of solution, so chemical deposition can contribute in an
important way to landform building in much karst, both on the surface
and underground. This is important not only in creating cave decorations
and barriers on surface streams but also in the more widespread effect of
reprecipitation of calcite in voids in limestone or calcareous sands to
case-harden the surface with calcrete (Monroe 1966; Jennings 1968).

Because its characteristics are best developed in limestone, karst has
sometimes been defined lithologically, usually restricting it to limestone
or at most to carbonate rocks. However, many of the relief and drainage
attributes mentioned above are formed in evaporite rocks also, seen best
in subhumid to semiarid climates. Admittedly, evaporites lack great
mechanical strength compared with most carbonate rocks, and this limits
cave and gorge formation. Nevertheless, the world's second longest cave
(in Podolia, USSR) is the result of simple physical solution of gypsum.
Exclusion of evaporites from karst-building rocks is defensible neither
logically nor practically (Priesnitz 1969).

On the other hand, not all carbonate rocks give rise to karst because
they may lack strength adequate for the support of cave roofs and walls.
Finally, all rocks suitable for the development of karst also need moving
water for this to happen; rain or meltwater and local relief to give power
for work underground as well as on the surface are required, though it is
now thought that occasionally both the water and its energy may be
provided in other ways.

Pseudokarst or Karst

Where the limit should be drawn remains debatable, and though we
should not let terminological debate distract us from substantive matters,
it can throw light on the latter.

There are some landforms, and even landform assemblages, that
resemble those of karst but are the products of quite different processes.
For them the term *pseudokarst* has been devised. Thus, in glaciers and
ice sheets, caves, ranging from shafts to tunnels, and melt dolines,
are the products of the melting of ice, and some small caves are also
produced by ice movement. Ablation is responsible for some minor forms

of karst character on glacier surfaces. These constitute *glacier karst* (Grimes 1975). On a lesser scale and ephemerally, similar features develop in snow. In periglacial regions, the melting of ground ice and of buried glacier ice gives rise to a variety of depressions and irregular relief in unconsolidatd deposits. This *thermokarst* may be difficult to distinguish from true karst effects in areas where the underlying bedrock is karstic and the climate now or recently has been periglacial.

Similarly, there is pseudokarst in young volcanic regions. Very long and even comparatively complex tunnel caves develop where the lavas are very fluid; to form them several mechanisms operate. There are other smaller caves in young volcanic provinces of quite different origin (e.g. gas bubbles, vent shafts). Collapse depressions and natural bridges develop from these caves. This complex has been called *volcanokarst*.

Caves and blowholes in littoral cliffs arising mainly from wave erosion; rock shelters and tafoni in inland crags and cliffs arising from the interplay of various weathering processes; caves within land-slipped masses; blockfields and weathering mantles – all have been classed as pseudokarstic; solution may have played a subordinate role in the development of some. A wide range of rocks is involved in all these.

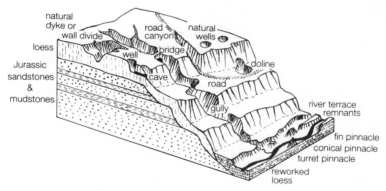

Figure 1 Pseudokarst features of the loess plateau of north China, some of which are anthropogenic.

More borderline in nature are features in loess (see figure 1), as in north-west China, where there are closed depressions of various kinds, interrupted drainage and caves, though they may be difficult to distinguish at times owing to the intense human modification of this malleable material. With calcium carbonate contents being commonly between 10 and 15 per cent, carbonate solution plays a significant role; nevertheless, mechanical eluviation – washing out of fine particles – is predominant. A related problem is that loess may only thinly blanket carbonate karst, as in the Loess Plateau of China, and features in the country rock show through.

Basically similar effects occur in carbonate-free mantles, e.g. in deep weathering mantles of lateritic type. In many parts of northern Australia, laterite plateaus are characterized by fields of shallow closed depressions, and small caves lead back from the 'breakaways' – scarped margins – of laterite plateaus.

Related but larger closed bedrock basins with intermittent to permanent lakes in them are common in granite in the Monaro plateau, NSW. Deep weathering of such coarse-grained igneous rocks has been shown from tin mining exploration in Nigeria to cause closed basins in the weathering front not present in surface relief (Thomas 1966). Their evacuation to produce topographic basins presents problems; eluviation of solutes along joints seems hardly adequate for this, while mechanical eluviation through bedrock as opposed to weathering mantles appears impossible.

Granites and related rocks frequently possess small outcrop sculpturing such as rounded runnels (Ger. *Silikatkarren*), best developed in the humid tropics as in Malaya. Twidale and Bourne (1975) attribute these and related features to subsoil chemical weathering with subsequent stripping.

At the basic end of the igneous rocks, a greater range of closed depressions in size and form is described, e.g. in the ultrabasics of New Guinea (Löffler 1978) and New Caledonia.

Though there is no intention of pursuing these pseudokarst questions here (see Twidale 1984), mention of them is useful because it draws attention to what is meant by 'solution' in this geomorphic context. As will be discussed later more fully, it is only with regard to evaporites that the term strictly signifies simple physical solution. With the carbonate rocks, it means predominantly the chemical reactions of carbonation. Some have therefore taken the view that there is no reason why the chemical weathering of rocks such as granite and eclogite, which produces some landforms resembling those of karst, should not also be lumped under 'solution' and the results labelled 'karst'. There is an important difference, however, in that the reactions of water with both mafic minerals such as olivine and felsic ones such as feldspar yield much insoluble residue, whereas pure carbonate rocks yield little. Residues tend to restrain the increase in permeability and the development of underground drainage that are crucial to the fashioning of karst. As a result, the bulk of the denudational products are not removed as solutes in the drainage system, which is the characteristic mode in karst. There is good reason, therefore, to leave these manifestations outside the pale of 'karst'.

This leaves the most problematic case of all. We now know that large cave systems, including some with big rivers in them today, huge dolines and extensive shallow closed drainage basins occur in rocks consisting entirely of quartz, the most chemically inert of minerals: only

4

very little quartz can get into solution in water at surface temperatures and pH conditions, and that at a slow rate. Minor surface features in quartz sandstone with siliceous cement and in quartzite may be explained by conversion first of a surface layer to amorphous silica, which has higher solubility (W.B. White *et al.* 1966). But this does not extend to the underground, and there explanation has resided in slow solution penetrating along crystal boundaries to free grains more than in fast solution (Martini 1981a). This yields sand residue instead of mixed textures, which have a greater resistance to removal by water (Jennings 1983a). It is possible that more time is needed for such cave development, and it is consistent with this that the best expression is in ancient shields of the Gondwanaland continents of South America (Szczerban and Urbani 1974), Africa and Australia. Study of all these features in quartz rocks, be they regarded as pseudokarst or karst, is still at a very early stage and for that reason will not be pursued further in this book.

Some General Aspects of Karst

This introductory book will emphasize landform and drainage elements and the mechanisms responsible for them. However, every karst has its own overall character; space will preclude much discussion of such regional personality here. Between the two are landform assemblages of different types; indeed, the elaboration of typologies has engaged a good deal of effort (e.g. Mazur and Jakal 1976). Various karst types will be discussed later, but it is convenient to touch on some general distinctions now.

An important contrast is between *bare* and *covered* karst, where bedrock outcrop predominates in the former and occurs only to a limited extent or not at all in the latter. The cover may be residual soil and vegetation litter, in which case the associated karst features are syngenetic, developing as insoluble fractions and organic residues accumulate. Alternatively, the cover consists of unconsolidated transported sediments of fluvial, aeolian and glacial genesis. Quinlan (1972) employs *subsoil karst* and *mantled karst* to distinguish between the two. Karst features beneath transported materials may be older or younger than their cover. Bare, subsoil and mantled karst often occur together like a patchwork quilt.

Most of the south-western half of Yugoslavia is made up of carbonate rocks, but there is considerable difference in development between the interior parts and the coastward region, recognized even before the end of the nineteenth century by one of the greatest of karst geomorphologists Jovan Cvijić. The coastward part, with widespread underground drainage and a whole gamut of karst landforms, consists dominantly of thick, pure limestones reaching deep below sea level; the inland, under the sway of surface drainage and displaying an incomplete karst morphology, has much impure limestone and much dolomite, with an impervious rock basement at shallow depth. Because slopewash and river action retain a prime role in the latter, Roglić (1960) has called it *fluviokarst* to separate it from karst proper. This distinction has been found valuable elsewhere and has been extended to areas where the country rock may be pure limestone but where for other reasons mechanical water action at the surface prevents full expression of the factor of solubility – e.g. Sweeting (1972b) with regard to the Peak District of England. Historical factors may have intervened, or, because of geography, sediment-laden rivers from surrounding higher relief on impervious rocks may have had a big influence.

A related distinction is between karst that drains directly to the sea, which can be termed *free karst*, and karst completely surrounded by impervious rocks through which the output of the karst must pass to reach general base level. This can be named *impounded karst* (Fr. *karst barré*). The smaller the karst, the more important this condition can be.

Solution may operate, and karst forms develop in karst rocks beneath other bedrock formations. This is not called covered karst but *subjacent karst* (Jennings 1965) or *interstratal karst* (Quinlan 1972). Where overlying rocks are conformable, karst features developed below must be younger than the deposition of the later rocks. Thus, along the North Crop of the South Wales Coalfield, the surface of the Millstone Grit has acquired a karst landscape through subsidence into the underlying Carboniferous Limestone because of solution of the latter (Thomas 1974). Subjacent karst can affect the surface in this manner through hundreds of metres of foreign rock, or it may have no effect at all despite elaborate development below.

Where the two sets of strata are unconformable, there is the possibility that karst features have been inherited from the time before the younger rocks were laid down. This condition is most readily recognized where old soil horizons are found at the contact and where the younger sedimentary rocks occur with undisturbed bedding in closed depressions or in caves in the underlying ones. Where residual karst hills are sealed in this way, the sequence of events is also clear, as is found in parts of the Swabian Jura in southern Germany (Büdel 1951). *Buried karst* is the best term. ('Fossil karst' would be appropriate if it had not been used as well for features never interred in this way.) It is most often seen in quarrying and mining.

Natural erosion may uncover such an old surface and its features; this produces *exhumed karst*. Thus, near Gascoyne Junction, WA, a karst topography of towers and corridors has been revealed by removal of sandstone (Jennings 1982a).

In karst, as in most other kinds of relief, there are often parts of the landscape that are not the product of present conditions but have been inherited from different circumstances in the past; *relict* is the appropriate term then. Thus, in southern Yugoslavia there is karst that Gavrilović (1969) considers, from its style and restricted sediment cover, to have formed during a Tertiary period with a tropical climate. It is not a question here of burial and exhumation.

The term *palaeokarst* has been variously applied by different authorities, and now is perhaps best used in a broad way to comprise any parts of a karst landscape that are of considerable age and are not adjusted to the present controlling factors.

It is by no means always easy to distinguish between active, relict, subjacent, buried and exhumed components in karst. This may be due to a paucity of stratigraphical sections but often is because of compound histories. Thus, both buried dolines and filled caves are likely places for a later resumption of solution and for fresh inputs of sediments. What was simply a buried feature may become also subjacent in origin. There is also the possibility of confusion with structural landforms in the sense of landforms reflecting geological structure. This applies to the Lower Carboniferous reef knolls of the British Isles. Some of these distinctive hills in east-central Ireland originated as compact bodies of pure limestone, which accumulated as patch reefs that were gradually buried by clastic sediments filling up the sea floor between them. Differential erosion at a later time removed the shales and impure limestones from around the reef masses for them to become terrestrial features for the first time. Others, however, like Crome Hill on the western flank of the English Peak District, are part of a surface of unconformity and appear to be mid-Carboniferous terrestrial erosion features, submerged and buried by shales, which were later stripped to create exhumed karst.

Increasingly, the role of biological agents is being recognized in influencing and indeed producing distinctive *biokarst* landforms (Viles 1984). Initial identification of microkarst phenomena produced under soil cover (Sweeting 1972a for review) has been supplemented by recent reports of the direct effect of plant and animal activity in producing both erosional and depositional karst forms (Bull and Laverty 1982). Most of this work has been related to the identification of bio-processes in present day landforms. Further attention is needed to relate these newly identified processes to more ancient karst features.

2 Karst Rocks

Although a basic knowledge of geology is assumed here, the lithology of karst rocks (cf. Chilingar *et al.* 1967), which exerts both broad and subtle influences on the expression of karst (Sweeting 1973), will be outlined.

Carbonate Rocks

Carbonate rocks are taken to be those where at least half of the rock is made of carbonate minerals; to be considered pure, they must have at least 90 per cent of such minerals. This works quite well for geomorphology, because Corbel (1957) estimated that, with limestone, 60 per cent of it had to be $CaCO_3$ for karst to begin to form and full development of it required the 90 per cent purity, though of course other factors may inhibit that happening despite such purity.

The proportions of calcite ($CaCO_3$) and dolomite ($CaMg(CO_3)_2$) give rise to the most important distinctions among the carbonate rocks (see

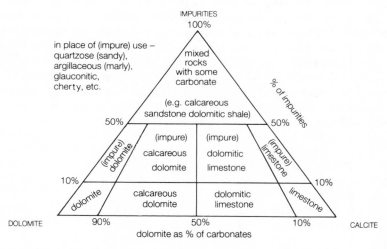

Figure 2 The classification of carbonate rocks according to Leighton and Pendexter (1962).

8

figure 2). Aragonite, another mineral form of calcium carbonate, is secreted by many marine organisms in addition to calcite, so many young limestones include it also, but gradually with time this inverts to calcite. The impurities in carbonate rocks are mainly clay minerals and quartz, but flint and chert can be very important in some of them. Oxides of iron act as colouring agents of the fresh rock and even more of weathered surfaces, daubing yellow and red the otherwise white, grey and black rock surface.

Marine carbonate rocks are the rule in karst, but locally limestone and dolomite deposited in freshwater lakes and limestone formed from calcareous dune sands can be significant. Limestone and dolomite are variously estimated to constitute between 10 and 20 per cent of all sedimentary rocks of the earth.

Limestones

No common rock name covers so much variety as does limestone. This is because a wide range of materials – detrital, organic and chemical – accumulates originally and because *diagenesis* – change at low temperature and pressure – is intense through their chemical susceptibility (Bathurst 1975). High temperature and pressure may also metamorphose them to marble, a mosaic of large, clear calcite grains, but limestones become so completely crystalline in diagenesis that they may easily be labelled marble without metamorphism.

Because of their complexity, many classifications of limestones have been constructed; that of Folk (1959) is set out in figure 3 because it depends mainly on texture, which influences permeability strongly. However, it may not be easy to apply fully in the field, where initially one may be content to use a simple division based on the main grain size: *calcirudites*, i.e. conglomerates with pebbles larger than 2mm diameter; *calcarenites*, of sand-sized grains (2 m–0.2 mm); *calcisiltites*, with grains 0.2 mm–0.02 mm; and *calcilutites*, which have such fine grains (<0.02 mm) that they appear quite smooth (aphanitic). Add *breccia limestones*, in which large angular clasts are cemented together, and one can make a start.

The first picture that comes to mind when we think how limestones form is probably that of marine organisms growing together so that their calcareous skeletons bind into a rigid body, with many voids into which detritus is washed or which are filled by chemical precipitates. Though not as common as one might imagine, these autochthonous fossiliferous limestones are important geomorphologicaly. They are called *biolithites* by Folk (type IV in figure 3), *boundstones* by Dunham (1962). Dominant life forms – corals, stromatoporoids, bryozoa and algae – serve to distinguish them further.

9

Karst Rocks

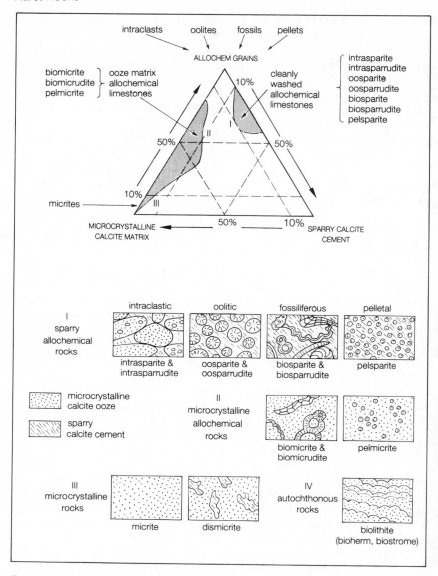

Figure 3 Major kinds of limestone according to Folk (1959).

But more important for karst is the overall form such limestones assume – either compact, upward-projecting masses called *bioherms*, or extensive tabular bodies called *biostromes*. These differences were first comprehended by reference to modern 'coral' reefs, where various colonial organisms, not solely corals, build up wave-resistant projections from the sea floor such as fringing reefs, barrier reefs with ribbon and patch elements and atolls. Their essential framework consists of biohermal limestone, but erosion and transport during construction ensures that many other facies of limestone enter into the reef structure (see figure 4). Indeed, in sheer volume the biolithites are subordinate. On the wave-protected flank of the reefs and in their lagoons, quiet conditions allow well-bedded limestones to accumulate horizontally, and biostromes are common among these backreef beds.

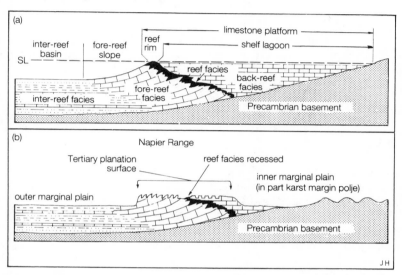

Figure 4 The Napier Range, north-western Australia: (a) Devonian reef facies according to Playford and Lowry (1966); (b) present relief.

Not all the rocks consisting mainly of organic skeletons that have accumulated where they lived belonged to such reefs. Shallow banks also form biostromal masses of less wave-resistant character and so are more associated with lower-energy coasts. Here algae can play an even larger part than on coral reefs; algal films trap lime sand, silt and clay to form stromatolites of different shapes (Logan *et al.* 1964).

In reef lagoons and on other calm, shallow sea floors, limestones of a completely different character may form from calcareous ooze, with grain so fine as not to be visible in the optical microscope. These have originated both as the finest products of attrition of coarser calcareous material and as chemical precipitates. These are called *micrites* by Folk (type III in figure 3) and *lime mudstones* by Dunham.

Most limestones are more composite than either of the above groups; they consist of larger grains set in either a matrix of dull lime mud *(micrite)* or a cement of clear, lustrous crystalline calcite *(sparite)*. Folk calls the larger grains *allochems* and recognizes four classes:

1 detritus eroded from only partially consolidated carbonate sediment: since the material was still weak, the fragments were readily rounded – *intraclasts*;
2 spheroidal precipitates formed in strong currents – *oolites*;
3 *fossils*, which include not only fragments of larger skeletons but whole smaller ones, e.g. foraminifera, sponge spicules;
4 rounded aggregates of micrite which are thought to be the faeces of worms, etc. – *pellets*.

Where bottom currents were weak, lime mud settles on the floor along with these larger constituents (type II in figure 3). If the grains are few they float in the mud, which supports them (Dunham named this rock *lime wackestone*); whereas, if the grains are many they support one another to give *lime packstone*. Both are found in the back-reef facies of coral reefs.

Stronger currents remove the ooze and pile the grains together supporting one another. If they remain like this, the large pores make them highly permeable; shelly limestones in this category are the *coquinas* of older classifications. More commonly, the voids get filled over time with sparry calcite, reducing permeability. All these fall into Folk's type I (figure 3) and Dunham's *grainstones*.

Rocks of this latter kind form on the steep seaward flanks of coral reefs, where there is erosion by strong waves and debris accumulates in steeply inclined beds with up to 30–35 deg depositional dip. This forereef facies includes much sparitic limestone with coarse intraclasts. The steep submarine slopes are unstable and tend to slump while still not much lithified, forming *megabreccias* (Playford and Lowry 1966) with very large boulders in them ('intrasparrudites' of Folk's terminology, which allows for further subdivision – figure 3).

Reef facies can be important factors in karst, for instance affecting the location of caves, including Carlsbad Caverns in the Guadalupe Range, New Mexico, with its Permian reef complex.

One of the most distinctive aspects of limestone is the importance of pressure solution, expressed in *stylolites*, or sutures in the rock where pressure solution has taken place, often marked by laminae of insoluble impurities left behind. In the Oligocene shelly calcarenites of the King Country, New Zealand (Barrett 1964), they strike the eye both in surface outcrop and cave walls, often as a wavy recessing suggestive of flaggy bedding (see plate 1). The effects are much more pronounced in the Devonian limestones of the limestone ranges, WA (Logan and Semeniuk 1976), where there is not only much stylo-bedding but also stylolamination. More important still is the presence of much *stylo-breccia*, in which each clast is margined by a pressure solution surface and the spaces between are filled with dolomite or insoluble impurities, which, if they include iron oxides, stand out as pink involute shapes in section.

Plate 1 An Oligocene marine limestone outcrop, King Country, NZ. Above, stylolites have weathered out to give the impression of flaggy bedding; below, smoothed surfaces have been created by solution by a formerly continuous cover of mosses, liverworts and other lower plants.

13

Sparry calcite veins are also developed to an intense degree, even to form calcite vein breccias. From the regional pattern of such features, Logan and Semeniuk argue for great tectonic stress from the south-west and dynamic metamorphism with both large and small-scale effects. Pressure solution may not yet have been fully appreciated in carbonate rock lithology.

Dolomites

Dolomites are dominantly crystalline and are best classified by grain size. Sometimes the 'ghosts' of fossils, intraclasts, etc., can be identified, though it is impossible to determine original proportions of ooze and sparry calcite. All this implies that they are formed secondarily by dolomitization of limestones. However, some dolomites, of very fine grain and lacking relicts of former limestone, are thought to be of primary origin, especially if they are associated with evaporites.

Despite Corbel's (1957) estimate that 60 per cent of limestone needed to be $CaCO_3$ for karst to develop properly, many predominantly dolomitic rocks contain fully established cave systems. The outcrops of the Praire du Chien dolomites near the Great Lakes (USA) contain hundreds of caves in a band extending from S. Wisconsin into Illinois and Minnesota. Undoubtedly there is much limestone in these outcrops but the cave systems follow structural or dominant palaeohydraulic courses rather than rigid lithologic ones.

Evaporites

Evaporites formed in warm coastal lagoons or marine embayments and in desert basins. There are many evaporite minerals, which occur as mixtures or interbedded in the rocks. The most important – halite (rock salt), anhydrite and gypsum – are those of concern to the karst geomorphologist.

Halite (NaCl) is a poorly bedded, coarsely crystalline rock, lacking joints. It yields plastically at low pressure and temperature, so it commonly occurs in diapirs to give salt domes. *Anhydrite* ($CaSO_4$) is usually bedded or laminated and granular in texture. It also may rise in diapirs. *Gypsum* ($CaSO_4.2H_2O$) is formed by the hydration of anhydrite during which it swells by 30–50 per cent, so that much crumpling may result. It can be fine-grained or coarsely crystalline, well or poorly bedded.

All occur together in the Permian Castile Formation in New Mexico and Texas to an exceptional thickness of 1200 m.

Permeability and Strength of Karst Rocks

How readily the rock allows water to pass through it and how well it can hold together are critical matters for karst development. These properties depend on many interacting factors.

Table 1   Physical properties of some common rocks

Rock	Porosity (% voids)	Coefficient of permeability ($l\,s^{-1}m^{-1}$ with hydraulic gradient 1 in 1)	Uniaxial Compressive Strength ($N\,cm^{-1}$)
Clay	50–60	3.5 (10^{-1}–10^{1})	-
Sand	30–40	3.5 (10^{5}–10^{8})	-
Gravel	25–35	3.5 (10^{8}–10^{11})	-
Shale	5–15	3.5 (10^{-4}–10^{0})	3600–23 100
Sandstone	5–25	3.5 (10^{1}–10^{6})	1200–23 500
Conglomerate	5–25	3.5 (10^{8}–10^{11})	16 600
Limestone	0.1–10	3.5 (10^{0}–10^{5})	3400–33 100
Coral rock	-	-	600–3500
Marble	-	-	4600–23 800
Chalk	14–44	1.8 (10^{9})–5.3 (10^{9})	1700
Dolomite	3	-	6200–36 000
Anhydrite	-	-	4100
Basalt	0.001–50	3.5 (10^{0}–10^{4})	8100–35 900
Tuff	10–80	3.5 (10^{0}–10^{4})	3500–26 200
Granite	0.0001–1	3.5 (10^{-4}–10^{-1})	15 900–29 400
Gneiss	0.0001–1	3.5 (10^{-4}–10^{0})	15 300–25 100
Quartzite	-	-	14 600–62 900

Sources: Waltz (1969), Martel (1921), Chilingar et al. (1967), Coates (1967), Jaeger and Cook (1969), Obert and Duvall (1967), Ineson (1962).

Reference to table 1 reveals that there is little relationship between porosity and permeability of rocks because the latter depends not only on the number of the pores but also on their size and interconnectedness. Porosity is determined on small specimens in the laboratory and is simply the percentage that the voids between the grains represent of the bulk volume. Permeability is the capacity of a rock to transmit water through it; this also can be determined for laboratory specimens, but measures from bores and wells, e.g. the rate of water yielded when pumped, relate to much larger bodies of rock and are more representative.

Intergranular porosity is related to the texture of the original sediments, their diagenesis to rock and any subsequent metamorphism. Micrites are usually devoid of pores, whereas a coquina is extremely porous, perhaps 60–70 per cent, and because its pores are large it also has considerable primary permeability. However, initial pores may get filled with lime mud or calcite cement. Even if pore infilling does not take place during deposition and diagenesis, porosity may disappear through later recrystallization. So many limestones have practically no intergranular porosity (less than 1 per cent).

Nevertheless, although table 1 shows a wide range of permeability for limestones, that range is on the high side and, of course, the very nature of karst corresponds with this. This permeability – secondary permeability – is of a different nature depending on joints and other planes of weakness in the rock, which become enlarged by solution. The Cretaceous chalk of France and England illustrates the point. It is very porous but the pores are fine, and this pure biomicrite is mechanically very weak. Water infiltrates rapidly into it because of the high porosity but the rock does not yield it so easily. Ineson (1962) reports laboratory tests for hydraulic conductivity on chalk as low as $365 \text{ l s}^{-1} \text{ m}^{-2}$, but well pumping tests show that it is commonly five to seven magnitudes greater in nature. This is due to movement along joints. Even so, karst is limited in its character in chalk. Poor karst development is also characteristic of the limestone in Barbados, which Tricart (1968) attributes to a combination of high intergranular porosity and poverty in joints. Despite very soluble rock, heavy rainfall and lush vegetation, there is failure to canalize underground circulation.

The nature, frequency and pattern of planes of weakness constitute the most important single factor of geological structure in karst because their effect on the mechanical strength of the rock masses is important, as is their direct influence on the hydrology (see Kastning 1984 for regional illustration).

Table 1 sets out the *uniaxial compressive strength* of some common rocks; this is the maximum stress that small cylinders of rock can withstand under compression in the laboratory in a single direction before bending or rupture. Triaxial compression is the usual field condition. *Tensile strength*, the maximum tensional force that rocks can undergo without deformation, is hard to measure and varies much more from one specimen to another. However, uniaxial compressive strength is usually a guide to variation in other strength properties of rocks, including tensile strength, which is, of course much weaker. It will be seen from the table that karst rocks are exceedingly variable in mechanical strength.

The Schmidt Hammer (Day and Goudie 1977) provides a convenient way of describing the surface hardness of different limestones, and of comparing them with other rocks. It has also enabled the assessment of case hardening, notably on limestones in the tropics (Day 1980). Some limestones can be extremely hard, and the magnificent limestone pinnacles of the Mulu area of Sarawak occur where R values reach 61.9. At the other extreme chalky limestones have values under 20. Some available data are given in table 2.

Table 2   Schmidt Hammer values for selected limestones

Material	Mean R value	Source
Calcrete hardpans	42	Day and Goudie, 1977
Israel chalk	14	Yaalon and Singer, 1974
Israel calcrete on chalk	51–4	Yaalon and Singer, 1974
Limestone aeolianite in Bahrain	14.5	Day and Goudie, 1977
Wind abraded dolomite in Bahrain	50	Day and Goudie, 1977
Puerto Rico Aymamon limestone,		
unweathered	12.5	Day, 1980
case hardened	53.4	
Yucatan, Mexico, unweathered		
Carillo Puerto	35.9	Day, 1980
Jamaica Browns Town	32.1	Day, 1980
Guatemala-Dolomitic Peten	39.7	Day, 1980
Belize-dolimitic	39.8	Day, 1980
Melinau limestone-Mulu, Sarawak	56.4	Day, 1980
Gunong Api pinnacle limestone, Mulu	61.9	Day, 1980
Mallorca limestone with pinnacles	52.7	A.S. Goudie (pers. comm.)
Barbados Pliocene	29.8	Day, 1982
Guadeloupe Miocene	33.4	Day, 1982
Antigua-Antigua formation	33.3	Day, 1982

Even more variable is the behaviour of large masses of these rocks in nature as opposed to laboratory samples because of larger-scale inhomogeneities, especially their planes of weakness. The range is from rocks such as halite, which cannot support wide cave roofs and needs active evacuation, and chalk, which cannot form cliffs except where subject to marked erosion by stream or sea, to compact, crystalline limestones, which stand in huge, nearly vertical cliffs without such basal attack and which form wide spans in cave roofs to the presently known maximum of 700 m by 400 m of Sarawak Chamber in Lubang Nasib Bagus, Mulu, Sarawak (Eavis 1981).

Bedding may involve (a) dividing surfaces only, (b) variation in lithology through the bed with greater impurity at the bottom, or (c) lithologic difference between beds. Cyclic change in bed lithology is common in formations that include limestone. Thin bedding may reduce the strength of the formation so as to make it unfavourable for cave development. Such bedding is often accompanied by insoluble materials in the bedding planes and by shale or clay interbeds; if too plentiful, they hinder underground drainage development. Widely spaced shale inter-beds may localize cave formation. With poorly bedded bioherms, the widely spaced parting planes are especially favourable to cave development, e.g. in the English Peak District (Warwick 1960), where many caves are associated with bioherms.

Joints generally favour karst, though rewelding by solute precipitation to minimize their effect is common in carbonate rocks. Joints are due mainly to release of strain energy, residual from earlier compression, during later uplift which permits extension (Price 1959; Hancock 1968).

Because of this dominant origin, most joints in limestone and dolomite are normal to the bedding. Minor joints lie within a single bed whereas major ones cut several over tens of metres of thickness. They usually occur in parallel sets, and frequently two sets intersect at angles of around 60° in a conjugate system owing to stress from a particular direction.

Joints are (a) latent – of hair thickness and apparent only when the rock is hammered, (b) closed – when they are visible but allow movement only of capillary water, and (c) open – when they allow free water movement. They may be too close together to permit adequate rock strength to support cave roofs. Cleavage joints are close-set joints at right angles to compressional forces and they make for weakness, as in Shatter Cave near the Goodradigbee River, NSW, so named because of its instability. But in general, jointing has been crucially favourable to the development of caves.

Finally, faults also transgress rocks, and movement along them may open up planes of weakness. Often, therefore, faults guide underground drainage and cave development; the Great North Road in Dan yr Ogof in South Wales (Coase and Judson 1977) illustrates the point aptly in its name. However, intense cleavage and mineralization, which often accompany faulting, may have a contrary influence in some circumstances. Thus in soft chalk, plastic material is injected along the fault zone, making it a partial barrier to groundwater flow (Ineson 1962).

3   Karst Processes

Many processes operate in karst landscapes; here only those that assume a peculiar importance in karst will be discussed. It must be recognized that processes that do not fall into this category may play a dominant role in particular karst types. Thus McDonald (1976, 1979) has stressed the importance of lateral erosion by surface streams in fashioning tower karst in both Sulawesi (Indonesia) and Belize. Nevertheless, this does not lead him into the unrealistic standpoint of Panoš and Stelcl (1968), who excluded similar terrain, for instance the Sierra de los Organos in Cuba, from karst on such grounds.

Solution and Precipitation

Limestone

The most calcite that can go into solution in pure water is only about 13 mg l^{-1} at 16° C and 15 mg l^{-1} at 25° C; aragonite is only slightly more soluble. So simple physical solution is not very effective in karst. Much greater concentrations are found in natural waters because these contain acids. The most important of these is carbonic acid from dissolved carbon dioxide, and the chief sources of the latter are plant root respiration and bacterial decay of organic matter (Pitty 1966). Rotting vegetation also produces an array of organic acids capable of attacking limestone, and this kind of action may be important with peaty waters (Bray 1975). Miserez (1976) thinks that as much as half the limestone under peat bogs and meadows in the Jura that goes into solution does so by reaction with humic organic matter; however, only 2 per cent of the calcium in Slovenian karst output is attached to humates.

A more powerful acid found in bogs, sulphuric acid, is a result of other bacterial metabolism. It can also be produced by the weathering of sulphide minerals such as pyrite. Interbedded shales may be a significant source of sulphuric acid and pyritic limestones are also known to yield it. Other sources of sulphuric acid that have been suggested are hydrogen sulphide from hydrocarbon deposits and the mixing of gypsum brine with freshwater. These will be supplied in the saturated zone, in contrast with the other supplies of acidified water which are surface inputs. This acid may therefore be important locally. On the other hand, the amount of nitric acid in rain as a result of lightning is negligible. The general view remains that carbon dioxide is the dominant factor in the chemical attack on limestone.

This crucial process in karst has in the past been incorrectly posed as a single reaction, producing the more soluble calcium bicarbonate from the less soluble calcium carbonate. Instead, there is a complex series of ionic dissociations and reversible reactions, governed by their own activity constants and saturation equilibria. As simple a presentation as possible will be made here, and the reader is referred especially to Picknett (1976).

Some water is always in a state of dissociation, so there are hydrogen (H^+) and hydroxyl (OH^-) ions in the solution from this source. Carbon dioxide is in solution even in rainwater (CO_2) and some of it has reacted to form carbonic acid:

$$CO_2 \rightleftharpoons CO_2^0$$
$$(\text{air}) \quad CO_2^0 + H_2O \rightleftharpoons H_2 CO_3.$$

Both of these actions proceed slowly. The carbonic acid dissociates into its constituent ions also.

The physical solution of calcium carbonate also proceeds slowly:

$$Ca\,CO_3 \rightleftharpoons Ca^{2+} + CO_3^{2-}.$$
$$(\text{solid})$$

However, two reactions follow extremely quickly:

$$CO_3^{2-} + H^+ \rightleftharpoons HCO_3^-$$
$$HCO_3^- + H^+ \rightleftharpoons H_2CO_3.$$

As indicated, all these actions are reversible and states of equilibrium can be reached. The amount of limestone dissolved thus depends on the hydrogen ion concentration, and this in turn usually depends on the carbon dioxide in solution.

This quantity is governed by the water temperature and the partial pressure of carbon dioxide (P_{CO_2}) of the air with which the water is in contact (Henry's Law). The temperature effect is inverse, – the lower the temperature, the more carbon dioxide can go into solution – whereas, the more carbon dioxide there is in the air, the more can go into solution until a balance is reached between molecules going from the air to the water and those coming from the water into the air. The two effects are also very different in magnitude. Between 0 and 20 °C, the amount of carbon dioxide in solution at equilibrium falls to one-half; between 0 and 35 °C (a very high temperature for meteoric waters) it falls to one-third. On the other hand, P_{CO_2} ranges from 0.03 per cent by volume in open air near sea level to 0.5–2 per cent commonly in soil and cave air, with extreme values a magnitude greater still. There is thus about a hundred-fold range in carbon dioxide in solution in natural waters equilibrated to these partial pressures.

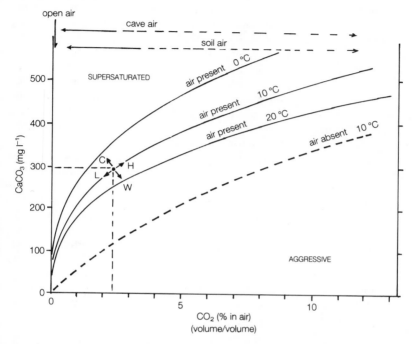

Figure 5 Saturation equilibrium curves for the solution of calcium carbonate in water at different temperatures in contact with air containing varying amounts of carbon dioxide. The broken line shows how much dissolves when water equilibrates with air containing the indicated amount of CO_2 and is then isolated from it (after Picknett 1976). If saturated water at 300 mg l^{-1} Ca CO$_3$ and 10 °C is cooled (C), it can dissolve more limestone; if it is warmed (W), it will throw some out of solution. If it comes into contact with air with less CO_2 (L), it will give off CO_2 and precipitate CaCO$_3$, whereas if it meets air with more CO_2 (H), it will absorb CO_2 and dissolve more limestone.

Figure 5 shows how much CaCO$_3$ can get into solution in these conditions, with the direct effect of carbon dioxide proving much greater than the inverse temperature effect. However, the continuous lines for saturation equilibrium are based on the condition that the water dissolving the limestone stays exposed to the air, from which it can renew its supply of carbon dioxide until equilibrium between air, water and rock is achieved. In such an open system this can take hours or even days, because some of the actions in the system are slow, as has been indicated. Commonly, however, before this has happened soil water will pass down into joint planes, filling them up so it becomes virtually a closed system. Saturation will be reached sooner but at lower concentrations. This is illustrated for 10 °c by the broken line.

21

So far this discussion has concerned itself with the question of how much limestone *can* go into solution with the help of carbon dioxide. It is an important question. For example, the average concentration in the springs of the Mendip is about 235 mg l^{-1} (Drew 1970) at about 10°c. Smith and Mead (1962) assumed that the average P_{CO_2} of the Mendip soils was 1.6 per cent and this would allow 280 mg l^{-1} of limestone solution, to which they considered the springs nearly adjusted. As we shall see later, they may have been mistaken in this, but such comparisons are vital to reaching an understanding of this major karst process.

Nevertheless, many springs in karst are far from their saturation equilibrium. Thus the 6 m^3 s^{-1} spring of the Atea River, New Guinea, carries only 60 mg l^{-1} at 14–16° c and is undersaturated (James 1980). Karst springs that are undersaturated much of the time are widespread (Thrailkill 1976). Moreover, we are concerned with what is happening as water passes through the karst before it reaches the output end, even if equilibrium is achieved there. The kinetics of the process are at least as important as the equilibria: at what rate does solution take place?

These kinetics are also complex (Plummer and Wigley 1976; Plummer *et al.* 1978; Dreybrodt 1981a; W.B. White 1984). Over the normal range of karst conditions, the rate of solution is controlled by both the rate of reaction at the rock surface and the rate of mass transport of reactants and products from that surface into the whole body of water involved.

The surface reaction rate is in direct dependence on temperature (in accord with Arrhenius' Law) and on carbon dioxide present. The mass transport depends:

1 directly on the difference between the solute concentration at the rock surface and the concentration of the mean flow (which is inversely related to temperature);
2 inversely on solute density;
3 directly on the diffusivity of the solution (which is itself directly related to temperature);
4 inversely on solvent viscosity (which is in turn inversely related to temperature);
5 directly on the velocity of flow;
6 inversely on the thickness of the flow;
7 on the nature of the flow with an abrupt increase at the change from laminar to turbulent flow;
8 on the geometry of the rock surface, causing planar or pipe flow, etc.

These factors vary greatly in importance, but the net effect is that the rate increases with water temperature and flow velocity, though there are qualifications to be made to this which affect diversely solution in different hydrodynamic situations (Palmer 1984).

So far, a homogeneous calcite surface and water with only carbon dioxide in solution has been assumed. However, in nature many 'foreign' ions are present also, with a diversity of effects. Thus, if substances in solution are present that have no common ion with the carbonate system, this enhances the solubility of the limestone by the *ionic strength effect*. A most important foreign electrolyte is sodium chloride, which can reach high concentrations in semiarid–arid climates such as the Nullarbor Plain, where in parts the solubility of the limestone is at least doubled. The question of mixing with sea water in coastal karst is touched on in chapter 12. However, if there are substances in solution that have ions in common with the carbonate system, calcium carbonate solubility is reduced by this *common ion effect*. This applies to calcium sulphate and magnesium carbonate.

Some metal ions in trace concentrations such as lead, copper and manganese are absorbed on to the calcite surface and reduce the solubility of the limestone. Phosphate also acts as an inhibitor, and there are many other interfering conditions not well understood.

If a body of water reaches saturation for calcite before it leaves the karst, it does not necessarily follow that solution ceases for it; its capacity to attack limestone may be renewed in various ways. Thus, if water has reached saturation at the surface or at shallow depths and descends further and is cooled – a happening likely in summertime – it becomes

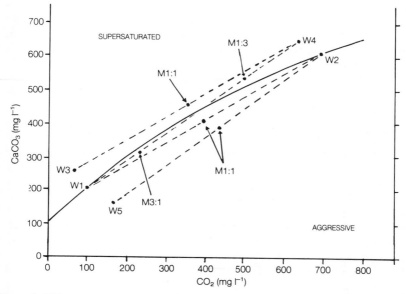

Figure 6 Mixing corrosion (after Bögli 1964a, Thrailkill 1968, Picknett 1976). Any mixture of saturated waters W1 and W2 gives aggressive water, e.g. M1:1, an equal mixture. Mixtures of saturated waters W3 and W4 remain supersaturated. Mixtures of saturated W2 and aggressive W5 are aggressive in any proportion. M1:3 (1 part saturated W1 and 3 parts supersaturated W4) remains supersaturated, but M3:1, the converse mixture, becomes aggressive.

23

B

aggressive again; Bögli (1964a) terms this *cooling corrosion*. This is a small effect.

Though not the first to recognize it, Bögli first stressed the geomorphic importance of *mixing corrosion*. Because the relationship between CO_2 partial pressure and calcium carbonate saturation equilibrium is exponential, the mixing of two bodies of water, both saturated but at different $CaCO_3$ concentrations, produces water that is undersaturated (see figure 6). When a large body of water saturated at low P_{CO_2} mixes with a small body saturated at high P_{CO_2}, such as when vadose seepage and vadose streamflow (see chapter 5) meet, the shift to aggressiveness is considerable; however, vadose streamflow is usually still aggressive in any case. In the water-filled zone at depth, percolation water at high P_{CO_2} is more likely to encounter saturated water moving slowly along pipes. This may be important in the early stages of cave development especially (Dreybrodt 1981b), but Bögli was concerned chiefly with the possibility of renewing aggressiveness at considerable depth in limestone relief, since the deeper the level, the greater the likelihood that water arriving there will already be at equilibrium.

If contents of magnesium vary, mixing may cause increased power of corrosion on that count (Picknett 1972; Picknett and Stenner 1978). From 0 to 10 per cent, increasing content of magnesium reduces calcium solubility, but above 10 per cent increasing magnesium content enhances calcium solubility. Therefore mixing saturated waters with contents above and below this limit makes the mixture aggressive. Water passing from one limestone to another with a different magnesium content has the same effect.

A third source of renewed aggressiveness is probably of more widespread applicability than has been yet been realized; this is new supply of carbon dioxide. Thus, at Bungonia Caves, NSW, James (1977) was able to relate unusually high CO_2 levels in the cave air to microbial breakdown of organic matter washed in from the surface by storms. Not all the microbia involved are aerobic; the generation of CO_2 can proceed without air. The Bungonia Caves are special because of their excessively foul air, but this is not true of Ogof Ffynnon Ddu in South Wales, a cave with normal atmospheric conditions. There, Bray (1975) has shown that loss of organic content in the water and increase in its hardness occur concomitantly (see figure 7); in his view there is a 'latent aggressiveness' which is the product of oxidation of the organic matter. Again, Atkinson (1977) analysed more closely the relationship between the chemistry of Mendip spring waters and soil CO_2 levels; the latter were not high enough or constant enough to account for the hardness and P_{CO_2} of the springs. He found high cave air P_{CO_2} in fissures in the caves where there was dark-coloured mud. Decay of organic material washed into the cave from the surface is thought to be the operative process.

Reprecipitation of the products of limestone solution is another

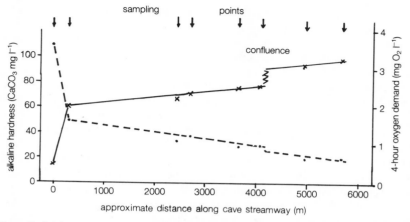

Figure 7 Calcium carbonate content and oxygen demand along the streamway of Ogof Ffynnon Ddu, Wales, after Bray (1975).

significant geomorphic process in karst. In the past it was attributed to evaporation, raising concentrations above saturation equilibrium. This may be important in the formation of calcrete and in the forward parts of caves in hot, dry climates (Jennings and Sweeting 1966); generally, however, in caves humidity is so high and air movement so limited that evaporation is minimal. The various reactions of the $CaCO_3–CO_2–H_2O$ system are reversible, and 'degassing' – loss of CO_2 from the water to the air – is a very important cause of deposition of calcite. Thus, where seepage water, which was enriched in CO_2 in the soil and became saturated in passing through joints in the limestone, enters a cave with lower partial pressure of CO_2 in its air than in the soil above, carbon dioxide diffuses from dripping and flowing water and causes $CaCO_3$ to be thrown out of solution. This is the major cause of calcite decoration in caves. Calcite is the mineral form of $CaCO_3$ normally precipitated, but if the solution gets highly supersaturated before there is deposition, e.g. through lack of solid calcite on which to nucleate, aragonite or (rarely) vaterite may form. The presence of magnesium, sulphate and organic substances also causes aragonite to form in preference to calcite. In Castleguard Cave in the Canadian Rockies, the formation of calcite speleothems beneath glacier ice is the result of solution of gypsum and dolomite causing the precipitation of less soluble calcite (Atkinson 1983).

Dolomite

Dolomite rock behaves in a similar way to limestone in natural waters, with carbon dioxide taking on the crucial role here also, and its solubility at equilibrium is much the same. However, its solution kinetics differ markedly, bringing equilibrium much more slowly (W.B. White 1984).

25

With deposition, dolomite crystallizes very slowly, so that other crystals such as calcite grow preferentially.

Evaporites

Simple physical solution is the rule with the evaporites, since they do not react with CO_2. Gypsum is most soluble at 37 °C; since this is above the temperature of most natural waters, in geomorphology the relevant fact is that there is rising solubility with temperature. More than ten times as much gypsum dissolves at saturation as calcite, and the rate at which it goes into solution is faster. Supersaturation leading to reprecipitation can occur through both evaporation of water vapour and cooling. In Castleguard Cave in the Canadian Rockies, the distribution of gypsum speleothems has been related to a zone where geothermal heat causes increased evaporation (Harmon and Atkinson 1981).

Rock salt is much more soluble still – more than a hundred times greater than gypsum. Temperature has little effect on saturation equilibrium and the rate of solution is very rapid.

Waters from deep sources as well as from the surface are effective in evaporite solution since there is no dependence on atmospheric gases as with carbonate rocks.

Piping

Piping or tunnelling is primarily a cause of various kinds of pseudokarst. It occurs in soils and unconsolidated sediments where percolating water transports clay and fine silt fractions internally, evacuating underground conduits usually to a width of a few decimetres in diameter (Parker 1964). The solution of soluble grains in the material may assume a supporting role in suitable materials (Rogers 1981). In coarser materials, open fabric provides primary permeability. In finer grained materials, cracking where there are swelling clays (e.g. montmorillonite) and dispersion of fines through a preponderance of alkalis over alkaline earths in the exchange complex are conducive to piping. Engineering excavations may induce it, but attention to piping on a wide scale was first drawn in semiarid-to-arid environments where overgrazing or other human interference had destroyed vegetation and exposed the land to gullying. Steep engineered slopes and gullies increase hydraulic gradients and this causes headward extension of pipes from the exposed faces. However, later studies have revealed a wide occurrence of this process under natural conditions. Bunting (1961) documented the occurrence of percolines on English moorlands – dendritic subsurface drainage lines extending the visible stream channels – and Löffler (1974) describes piping and related surface features well developed in tropical lowlands in New Guinea.

Although still little studied, it is evident that piping is important in karst where the hydraulic gradient in the regolith is provided by the opening and enlargement of cavities in karst rock beneath (Pitty 1971; Carson and Kirkby 1972). Piping is generally accompanied by subsidence forming shafts and closed depressions (Clausen 1970).

Subsidence

The removal of support from below, inducing centripetal mass movement, is an outstanding characteristic of karst. This infall will be discussed here under two headings – subsidence and collapse. *Collapse* will be retained for geologically sudden mass movement of the karst bedrock, and *subsidence* wil be applied to the mass movement of soils, weathering mantles and superficial deposits that is often gradual. With many rocks this distinction would be of little value, but with the enhanced solubility of karst rocks there is usually an abrupt break between bedrock and regolith – indeed, it produces some of the sharpest weathering fronts known – making it useful in this context.

It is also useful to consider generally the special influence that karst conditions have on slope processes. Because of the low proportion of insolubles in karst rocks, residual soils tend to be shallower than on many other rocks, minimizing superficial mass movement. Furthermore, the ready reversal of the solution process leads easily to cementation, reducing mobility, as for example in talus. Moreover, because of rapid downward percolation in the bedrock, covers dry out more quickly and more markedly than on other rocks, where this will depend more on runoff and lateral percolation. For this reason the more water-aided mass movements – block (rotational) slump, debris slide, debris avalanche and debris flow (terminology of Varnes 1958) – are proportionately less active in modifying karst landscapes than other landscapes in the same climatic conditions. Desiccation of covers is not entirely a restraining factor in mass movement, because with swelling clays it readily creates deep cracking. Rapid infiltration down such cracks is a common trigger of block slumping.

Despite the generally unfavourable factors towards mass movement, creation of space below soils and superficial covers inevitably leads to their deformation. Dry soilfall and slow earthflow can assume unusual importance in this context. For example, dry soilfall appears to be the dominant process in the Maiden's Tresses Chamber of Easter Cave, Augusta, WA, where sandy loam has been fed vertically from a choked solution pipe in virtually single-grain state to build a conical pile below.

In wetter climates the gradual descent of surface materials in slow flow, or slide down joints and other solution-widened planes in the bedrock with a modest degree of pore water pressure, is widespread. Surface clays and loams gradually incorporate clasts of the karst bedrock on their way down, producing an important category of cave sediment of the character of a diamicton. They have commonly been labelled breccias in the past; in so far as no fluvial action is involved this is justified, but subsoil weathering of limestone and dolomite clasts rounds and smoothes them, so that in purely descriptive terms the mixtures often take on the aspect of conglomerates.

However, removal of unconsolidated material by piping to create voids of some size can cause sudden and substantial block slumping to create fresh surface depressions (Ger. *Erdfall*). Debris slides contribute in this circumstance also.

Collapse

In no morphogenetic system are rockfall, block slide and rock slide (Varnes 1958) as significant as in karst. Since soils are generally thin, bare rocks and cliffs in regions where these processes operate assume a more important role in the landscape. Solution acts as freely both laterally and vertically to a degree not so true of other erosive processes, so that undercutting of slopes by streams is more effective in karst than in less soluble terrain. Most importantly, solution produces caves where roofs as well as walls are subject to fall (White and White 1969; Renault 1967–8).

The laws of rock mechanics have been determined on small bodies of rock in the laboratory or by observations in tunnels and cuttings for engineering purposes, where the stresses are applied virtually instantaneously in geological time. These findings have to be applied with care in nature, where the enlargement of a cave or the widening of a valley proceeds exceedingly slowly in comparison. Shear strength varies complexly because of variations in lithology and the presence of bedding and joint planes. In addition to the force of gravity, there are permanent tectonic stresses in the rocks and also in the load imposed by the mass of overlying rocks (lithostatic load). Erosion causes decompression, which opens up joints and permits rockfall on the surface and roof collapse underground. Changes in surface form or cave shape as a result of solution, corrasion and transport of cave deposits can upset a previously established equilibrium of forces so that breakdown occurs to restore a fresh temporary equilibrium. The draining of a previously waterfilled cave causes a sudden loss of roof and wall support, which has been considered by Davis (1930) and later by Davies (1977) as a potent factor in cave evolution. However, Bögli (1978) thinks the fluctuation in water support that occurs in the parts of a cave liable to intermittent flooding is more important.

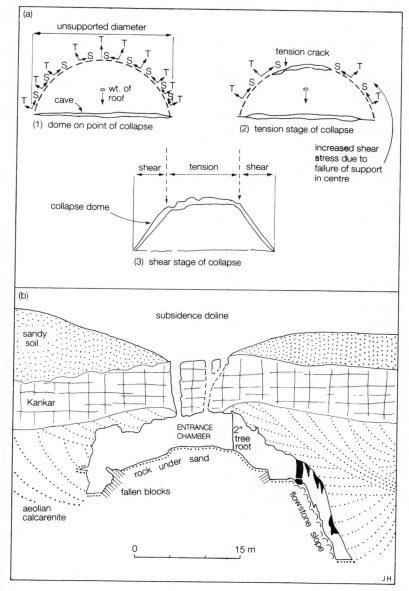

Figure 8 Collapse dome formation in weak limestone: (a) the sequence according to A.L. Hill (in Jennings 1968): S = shear, T = tension; (b) an example in aeolian calcarenite, Easter Cave, Augusta, south-western Australia. Soil thickness from Lowry (1967).

Stresses in cliffs in the open and on cave walls and roofs tend to drive them into space; falling and sliding of masses of rock result. In the confined condition of a cave, the continuity of the roof from wall to wall results in local compression. Tensional and shear components in this compression tend to produce dome or Roman arch forms. How well this will be achieved depends on the consolidation of the rock, the spacing of the planes of weakness and their attitude, and on the pressure of the overlying rocks. The semi-consolidated dune limestones of Australia are particularly prone to piecemeal collapse, creating domes (figure 8), but the collapse material may pile nearly to the roof through lack of much solution to remove the bulky material. The chalky bryozoal limestones common at depth in the Nullarbor Plain, Australia, are also weak enough to produce barrel arches, apses and high domes in profusion (see plate 2).

With strong rocks near the surface, rock structure maintains angular forms. Quadrangular cross-section is found not only with horizontal bedding (figure 9(b); plate 37) but also with vertical; however, collapse in rocks of intermediate dip commonly gives rise to triangular cross-section, as in many of the Mendip caves in England. As the cave slopes towards the surface through successive collapses, eventually the roof sags and then falls down, opening the cave to the sky. Cave collapse may expose prominently joints that have not played an important role in the cave formation; this can be misleading, as Bögli (1978) says.

Below a critical depth, the mechanical response of the rock will be different, a plastic regime taking over from an elastic one. Here an elliptical form with a vertical major axis should develop, though collapsed material will interfere with the system of forces if not removed

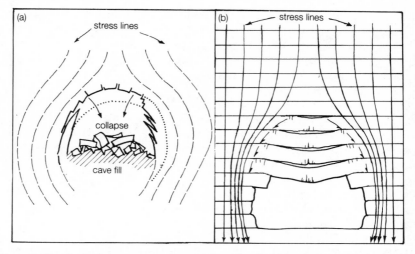

Figure 9 The effects of stress on cave cross-section: (a) under high rock pressure at depth, after Trimmel (1968) and Bögli (1978); (b) in a shallow cave, after W.E. Davies (1951).

Plate 2 A dome in Abrakurrie Cave, Nullarbor Plain, Australia. It was formed by breakdown in weak, horizontally bedded Eocene chalky limestone.

(figure 9(a)). Trimmel (1951) and Bögli (1978) interpret the shapes of various Alpine caves along these lines, but plasticity is not relevant to most caves (Renault 1967–8). The peeling rock tends to form curved flakes with thinning margins, which cut across the bedding.

With greater depths still, the load will be so great as to close all voids quickly; Waltham (1972) thinks that the apparent absence of caves in carbonate rock parts of the Himalayas is due to high plasticity of the rocks present. Chalk behaves more plastically than many limestones. Gypsum and halite have much greater plasticity still, so this is a great constraint on cave formation in the evaporites.

Many of the factors governing the stability of cliffs and caves are permanent in terms of human observation, yet rockfall and rockslide are known to be intermittent. Triggering actions must be involved. Earthquakes create temporary additional stresses, but there is no evidence that they have greater effects underground than on the surface, or in karst than in other terrain. Rock-blasting and heavy vehicular traffic can happen very close to caves without obvious damage; this was true of the Dark Cave at Bukit Batu in Selangor (Malaysia) in 1962, for example, and applies to several caves at Mt Etna in Rockhampton, Qld.

Hydrostatic water pressure in cracks may increase after heavy rain. Other possible triggering forces are swelling after the wetting of shale interbeds or films of colloids along slightly opened planes of weakness. There is also the force of crystallization of minerals (salt wedging) to be considered. Conversely, it has been suggested that the drying out of clay interbeds and breccia fills in fissures may reduce cohesion and shear strength. However, the probability is that the commonest trigger will be the simple progress of solution by percolation water along planes of weakness and lateral migration of cave streams eroding the base of walls.

Cave Weathering

Most caves possess an equable atmosphere and many higher latitude caves are lacking in much biological activity; therefore many weathering processes that depend on atmospheric fluctuations and biotic factors are absent or minimized in caves. There are important local variations from this principle, however, so that solution and cave breakdown as already described are not the only factors involved.

Thaw–freeze action penetrates into the forward parts of caves and its products may fall or sludge in farther still. Some caves or parts of them are dry enough to allow crystallization of salts by evaporation and so salt wedging can become important. Gypsum is the more widespread mineral to form and act in this way, but its effects are small in comparison with

Plate 3 The Dune in Mullamullang Cave, Nullarbor Plain, Australia, a 9 m pile of sand and fine-gravel-sized breakdown formed by salt crystallization from Eocene limestone.

those of halite in Nullarbor Plain caves (Lowry and Jennings 1974); roof dome formation here may owe much to this process, and the products pile up in dune-like forms (plate 3).

In biological weathering, there are disputed claims about bats scratching bell holes in cave roofs (King-Webster and Kenny 1958; Hooper 1958), but there is the undoubted fact of corrosion of bedrock and speleothems by bat guano and possibly urine (Jennings 1963). New minerals are formed from the reactions. Bacteria are now thought to be widespread in caves and they have been claimed to have both corrosional and depositional actions (Smyk and Drzal 1964); they may be responsible for the formation of moonmilk (Caumartin and Renault 1958).

Whilst biological activity is relatively restricted in higher latitude caves, it is becoming increasingly obvious that biological weathering (by both physical and chemical means) is very important in the equatorial regions. Here, hot, (20–25 °c) humid conditions in caves often provide excellent habitats for a whole range of vertebrates, invertebrates, fungi and bacteria. The intricate chain of life from the smallest bacterium or fungus through to cockroaches, spiders, centipedes and snakes, is now well documented from the caves of Mulu, Sarawak (Eavis 1981) and popularized by many television programmes. With such an amount of life in these caves, excreta and other waste products accumulates and in turn affect the water chemistry of the cave environment. This effects both weathering of the limestone rock and the production of many rare minerals. These are the neglected processes of tropical cave development.

4 Drainage

It is difficult to write about the drainage of karst without presuming a knowledge of karst landforms, but it is harder still to attempt to explain the forms without a background knowledge of the way water passes through karst, because this is the main operative agent. Therefore on both theoretical and practical grounds this subject is taken up here. The

Plate 4 The River Andabara, in the central highlands of PNG, piercing a Miocene limestone strike ridge. The flat-floored closed depression beyond has partly developed on impure limestone.

essence of the matter has already been posed: marked permeability enables underground drainage to take on the task of moving water to the sea or at least into surrounding country to various degrees in space and time (see plate 4). As a result, surface drainage can become intermittent, widely spaced, subdivided or absent.

Areal Input

Only recently has study begun on what happens to water falling onto slopes in karst. Even now, what can be said must rely largely on qualitative observations and theoretical assumptions rather than actual measurement. Perhaps the best study yet made (Gunn 1981) has the limitation that it deals with karst with relevant special characters. The broad standpoint that offers itself is that in karst:

1 there is rapid and substantial infiltration into outcrop and soil;
2 overland flow (whether Hortonian, with rainfall intensity greater than infiltration capacity, or saturated, when the soil no longer accepts rain) and return flow (where water is emerging areally from the soil) are restricted and rarely reach stream channels;
3 throughflow (where water is moving laterally through the soil, either saturated or unsaturated) is modest.

These generalizations need amplification and qualification. On out-crops in karst, rain usually flows only short distances before infiltrating. The coarse porosity of emerged coral reefs usually causes immediate absorption, so that lack of surface water can be extreme even with annual precipitation of 2000 mm and more. Rapid infiltration is also characteristic of chalk, despite its micritic texture and very fine inter-granular porosity. With compact karst rocks lacking intergranular porosity, water flows over the surface until it encounters planes of weakness. Here the frequency, openness and continuity of these planes control infiltration. Aubert (1969) contrasts the numbers and openness of joints, particularly strike joints, along anticlines in the Jura Mountains of Switzerland with their paucity and tightness along synclines. Very fine joints characteristic of argillaceous limestone hinder infiltration because of high surface tension and blockage by weathering residues. Those joints wide enough for infiltration are enlarged preferentially by solution so that initial permeability is accentuated. Close fields of grikes (solution-widened joints) bring about virtually immediate loss underground. But in thick beds lacking porosity, water may be held until it is entirely lost by evaporation in solution pans and even larger solution hollows such as the rockholes of the Nullarbor Plain (where calcretization is involved – Lowry and Jennings 1974). The more intense the rainfall and the steeper the surface, the longer overland flow can be, as witness solution flutes several metres long and solution runnels several tens of metres long on nearly vertical faces in the perennially or seasonally humid tropics (Jennings 1982b).

With covered karst, behaviour varies with the nature of the soil or superficial deposits. Many residual karst soils allow high infiltration rates. This is true of rendzinas, common in mid-latitude karst forms; these soils are dark, alkaline, shallow loams with crumb structure and often including rock fragments. On steep slopes there is throughflow in such soils, but otherwise the tendency will be to pass almost vertically through the soil to the bedrock surface where there may be lateral movement to joints.

However, other residual and transported soils in karst behave differently. Prolonged leaching of weathering mantles may result in dense, acid, fine-textured soils which consist of clay minerals and iron sesquioxide residues from the bedrock. Some at least of the 'terra rossa' soils of the Mediterranean and the heavy yellow podsolics of the south China karst are of this nature. These restrain infiltration, especially when they are cleared of forest, grazed and cultivated; they also tend to block joints below. Longer overland flows result prior to infiltration. Heavy clay soils seal the bottoms of depressions, leading to hydromorphic soils, swamps and even ponds.

Superficial deposits are as various as soils. Colluvia on steep slopes on carbonate rocks are generally coarse and promote vertical infiltration to the rock. Alluvia within karst vary much in texture because materials from outside the karst may be involved as well as those derived from the karst rocks, so the balance between downward percolation and lateral deflection as surface runoff to the margins of the alluvial flats varies a great deal. Glacial moraine derived from karst itself is commonly permeable with little overland flow. Loess behaves similarly in natural conditions, though ancient loesses have developed much clay pedogenically. Volcanic ashes are similar, but these are found in humid climates as often as dry (to which loess is largely confined) and so quickly develop clay contents inhibiting infiltration and promoting lateral movement of water (see below). Bauxitic clays in Jamaican karst are thought by some to be of such volcanic origin. What is certain is that, in its vigorous cockpit relief, there is much stripping from higher relief and concentration in the lower parts of the landscape (Smith *et al.* 1972). Thus there can be sharp variation within and between types of karst in the relative importance of infiltration, runoff and throughflow.

Vegetation also has a great influence on infiltration, promoting it by increasing stemflow and providing root channels. However, perhaps even greater is the contrary effect through transpiration of different plant covers. Thus, Holmes and Colville (1970 a,b) showed that, with the same limestone and soil in south-eastern South Australia, pine forest causes twice as much loss to the atmosphere as grassland, reducing input into the limestone to nil. Both are anthropogenic in nature, but equivalent differences in cover do occur within karst forms in a nearly natural state.

The karst surface is commonly a mosaic of outcrop and soil, the latter often on patches of transported sediment. The interaction between these elements can be important. Outcrops may export still aggressive water to soils around, for often the rock stands higher and this export can help perpetuate the topographic relationship between the two (Jennings 1978b). At the same time, their contact may become an especially favourable locus for solution attacking the basal margin of the projecting rock.

The hydrology of the closed depression is clearly central to karst development but has rarely been investigated in a thorough manner. Williams (1972a) argued from an analysis of the form of closed depressions in much tropical karst to stream flow down a pattern of gullies, fed by overland flow, throughflow in soil and litter, and lateral subcutaneous flow in the much weathered, upper few metres of the bedrock. Thus autogenic recharge of the limestone is concentrated to a few point inputs.

However, from more localized but repeated observation in Jamaican depressions, Day (1979) came to the conclusion that surface flow is of very restricted importance – indeed, significant only in the lower parts of those depressions with thick bauxitic clay covers, where small gullies were encountered. Even here it needs exceptional storms to produce flows in them, when ponding of the floors occurs also. Vertical infiltration is apparently the dominant hydrological mode here, especially where superficial covers are absent and open shafts present. In this case waters enter the underground in a diffuse way.

The most continuous observations have been made in two depressions in the Waitomo karst, New Zealand, over the course of a year by Gunn (1981). Regular sampling of water from various points and correlation of their chemistry with antecedent rainfall permitted a preliminary picture of their hydrology (see figure 10). Overland flow is infrequent, only after intense or prolonged rainfall, but sustained lateral flow occurs within the soil, the throughflow consisting of both a rapid component near the surface and a slower flow lower down. Subcutaneous flow takes from two to ten weeks to reach the centre of the depression, but storms have an immediate effect by shunting threads of water through the rock. Gunn's subcutaneous flow corresponds largely with the ideas of epikarstic storage and delayed infiltration of Mangin (1974–5) and Bakalowicz (1981) in a zone near the surface of more intense jointing as a result of exogenic factors.

Gunn also distinguishes three components in the vertical transmission of water through the rock. Through tight joints vadose seepage feeds slow drips in caves below, which take from a few hours to as much as ten weeks to respond to rainfall events. It is the smallest component of the

37

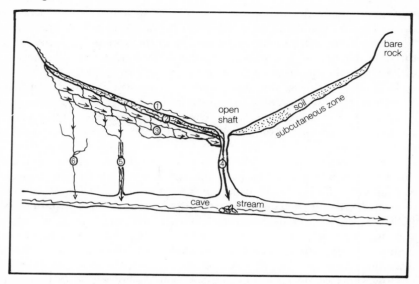

Figure 10 The hydrology of a closed depression, Waitomo, NZ, after Gunn (1981). 1, overland flow; 2, throughflow; 3, subcutaneous flow; 4, shaft flow; 5, vadose trickle; 6, vadose seepage.

three. Vadose flows ('trickles' of Smith *et al.* (1976) is a less confusing term to apply to them) descend solutionally enlarged joints, which are either open or choked with sediment, and reach caves as fast drips or streamlets (often called 'inlets' by cavers). These respond rapidly to rain, but how long flow lasts depends on whether the channels they follow are open (up to 6 weeks) or filled (up to 15 weeks). Shaft flow provides the largest inputs made up of varying proportions of overland flow, throughflow and subcutaneous flow. The differences between Gunn's assessment and that of Day derive only in part from the 2–6 m covers of Pleistocene ash over the Waitomo karst from the volcanoes to the east, which develop loamy soils deflecting flow laterally, because subcutaneous flow is more important than throughflow there. Moreover, there is much agreement between Gunn's findings and those of Friederich and Smart (1981), who carried out dye tracing from small surface depressions into G.B. Cave in the Mendip Hills where there are no comparable transported covers on the limestone. Also, Williams (1983) interprets drip rates and cave pool levels in Carlsbad Caverns in the semiarid, bare karst of the Guadalupe Mountains along similar lines. The system revealed by these investigations is one of important lateral concentration on to point inputs into the underground, favouring the development of large cave passages below (Gunn 1983).

Gunn's chemical results showed expectable responses in terms of amounts of limestone dissolved. Overland flow and throughflow have low values but the remainder have high ones, with subcutaneous and

38

shaft flows the highest. This is through longer contact with the bedrock. Among the vadose flows where there is greatest variance, those through soil-filled joints yield lower calcium concentrations because of reduced contact with the rock itself. Gams (1979) gives an important role to hygroscopic and capillary waters retained for long periods in soils and joints and then shunted into caves by gravitational water after rainstorms; this is responsible for bringing many waters to saturation, in his view.

Surface Rivers

Surface streams are usually few in karst. In the whole Dinaric karst of Yugoslavia, only four rivers – the Neretva, Cetina, Krka and Zrmanja – cross it to reach the sea, and only the first crosses the whole width of the fully developed karst. One-quarter of the karst drains directly to the sea without any help from surface streams (Gams 1969).

In very humid climates and on less pure karst rocks river systems are found, but generally the drainage density is less than on other rocks in the region. With well developed karst this is self-evident, but analysis may be needed. Miller (1953) did a morphometric analysis of Horton first- and second-order streams in the Clinch Mountains in Virginia and Tennessee, comparing the dolomite Copper Ridge area with the sandstones and shales around Blountville and the sandstones, siltstones and shales around Pennington. All have similar local relief and dendritic drainage, but streams are longer and basins larger on the dolomite than on the others, giving it a smaller drainage density.

The four rivers that cross the Dinaric karst have their headwaters on impervious rocks (i.e. they are *allogenic*) and have practically no tributaries as they pass through the karst, though springs do augment their flow. Allogenic rivers are common in karst. Rivers that begin their surface courses on karst rocks (i.e. *autogenic* streams) commonly do so in springs. These are often large, so that autogenic karst streams are often born adult.

To cross karst on the surface, both kinds of rivers frequently depend on alluvium sealing them off from the permeable bedrock. Some tropical karst forms consist largely of broad, alluvial plains on limestone, with perennial rivers meandering over it as in the Kinta Valley, Malaysia. In Guadeloupe, dendritic valleys occupy much of the karst with intermittent streams along their bottoms where 'terra rossa' has accumulated thickly (Lasserre 1954). The karstic central lowland of Ireland abounds in streams and lakes. This is due partly to a mantle of Pleistocene glacial deposits, some brought in from other rock areas. It is probably also a consequence of an earlier reduction of the region to a corrosional plain near to sea level on which a residual red clay cover had developed (Williams 1970).

Drainage

Away from dunefields, deserts on impervious rocks rarely lack stream courses, however impersistently used. Karst in semiarid and arid climate is usually without them, as for instance the Nullarbor Plain, Australia; all its meagre water goes underground to the ocean.

River Regimes

The more underground drainage participates in a hydrological system, the more efficient the latter becomes and the more of the water is available for geomorphological action. Rapid infiltration means that water escapes the surface heat, low humidities and wind, reducing evaporation. Plant roots search deeper, it is true; tree roots 20–30 m underground are common, and in Lake Cave, south-western Australia, living roots have been found 60 m down. Nevertheless, biological productivity is usually less on limestone than on many neighbouring rocks so that increased transpiration does not balance reduced evaporation.

Because of these factors, limestone areas discharge more of the precipitation falling on them than does impervious terrain. Pardé (1965) estimates evapotranspirational losses at 600 mm from impervious catchments in the central Apennines, Italy, whereas calcareous catchments such as that of the Nera River lose only 500 mm, a saving of 15 per cent. The Tarn in the Grandes Causses of France is even more efficient with a saving of 30 per cent.

The bottlenecks in underground flow and the water storage capacity of karst dampen down river regimes and so affect their geomorphic behaviour. Although only exceptionally will the voids in caves and enlarged planes of weakness in karst bulk more than 1–2 per cent of the whole mass, they sustain higher base flows longer, and flood peaks in karst rivers are moderate compared with those of rivers on impervious rocks. White and Reich (1970) have shown that in Pennsylvania the mean annual flood (the flood with a recurrence interval of 2.33 years) is low in carbonate rock basins compared with basins without karst rocks. This behaviour is found in karsts with elaborate cave systems above valley bottoms (below which all voids will be filled with water) and ceases in winter when frozen ground limits entry underground. Mountain relief will, however, make for big flood peaks even in karst country (Williams and Dowling 1979).

Pardé (1965) shows the general effect by graphing mean monthly discharge as a decimal fraction of mean annual discharge for the River Nera, a karst river in central Italy, where the lowest month has 0.83 and the highest month 1.06, and for the Tiber, a normal river, with corresponding figures of 0.18 and 1.95 (figure 11).

Examining the lower flows, especially by studying the mean of all flow

(a)

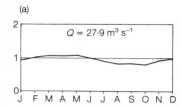

(b)

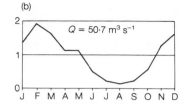

Figure 11   Mean monthly discharges as proportions of the mean annual discharge of (a) a karst river (the Nera River at Torre Orsina), and (b) a normal river (the Tiber, at Ponte Nuovo), after Pardé (1965).

peaks below the mean annual flood for many Appalachian catchments with carbonate rocks in them, E.L. White (1977) was able to make a further distinction between dolomite karsts, where caves are not so well developed and where low flows through smaller voids were very well sustained, and limestone karsts with elaborate karst development, where water passed through more rapidly and low flows were not so well maintained.

The damped flow regime in karst can be expected to minimize mechanical erosion there since it is in floods that rivers accomplish most of this kind of fluvial erosion, whether they be rare events of exceptional magnitude or more numerous ones of lesser magnitude. However, this argument does not apply so extremely or so widely in relation to corrosion. Many karst rivers have been found to have an inverse relationship between carbonate solute concentration (total hardness) and discharge; figure 12(a) shows this for the Green River, Kentucky. Various factors may combine to account for this relationship. With low flows there will be longer contact time between the channels, both surface and underground, and the karst rock, and yet the water will be turbulent enough to ensure mass transfer from the interface. Where low flows correspond with the growing seasons for plants (and in the warm season, evapotranspirational losses may cause this to be the time of low flows), greater carbon dioxide production can enhance hardness in waters reaching the river.

However, nearly always is the solute load greater at time of high flow than at low, because the range in discharge is far greater than the inverse range in carbonate hardness (see figure 12(b)). Thus karst rivers remain geomorphically effective despite their moderated flow regimes.

With some rivers, hardness is independent of discharge (Fergus River, Ireland: Williams 1968) and there are even examples where there is a direct relationship between the two (the Thames, England: Douglas 1968); in these cases the increase in solute load with rising discharge will be even greater. However, these rivers may have reached saturation, and transport or even deposition, rather than corrosion, may be their main function. Williams (1968) shows this is the case, for example, with the large Shannon River in Ireland.

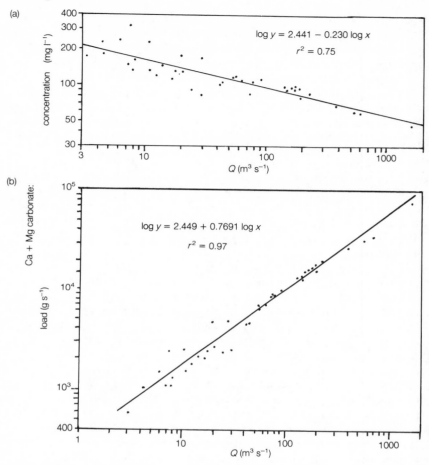

Figure 12 Regressions of (a) calcium and magnesium carbonate concentration and (b) load on the discharge of the Green River at Munfordville, Kentucky, for 1961–2.

Sinking of Rivers

Rivers entering karst or within it are liable to lose all or part of their volume underground. Where a stream can be seen to enter a cave either horizontally or vertically, or to disappear into fissures in the bedrock, the fact of karst loss is evident whatever the climate. In Slovenia there is the classic case of the Pivka River, which is barred by Sovic Hill under which it passes quietly into the famous Postojna Cave. In Craven, England, the stream flowing out of Malham Tarn sinks into fissures in its bed.

The loss is evident even when it takes place gradually into alluvium in the river channel or in swampy areas over karst rocks, provided it is

42

substantial or complete, and the climate is humid. In Nelson, the Takaka River is liable to disappear into its gravels, whereas other rivers in the area with impervious catchments flow perennially over gravel beds to the sea. Where only a small part of a stream is lost in these ways, the loss may be difficult to detect even in a truly humid region.

But in subhumid or semi-arid climates rivers are intermittent in flow, and may reach only partway along their courses as a normal rule because of evaporation, percolation into alluvium and failing supply. Here, additional loss into underlying permeable rocks may not be readily discovered. At Wee Jasper, New South Wales, an area with a subhumid climate, a creek along a limestone hill flank feeds water underground through joints to Dogleg Cave in a way that leaves the appearance of the channel no different from those of other streams nearby which do not encounter limestone but which are all intermittent in flow.

Frequently a stream will have a series of sinking points, or swallets, along its course into which it loses successive fractions of its volume. In the English Peak District, the Manifold River usually fails to flow over 7 km of its bed for one to three months each year in dry weather (Warwick 1953). This happens at Wetton Mill, where the stream flows on to reef limestones from interbedded limestones and shales. Its discharge decreases through losses into a series of *streamsinks*; some are shallow, bouldery depressions in the bed as at Wetton Mill itself; others are inflow cave entrances such as Redhurst Swallet. With falling stage, the one furthest downstream first becomes the limit of surface flow; then, successively, each upstream one in turn becomes the limit until the Manifold gets no further than Wetton Mill itself. With rising stage, the Manifold exceeds the capacity of each sinking point in turn downstream and eventually has continuous flow over its whole course again.

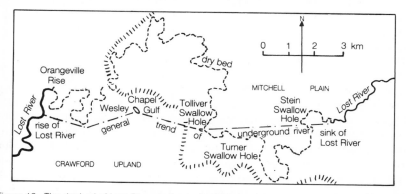

Figure 13 The dry bed of Lost River, Indiana, after Malott (1952).

The Lost River in Indiana provides a larger-scale example (figure 13). Its bed is commonly dry over 35 km, mostly over the Mitchell Plain but penetrating along entrenched meanders into the Crawford Upland, before perennial flow resumes (Malott 1952). Floods take the stream from its upstream sink (plate 5) to other points of engulfment down the dry bed, which occasionally is fully reoccupied right to Orangeville. Again, there are both seepages into coarse sediment in bed hollows and entrances into caves as at the big Tolliver Swallow Hole (though this is liable to be blocked with driftwood).

Plate 5 The Lost River, Indiana, sinking gently into its gravel bed on the Mississippian limestone of the Mitchell Plain.

Loss and resumption of surface flow are not always simple retreats up and advances down the dry bed. The process is complicated by groundwater additions and withdrawals along it, so that reaches of dry bed and of flow may alternate along the courses of karst streams, e.g. along North Branch at Cooleman Plain, NSW.

Equally common are streamsinks that put an end to surface flow at all times, often close to the contact between impervious and karst rock. This disruption of surface drainage gives an impression of disorder. However, Williams (1966a) showed that this was not so in the Ingleborough area in Craven, England, where he analysed the streamsinks by a modified form of Horton-Strahler stream ordering (see figure 14). In this a first-order stream has no tributaries, whereas a second-order stream has tributaries that are only first-order streams. A third-order stream may have tributaries that are second- as well as first-order; and so on with higher orders. A streamsink takes on the order of the stream disappearing into it. Dry valleys on impervious rocks that are parts of streamsink systems are included in the count because at times of favourable water balance streamflows are likely. On the other hand, sinking streams fed from large springs (which are where surface streams reappear) are excluded because they usually cannot be ordered. A higher-order streamsink may enclose lower-order ones, which must be excluded from the former's catchment area.

In the Ingleborough area, Williams found that, as with normal streams, the frequency of streamsinks varies inversely and geometrically with sink order, and streamsink catchment area has a direct relation to sink order. Furthermore, the mean distance apart of swallets of the same order increases geometrically with order number. Other measures confirm a picture of an orderly system.

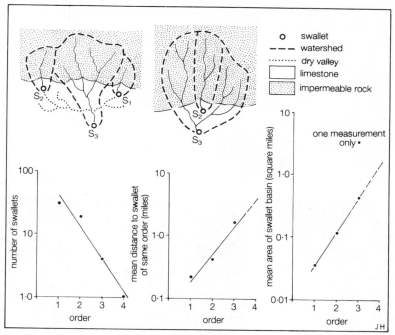

Figure 14 A method of ordering streamsinks and streamsink relationships in part of Craven, England, after Williams (1966b).

Williams worked from large-scale maps, but even they conceal the complexity of reality. Hanwell and Newson (in Weyman 1975) mapped the functioning stream courses in the Swildons Hole streamsink catchment in Mendip and found that in drought their length gave a density of less than 1 km km^{-2} but in flood the tentacles of drainage reached throughout the basin, giving a density of 47 km km^{-2}, the contributing area ranging between 14 and 100 per cent. The variable source area concept for runoff applies as well to these catchments contributory to karst as elsewhere.

Drainage

Some streamsinks behave in a way without complete parallel in surface drainage; these invert their function in time of flood and discharge water instead of receiving it. This happens because the cave fed by the streamsink receives other feeders underground, and in floods the total flow underground cannot pass through bottlenecks farther in and backs up. The French name *estavelle* is commonly used for such points of alternating action. The behaviour can be likened to overbank flooding above a gorge in a surface stream.

Streamsinks, and even apparently gradual disappearance of water along alluviated channels of allogenic rivers, imply a supply to ground-water at comparatively few points. However, in caprock situations where relatively thin covers allow vertical infiltration to the karst rock below, there can be allogenic supply to karst in small amounts at many points, amounting to a diffuse input.

Springs

In most kinds of terrain, throughflow in soil and waste mantles and subcutaneous flow ('interflow' of Chorley 1978) in weathered rocks give rise to small and intermittent springs. In karst, springs are larger, and more of them are permanent because of greater infiltration and because of the input of streamsinks fed from neighbouring impervious rocks. Important differences in behaviour distinguish *exsurgences* from *resurg-*

Plate 6 The River Lagaip resurging from a cave near Laiagam in the central highlands of PNG.

ences (Mangin 1974–5), though there is every stage of transition between them. The exsurgence is fed entirely by seepage through the karst rocks, whereas the resurgence is the reappearance of a former surface stream, always, however, with a lesser or greater contribution from percolation.

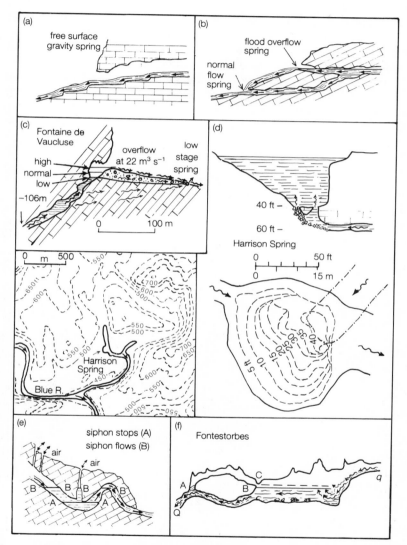

Figure 15 Types of springs: (a) gravity spring; (b) flood overflow spring; (c) spring rising under hydrostatic pressure, after Martel (1921) and Cousteau; (d) alluviated spring with rise pit, after Magerlein (in Palmer 1981); (e) ebbing and flowing spring, after Trombe (1952); (f) reciprocating spring, after Mangin (1974–5).

Drainage

Many springs flow out under gravity alone (figure 15(a); plate 6), either from the open mouths of caves, as with Mocilnik, one of the major springs of the Ljubljanica River in Slovenia, or through the interstices between rubble that has fallen to conceal the entrance, e.g. Grady Spring, Kentucky. At the Efflux, Bungonia Caves, NSW, the level of outflow was raised at least 9 m in this way.

An alternative name for a spring is a 'rising', and this name is applicable literally to many karst springs, which well upwards quietly through sediments, swamps or narrow fissures, or vigorously, through more open orifices. There is quiet upwelling through gravels and in wide swamps at Kirk Goz in the north of the Plain of Pamphylia near Antalya in southern Turkey. In the valleys of Kentucky and Indiana, deeply alluviated in the course of Pleistocene climatic oscillations, many springs issue from the bottoms of *rise pits* or *pools*. This is true of Harrison

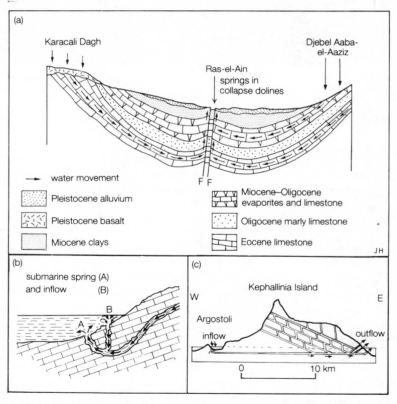

Figure 16 (a) Artesian spring, after Burdon and Safadi (1963); (b) submarine freshwater spring and associated seawater intake in a branch passage through the venturi effect; (c) Sea Mills of Argostoli, Kephallinia, Greece, feeding brackish subaerial and submarine springs on east coast, after Zötl (1974).

48

Plate 7 Waikoropupu Spring near Takaka, NZ, an artesian 'boiling' spring rising under pressure from limestone covered by impervious beds.

Spring, Indiana, with a peak flow of nearly 30 m³ s⁻¹, which can carry sand up from a cave passage in limestone 18 m below. A natural levee partly surrounds the pool (figure 15(d)).

Vauclusian springs, where the water is rising under pressure up bedrock passages, have their type in the Fontaine de Vaucluse at the head of the River Sorgue east of Avignon, France (figure 15(c)). It has a bedrock passage rising at about 45° to a little round cave in which it forms a pool. Normally it percolates through a shallow talus barrier, but it overflows this in floods. Divers have descended more than 100 m but have not reached the other side of the inverted siphon that provides the pressure head.

Vauclusian springs resemble artesian springs (figure 16(a)), where, however, the pervious beds are overlain by impervious beds. The waters descend in confinement down the dip and rise to the surface up faults or as a result of reversal of dip in synclinal structures.

Set in a gravel plain, Waikoropupu Springs near Takaka, NZ, with a mean flow of 14 m³ s⁻¹ (Williams 1977), include perpetually 'boiling springs' (plate 7). Velocities of more than 2 m s⁻¹ prevent divers from penetrating openings in the rocks below. These are in coarse Tertiary sandstones that act as an aquiclude over Palaeozoic marble which is the main supplier of the water. Thus these springs are artesian in character.

Frequently a perennial spring has associated with it one or more higher springs which function only after heavy rain. At these times the passage to the lower spring fills to capacity, so water banks up behind and overflows through a distributary passage to a higher outlet (figure 15(b)). This is the relationship of Ingleborough Cave to Clapham Beck Head in Craven, and on a larger scale of Hölloch Cave, Switzerland, to its perennial spring, the Schleichende Brunnen, 100 m lower down in Muototal.

Peculiar to karst are 'ebbing and flowing wells', springs with a regular period in their flow. Completely intermittent springs of this kind have been explained by a true siphon action (figure 15(e)). When the level behind the siphon builds up to B, the siphon functions and the level drops to A rapidly. However, there are difficulties in this explanation, and in any case most of the springs of this broad kind are 'reciprocating' (Sweeting 1972a); that is, they do not cease to flow in the low-stage intervals. These are more simply explained by air getting into an upper passage periodically, which reduces the hydraulic head for a lower passage, reducing the flow from the spring (figure 15(f)) (Mangin 1974–5). Mangin was discussing the Fontestorbes spring in the French Pyrenees; a similar spring is that at Buckhaw Brow in Craven.

Many features indicate the presence of a spring. Underlying impervious rocks cause springs at the base of the karst rock. Thus, in Craven, Austwick Beck Head emerges at the unconformity between Carboniferous limestone and Precambrian metamorphic rocks. Fault contacts of karst and impervious rocks are also likely spring locations. Glacial moraine banked against hillsides of limestone and dolomite sometimes causes springs along its top margin and alluvial river terraces have the same effect. Without the intervention of impervious materials, springs emerge entirely within the karst at points in valley bottoms or at sharp breaks of slope; here, the top of a saturated zone of the rock is intersecting with the surface. The Blue Waterholes, Cooleman Plain, NSW, rise within the limestone but not much above the level of a fault contact with igneous rocks which acts as a threshold to the karst. Springs also occur high up valleysides without obvious topographic or geological cause, e.g. the Golling Falls, 100 m above the Salzach River in Austria. In some cases this is due to such rapid downcutting of the valley that as yet the lower parts of the karst rock have not developed the necessary secondary permeability and cave development to lower the outlets to local base level.

Sea level is another important control of spring location; for example, Ewens Ponds and Piccanninie Ponds, SA, emerge at about sea level, and there are nearby springs in the beaches. Nevertheless, there are subaqueous springs beneath sea or lake level where karst rocks descend below it. The Bourbioz spring lies 80 m below the surface of Lake Annecy in the French Alps where relief can provide ample hydraulic head. The writings of classical Greece and Rome have made famous the submarine springs of the Asia Minor coast, e.g. in the Gulf of Edremit near Akcay, the *vruljas* of the Adriatic coast of Yugoslavia and around Greece itself (figure 16(b) and (c)). Submarine springs called *posas* are common around the low limestone plateau of the Yucatan.

Mistardis (1968) cites several submarine springs at depths of 30–40 m around southern Greece. Four hundred metres off the Kynourian coast below the high Parnon Mountain, Anavalos spring opens on the bottom at −36 m and has been divided to a depth of −75 m. Mistardis follows a well accepted attribution of such springs to cave development during Pleistocene glacioeustatic low sea levels with subsequent drowning. Theoretically, deep phreatic solution (see chapter 7) should also be capable of forming caves beneath the sea, and some Floridan submarine springs are artesian on origin (Springfield and LeGrand 1969a).

Sinking points of sea water are counterparts of submarine freshwater springs, as is the case with the famous 'whirlpool' in the Sea of Argostoli on the west side of the Ionian island of Kephallinia (figure 16(b) and (c)). These 'sea-mills' supply water to brackish submarine and coastal springs on the eastern side of the island. Precipitation on the mountainous core of the island drains underground down the dip of the limestone to the east coast; these currents act like ejectors accelerating water flowing across the island in caves formed below sea level in the Pleistocene (Zötl 1974).

Patterns of Underground Connections

The course of water underground has been established in many parts of the world now by direct exploration, by chemical analysis of the waters, by flood pulse analysis and by the introduction of various tracers. Sometimes this just replaces a part of the surface drainage; in other cases there is diversion elsewhere (Gèze 1958).

The simplest circumstance is where an underground course takes over from a surface course during normal and low stages along virtually the same line. This is the case between the Owenterbolea streamsink and St Brendan's Well rising on the Poulnagollum Cave–Gowlaun River drainage in northwest Clare, Ireland (Collingridge 1969). In the development of such an arrangement, sinking occurs at successively more upstream swallets, and successively more downstream resurgences take over from one another, but all remain in the line of the surface course, which formerly functioned at all stages of discharge. Surface and underground flows may reach the same point even when the underground connection follows a different route. Thus at Wombeyan Caves, NSW, Wombeyan Creek in flood flows through Creek Cave, which runs directly beneath the saddle of the old valley linking its upper and lower surface courses, but its lesser flows pass through Fig Tree and Junction Caves on a more direct course, the water emerging in a spring, which falls some 7 m directly into the flood channel (Jennings *et al.* 1982).

Drainage

Even when the surface course ceases to take flood overflow and the intervening dry valley has become a string of closed depressions, the relationship can still be close. At Yarrangobilly Caves, NSW, the stream entering Bathhouse Cave emerges 1.3 km away in Coppermine Cave in the bottom of the Yarrangobilly River gorge, only 425 m upstream of the junction with the gorge of the disorganized dry valley running down from the upper cave's blind valley. In the Takaka karst, NZ, a high, precipitous rejuvenation head separates the former streamsink at the 176-m-deep Harwood Hole from the former resurgence at Starlight Cave. But now Gold Creek disappears 2 km farther upstream, whereas

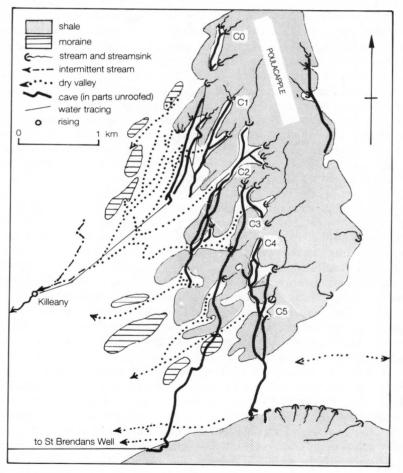

Figure 17 The relationship of Cullaun Caves, Clare, Ireland, to surface streams and dry valleys, after Ollier and Tratman (1969).

the active spring has shifted a kilometre down the gorge of Gorge Creek (Williams 1982a). The water soon sinks again in the gorge, but this time it departs underground from the original drainage line to rise finally a kilometre south of the mouth of the gorge.

Various degrees of departure of underground flow from the former surface flow are more common, and the geological structure is frequently the cause of the severance. Partial departure is exhibited by the Cullaun caves on the west of the shale ridge of Poulacapple, Clare (Ollier and Tratman 1969). The pattern of surface streams in valleys cut in the shales is continued south-westwards to the Killeany rising and stream by dry valleys cut in to glacial moraine down to the limestone (figure 17). The streams sink into the limestone and at first the shallow caves follow the dry valleys. But then they are deflected SSW along major joints. In this way they pass under divides south of their originating valleys and join the Killeany system at St Brendans Well south and west of the former surface drainage. The southernmost of the series, Cullaun 5 Cave, extends beneath the shale ridge of Knockvoarheen, closing off the Killeany lowland on the south and escaping the system altogether.

Faults sometimes provide favourable zones for cave development and may deflect flow until they meet a deep valley and thus disrupt the original pattern grossly. Gèze (1958) cites the example of the Bueges, which is deflected along a fault to emerge in the Hérault River gorge 10 km downstream of the junction of the Bueges River valley (figure 18(a)) with that of the Hérault.

Geomorphological history may have to combine with the tectonic structure to cause such deflections. At Mole Creek, Tasmania (figure 18(b)), the general trend of the drainage is north-eastwards from the northern flank of the Central Plateau of Jurassic dolerite across the axial trends of a synclinorium in Ordovician limestone and sandstone. These courses have been superimposed on the underlying folds from overlying rocks since removed. Marakoopa Creek is one of these streams and has a surface course channel across a limestone syncline and then along Sensation Gorge slicing through a sandstone anticline. However, it rarely flows through this gorge now but normally its discharge passes underground along the trend of the syncline to join Sassafras Creek, which passes round the nose of the pitching anticline of sandstone.

It is common for a number of streamsinks to feed a common spring, and in this respect the underground drainage matches a dendritic surface stream system. In the Poulacapple area (figure 17) several sinks resurge at the Killeany rising and another group feeds St Brendans Well.

In the King Country, NZ, where more or less horizontal limestones were formerly covered by mudstones and siltstones, stripping of these overlying formations and progressive disappearance of dendritic surface drainage has ultimately resulted in a total hydrological reorganization

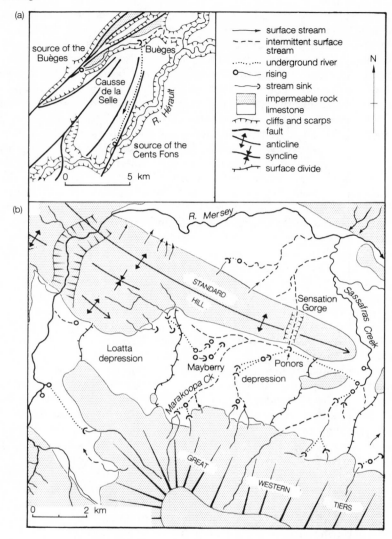

Figure 18 Structural deflection of underground drainage from the surface pattern: (a) by faults, after Gèze (1958); (b) by folds.

into small, polygonal, centripetal surface basins feeding dendritic cave river systems, which are arranged quite differently from the original surface drainage; see figure 19 (Williams 1982a).

Many instances are now known where a streamsink supplies more than one spring either at all times or at different stages of flow. The full

Drainage

range is present in the central Kentucky karst (Quinlan et al. 1983) (figure 20).

Only small systems have the one resurgence; these include the Double Sinks and Mill Spring catchments. The large catchments are complex. Bear Wallow incorporates three sub-basins, one of which is the Three Springs catchment that has two rise pits in alluvium and one composite spring through rubble.

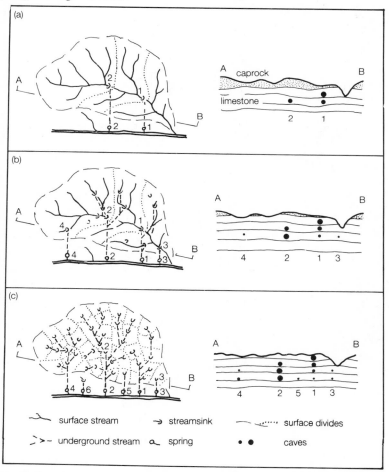

Figure 19   Karst drainage development and cave size in King Country, NZ (after Williams 1982a): (a) underground capture 1 creates a large catchment to form a big cave, but its lower level, formed through main river incision, is smaller because capture 2 has reduced the sinking catchment; (b) further removal of caprock allows more streamsinks and collapse dolines to form, which leads to more but smaller centripetal catchments and cave passages; (c) competition between surface basins produces a more uniform pattern of surface relief. Passage sizes adjust to the dendritic underground catchment discharges.

55

C

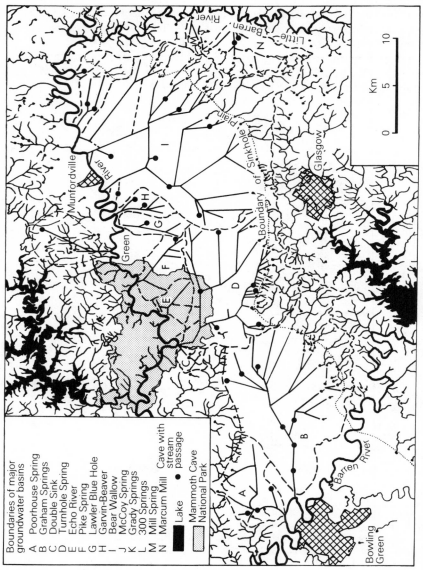

Boundaries of major
groundwater basins

A Poorhouse Spring
B Graham Springs
C Double Sink
D Turnhole Spring
E Echo River
F Pike Spring
G Lawler Blue Hole
H Garvin-Beaver
I Bear Wallow
J McCoy Spring
K Grady Springs
L 300 Springs
M Mill Spring
N Marcum Mill

● Cave with
   stream
   passage

▬ Lake

▨ Mammoth Cave
   National Park

Figure 20 The hydrology of central Kentucky, after Quinlan and Rowe (1977).

through rubble. Bear Wallow catchment feeds springs along 5 km of the left bank of Green River with eight major springs or groups of springs forming a big distributary system resembling a delta's hydrology. The Graham Springs catchment on the western margin of the Sinkhole Plain is mainly a very elaborate dendritic system but there is an overlap with the Turnhole Spring catchment to the east. Here, Madison Spring in base flow contributes to both basins, and Little Sinking Creek, which normally flows northward underground to Turnhole Spring on the Green River, in flood overflows its valley westwards to supply some water to Graham Springs on the Barren River (Quinlan 1976).

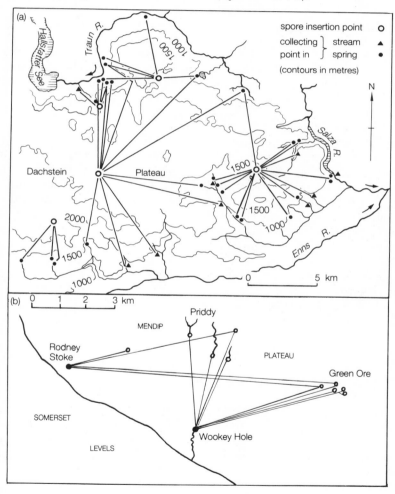

Figure 21 (a) The hydrology of Dachstein Plateau, Austria, after Zötl (1974); (b) crossing of underground drainage systems in Mendip, after Smith and Drew (1975).

57

Drainage

More extreme distributary underground systems have been demonstrated by Zötl (1957, 1965), employing spore drift in the Austrian calcareous Alps. In high limestone plateaus surrounded by deep valleys such as the Dachstein and the Totes Mountains, spores fed into streamsinks near the plateau margin reappeared in a few springs close together at the foot on one side. But when sinking waters farther and farther into the plateau were tagged thus, springs on wider and wider sectors of the margin were reached by them (figure 21(a)). Such a pattern can scarcely be likened to that of a river delta.

Underground drainage has one quirk of behaviour in its repertoire that cannot be matched at all on the surface, namely independent lines of flow at different levels crossing one another without interference. Water tracing suggests that this must be the case with the neighbouring spring catchments of Rodney Stoke and Wookey Hole in the Mendip (figure 21(b)) (Drew 1975). Water sinking near Priddy flows only to Wookey Hole, but streamsinks well to the east supply both Wookey Hole and Rodney Stoke, crossing the other flowlines without mixing. Normally it would not be wise to suggest this on the basis of water tracing only, but this is one of the most studied karsts in the world so the risk is less. This crossing of underground streams at different levels is supported by exploration of caves beneath surface streams on the limestone surface above, as in the case of Doolin Cave running beneath the Aille River in Clare, Ireland. In the Muller Plateau in New Guinea, the Ugwapugwa Streamway branch of the Atea Kananda cave passes beneath the surface course of the Atea River before the latter sinks; and it may also flow beneath the underground course of another tributary, Yu Wadaga, but as yet that is a matter of inference (James and Dyson 1980). Several instances of both kinds of behaviour are known in the Peak District (Christopher et al. 1977). Merlin Cave passes beneath streams in Cucklet and Middleton Dales, and water from the River Hamps crosses underneath the River Manifold at Ilam (Beck 1975).

Regimes of Karst Springs

Although basaltic lavas give rise to large springs, most of the large springs of the world are in karst. On present knowledge, the springs at the source of the Manavgat River east of Antalya in southern Turkey are thought to be together the largest, with a mean flow about 125–130 m^3 s^{-1}. The largest single orifice at Dumanli yields 50 m^3 s^{-1} as an average, with a total outflow annually of 1.6×10^9 m^3 (Karanjac and Gunay 1980). These drain a much larger area of the northern slopes of the limestone Taurus Mountains and the central Anatolian plateau than of the southern flank of the range.

In north-eastern Syria, the Ras el'Ain discharges on the average 39 m^3

s^{-1} from 13 individual springs, which tap two artesian aquifers along a fault plane (see figure 16(a)). The lower is of Eocene limestone, which has an intake area of basalts and that limestone, and the upper is of Miocene limestone and evaporites, and contributes only to a southern group of the springs (Burdon and Safali 1963). The springs are in circular ponds which are thought to be due to the collapse of a Quaternary conglomerate into cavities dissolved in the evaporites beneath.

One of the largest springs in China is Chingshui in Guangxi Province, with a mean flow of 33 m^3 s^{-1} supplied from a catchment about 60 km long and 30 km wide; it ranges from 4 m^3 s^{-1} to a mighty 390 m^3 s^{-1}. The main underground artery is 50 km long (figure 22).

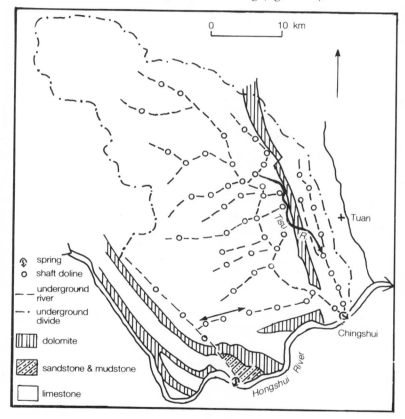

Figure 22 The underground drainage of Tuan County, Guangxi Province, China, after Guangxi Chuang Autonomous Region Geological Bureau (1976).

In Europe perhaps the most famous but not the largest karst source is the group of 16 springs at San Giovanni at the foot of the Istrian Plateau near Trieste, Italy. The mean flow is 26.5 m^3 s^{-1}, which forms the River

Drainage

Timavo for a very short course to the sea. However, the springs are the resurgence of the Reka River, which sinks into Skocjanska Cave 30 km away in Slovenia. In the United States there are the always limpid but 'boiling' pools of Silver and Blue Springs in northern Florida, each discharging 14–15 m^3 s^{-1}.

Karst springs usually have a more even flow than karst rivers, which do not depend entirely on underground supply. Ras el'Ain has monthly mean discharges ranging between 0.93 and 1.08 of the annual mean, with the extreme minimum recorded only 0.77 of it. Flood discharges of the Silver and Blue Springs are never more than three times the mean flow. These characteristics are due to slower movement underground, tight bottlenecks in cave passages and big storages (estimated at 2×10^9 m^3 for the Dumanli spring).

Not all are so well regulated. The Fontaine de Vaucluse, a big spring with its mean of 26–27 m^3 s^{-1}, has floods of about seven times that rate of discharge and then disgorges muddy water. It has an open cave system with big drops behind its inverted siphon. Elsewhere, unreliability of rainfall and liability to high intensity in precipitation can also induce liveliness in springs. With modest relief and modest precipitation, the Blue Waterholes at Cooleman Plain, NSW, have nevertheless recorded a range of 0.17–2.19 m^3 s^{-1} and muddy water is churned out in floods. This is despite routing patterns of underground flow that damp down peak flows. Nevertheless, such damping is characteristic compared with surface channel flow. Springs generally respond to rain more slowly than surface rivers. At the Blue Waterholes, Cooleman Plain, flood waters take 24–28 hours to pass through the underground with straightline distances up to 5 km between streamsink and spring. The flood pulse arrives earlier because of a hydraulic ram effect through the water-filled section of the caves; increased head above this part is reflected immediately at the bottom end in greater discharge. The caves of Clare respond more quickly than the Blue Waterholes – within a few hours – because of freer

Table 3 Straightline velocities between streamsinks and springs

Area	Mean velocity (km d^{-1})	Standard deviation	Number of traces	Source
Craven, England	3.3	3.7	11	Smith and Atkinson (1977)
Central Mendip, England	7.4	5.9	23	Smith, Atkinson and Drew (1976)
Eastern Mendip, England	6.0	1.7	16	Smith, Atkinson and Drew (1976)
Jamaica	3.5	4.1	40	Smith, Atkinson and Drew (1976)
Southern Turkey	2.4	1.8	4	Karanjac and Gunay (1980)
Central Kentucky	Range 0.24–9.6 km d^{-1}		300	Quinlan (1976)

circulation and lesser storage in their shallow systems. At the other extreme, Ras el'Ain changes its discharge slowly and responds only seasonally; the control appears to be surface runoff on the intake beds of the artesian system one year earlier.

Rates of passage of the water on the straightline basis have been gathered for various karsts; those in table 3 are typical. Even allowing for a tortuous course through cave systems, which would increase the real velocity, movement underground is in general slower than on the surface, where 50 km d^{-1} is typical in low stages, rising to 350 km d^{-1} in floods.

The above discussion has made it clear that seepage or percolation water passes into an underground system much more slowly than stream inputs from surface catchments. Consequently, the behaviour of a karst spring varies greatly according to the proportions of the two components (figure 23) (Smith *et al.* 1976). Where stream inflows dominate, response to rainfall is faster, the hydrograph is sharply peaked with rapid recession, and peak flow is great. Where the spring is fed mainly from percolation water, response to rainfall is delayed, increase in discharge is modest after rainfall, and return to normal flow is delayed. Where a spring has a balanced mixture of supply, hydrographs take on an intermediate character between the two extremes.

Williams (1983) has shown how in some cases the delayed flow comes primarily from the subcutaneous zone, where it is stored in a perched water body of greater magnitude than the water in the deep saturated zone. This kind of contribution makes the task of interpreting karst spring hydrographs more difficult than was previously envisaged.

Karst springs are dominantly bicarbonate waters, except where evaporites enter into the structure when sulphate and/or chloride dominate or where arid climate enhances a sodium chloride contribution to the groundwater. Chemical contents also vary in relation to weather events and climatic seasonality, but responses differ, as is evident even within a single karst such as the Mendip. There, some springs have a virtually constant calcium carbonate hardness but there is a graduation to regimes with large variations. These differences are related to the proportion of streamsink water from inliers of non-karst rock within the limestone plateau, which causes a reduction in hardness. Since this water increases relative to percolation water through the limestone as total flow rises, there is an inverse relationship between discharge and hardness (Smith and Drew 1975). The Mendip springs are usually saturated with $CaCO_3$ because the allogenic inputs are never great. A case of direct relationship between discharge and hardness is more appropriately discussed in chapter 7.

Where the karst part of the basin is smaller, not only is there an inverse correlation between spring hardness and flow, but also the water remains aggressive most or all of the time. This is true for the Clare risings in

Drainage

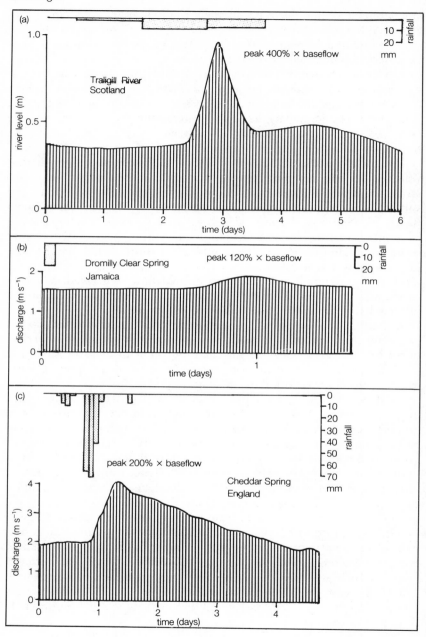

Figure 23 Flood hydrographs from (a) a conduit flow spring; (b) a percolation spring; (c) a mixed flow spring, after Smith *et al.* (1976).

Ireland, which can range over 120–205 mg l^{-1} within the month (Smith *et al.* 1969). It is also the case with the Blue Waterholes at Cooleman Plain, where the karst rocks constitute only 29 per cent of the surface of the basin with a further 16 per cent of limestone buried under other rocks, and with the Orangeville Rise in Indiana (figure 24(a)) (Bassett 1976).

In all cases, the absolute amount of limestone removed increases with discharge because the latter varies much more than the hardness concentration. The Orangeville Rise (figure 24(b)) shows the typical direct relationship.

But the contribution of different flow stages to the annual solute load (Gunn 1982) is distinctly different from one karst to another, as is illustrated in the magnitude–frequency bar graph of figure 24(b). The Riwaka River catchment in the Southern Alps, NZ, is mountainous and suffers intense storms; as a result, the contribution of big but infrequent floods is greater here than in the other catchments. At the other extreme,

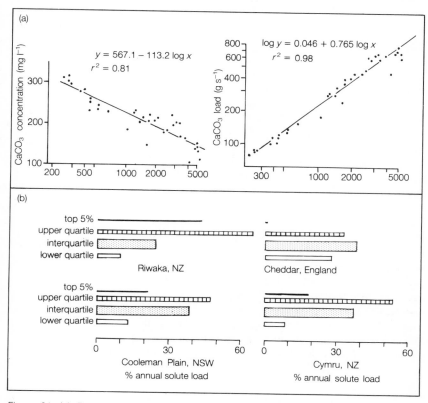

Figure 24 (a) Regressions of calcium carbonate concentration and load on discharge at Orangeville Rise, Indiana, after Bassett (1976); (b) the contributions of different frequency classes of discharge to solute load in representative karst catchments.

Drainage

Cheddar Spring in the Mendips depends on flows of low magnitude but higher frequency to a much greater extent; percolation water is dominant here, with a small allogenic input from gentle relief. The other two karsts fall into an intermediate position, with middling flows looming very large. In the case of Cooleman Plain, there is much less relief and less intense rainfall than in the Riwaka, though a higher proportion of non-karst rocks. With the small Waitomo catchment, NZ, virtually the whole catchment is of limestone bedrock, but volcanic ash covers speed up the hydrologic circulation, cutting down contact time so that hardnesses do not reach so high as at Cheddar.

Thus, in the effect of magnitude and frequency of discharges on solute removal, several factors, including available relief, proportion of catchment in karst rocks and nature of surface covers, interact to give a range from cases not far removed from normal river behaviour in their dependence on high flow to the other extreme, where it is persistent low flows that count most. Departure from normal river behaviour depends essentially on the fact that the critical velocity thresholds governing erosion and transport of clastic sediment do not apply to solute removal (Ford and Drake 1982).

Theory of Karst Hydrology

Although more knowledge can be gained by direct observation about the movement of water underground in karst than about subterranean circulation in other terrain, great controversy has raged in the past about karst hydrology, hinging essentially on the applicability of ideas established in other rocks to karst rocks.

These basic ideas derive from the study of water movement in sands and gravels through intergranular pores, i.e. primary permeability. Water escaping from the zone of soil moisture passes through a zone of aeration first. Here pores are only transitorily and not universally filled with water. Thence it enters a zone of saturation, where all air is displaced through hydrostatic pressure exceeding atmospheric pressure. The upper surface of this saturated zone is the *water table*, where hydrostatic pressure and atmospheric pressure are equal. The water table parallels in a subdued mode the land surface, and the groundwater moves down the slope of the water table, i.e. the pressure gradient. The Frenchman, Darcy, experimented with water movement through columns of sand and found that flow through such an isotropic medium varies in a linear way proportional to the loss of head, i.e. the pressure gradient:

$$Q = K \cdot a \cdot \frac{h}{l} \text{ or } K \cdot a \cdot \frac{\mathrm{d}h}{\mathrm{d}l}$$

where Q = flow, K = coefficient of permeability, a = cross-sectional area of flow, h = loss of head between two points and l = distance between these points. The total head is the sum of the head due to gravity (elevation head) and the head due to the pressure of the water column. The flow is laminar in these conditions.

However, in caves the dominant observed flow is along channels and through pipes and is generally turbulent (though in small pipes less than about 1 cm it is laminar). The flow in these conditions is governed not by the linear Darcy's Law, but by the quadratic Darcy–Weisbach equation, also determined in laboratory experiment:

$$\frac{Q^2}{a^2} = \frac{2d.g}{f} \cdot \frac{dh}{dl}$$

where, in addition, d = diameter of pipe, g = gravitational acceleration and f = friction factor. The friction factor depends on the roughness of the channel and the Reynolds Number (effectively, the product of the velocity and the diameter of pipe). The roles of these different modes of flow are clearly of vital importance.

Both formulae remind us that hydraulic gradients provided by the available relief are just as necessary to provide the energy to drive underground drainage as they are to surface river systems. It is not sufficient to have suitable geological structure and precipitation.

Karst water table and single aquifer

Until recent decades Anglo-American literature assumed that karst water behaved in essentially the same way as it does in moving through sands and gravels, and the notion of water table was transferred unmodified. In this they followed the Austrian Alfred Grund (1903), and the Serbian Jovan Cvijić in his earlier writings (1893).

Three hydrological zones are distinguished.

1 In the *upper vadose zone* the voids may be dry in space and time. *Vadose seepage*, which refers to rain or soil water percolating downwards, often in tight fissures (closed system), is distinguished from *vadose streamflow*, which takes place in open passages, laterally at least as much as downwards.

2 In the *lower phreatic zone* all cavities are perennially full of water. This permanent body of water, the *phreas*, has the water table as its surface, and springs occur where this surface intersects with the land surface.

3 In the *intermediate zone*, caves are intermittently flooded to capacity, a zone through which the water table rises and falls. It also has surface expression in the winter flooding of *poljes* (large, flat-floored closed depressions; see Chapter 7) through the water table rising above their floor levels.

65

Karst conduits and rest levels

However, it was early maintained by others such as Katzer (1909), from knowledge of the Dinaric karst on which Grund and Cvijić rested their ideas, and Martel (1910, 1921), the great French speleologist who travelled widely through Europe, that many facts did not fit this simple picture. Wells and bores put down close together in limestone often reach water at different levels; dry holes occur cheek by jowl with good yielding ones. Tunnels driven through limestone reveal dry and water-filled fissures close together, even with water-filled ones overlying empty ones. Underground water connections can cross one another without interference and vadose caves can pass under surface streams. In the same karst area poljes behave differently, some flooding and others not, even though they are at the same level. Sometimes higher poljes flood before lower ones. When some poljes flood, their streamsinks do not act as estavelles but take in more water. In Livanjsko Polje there are three separate flat floors, each with its own springs and streamsinks. When their streamsinks were opened up for agricultural improvement in the late nineteenth century, each behaved differently, demonstrating their hydrologic independence.

Therefore Katzer, Martel and their school maintained there is no karst water table: instead, independent conduit systems operate like rivers but in a three-dimensional space rather than over a single surface (figure 25). Parts of these underground systems are free-surface streams, only partly filling caves and flowing under gravity alone. Other sections of the

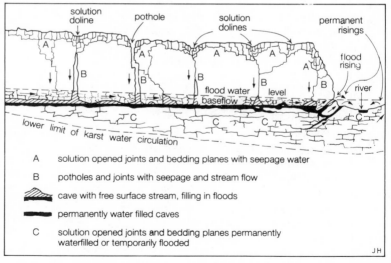

Figure 25   A karst hydrologic system based on the concept of independent conduits, after Cavaillé (1962).

streams fill the caves, and water can bank up behind constrictions, developing hydrostatic head. This may drive water uphill; thus in the French Alps rising water currents under pressure are known to carry pebbles with them up heights as great as 100 m. In the La Luire pothole, water can rise at great speeds comparable with those in surge shafts in hydroelectric systems.

To fit with this view, instead of water tables, separate *rest levels* for water in independent threads are envisaged (Sweeting 1958), and Mangin (1974–5) argues against the use of the term 'phreas' for the saturated zone in karst because it was conceived in relation to water movement through intergranular pores to be regarded as a single aquifer. In fact, karst water moves anisotropically through narrow fissures and large caves which Thrailkill (1968) suggested could be regarded a separate aquifers.

Compromise views

Difficulties face both of these schools of thought, so compromise views go back even to Cvijić in his later writings (1918, 1960). Otto Lehmann, a hydrologist, followed the Yugoslavian geomorphologist in attempting to reconcile the two views on an evolutionary basis (1932). The development of secondary permeability produces a mature karst hydrology, with many independent but complicated, branching and net-like passage systems. There is neither free intercommunication between them nor a single water table. Each conduit system has many input points, but streams join underground to feed a single or a few outlets. However, there follows progressive widening of passages and removal of barriers; fissures link neighbouring caves and free-surface flow predominates in very elaborate systems. Eventually, projecting limestone masses are reduced in size and riddled with passages. Lehmann regards this as a degenerate stage in karst hydrology when something approximating a karst water table is established.

Latterly, empirical evidence rather than theoretical reasoning has been the basis for compromise. Thus Zötl interprets his eastern Alpine broad plateau distributary patterns as being due to interconnections between underground arteries that were established earlier than Lehmann concedes. The major underground rivers constitute these arteries, and tracers injected near to them travel to a single rising or to a few neighbouring outflows.

In the chalk of eastern England and northern France, water levels in wells and bores permit the mapping of a single water table with ease (cf. Balchin and Lewis 1938). Nevertheless, Lewis also argued that the wide spacing of large springs along the foot of chalk scarps indicated a marked gathering of underground drainage along faults or joint zones. Pinchemel (1954) and Ineson (1962) gather evidence for concentrations of linear flow along joint systems beneath dry valleys. Straightline velocities of over 2 km d^{-1} by dye tracing in chalk in Hampshire (Atkinson and Smith 1974) are close to those in conduits.

Empirical evidence conversely points to slow, laminar seepage as an important component in the hydrology of virtually non-porous, compact carbonate rocks in addition to the undoubted conduit flow. Thus, Pitty (1966, 1968a) related cave drips to antecedent surface conditions and found that this seepage water took as much as two or three months to pass through a few tens of metres of rock in the Peak District and Craven in northern England. This water is considered to be passing through a network of joints to be likened to a degree to Darcy flow through pores. Nevertheless, neighbouring drips can behave very differently so that it is misleading to think of an integrated body of percolating water.

An important relevant study was that of Atkinson *et al.* (1973) in determining the nature of water movement between the streamsink, Stoke Lane Slocker, and the spring, St Dunstan's Well, in the Mendip. Fluctuations in discharge during a flood pulse seemed explicable only on the basis of export of water from the stream passages into surrounding joint fissures and the later return of this stored water to those arteries. This happens because water levels rise and fall more rapidly in the conduits than in the fissure networks. From his work in the Pyrenees, Mangin (1974–5) regards such *systemes annèxes* of considerable importance in karst hydrology.

There is thus both *conduit flow* and *diffuse flow* (White 1969) in karst, and their relative importance varies from one area to another as the behaviour of the outflows – the springs – discussed above indicates. In high mountain country with compact or crystalline carbonate rocks such as the Pyrenees, the hydrology can be analysed in terms of conduit flow (e.g. Mangin 1974–5), whereas in the horizontal limestones, many of them porous, of the low plateau of the Nullarbor Plain the levels of cave lakes with only slowly moving water suggest an almost horizontal water table of wide extent (Lowry and Jennings 1974). Nevertheless, the presence of long caves crossing the plain at intervals point to concentrated lines of flow, which may however be a product of times of more effective precipitation in the Pleistocene.

Finally, it is necessary to stress the role of the subcutaneous or epikarstic zone, which is capable of transmitting water both rapidly to karst outlets and by storage to delayed flow, which maintains springs and autogenic rivers in steady action (Mangin 1974–5; Williams 1983). Many factors control its importance relative to other components of karst drainage, including the nature and extent of soil and other covers, the lithology of the karst rock and the length of time that has been available for development of competitive vertical circulation. Where the role of the subcutaneous zone is great, it reduces the contrast between karst and normal fluvial hydrology.

Each karst needs appreciation in its own right as to its hydrology. What remains general is the need to recognize that use of the notions of water table and piezometric surface in karst can be done only at risk until investigation reveals the actual degree of their applicability.

5   Surface Weathering

Weathering etches minor forms of diverse nature in many rocks, but the greatest variety is found in karst because of the susceptibility of its rocks to solution. Unfortunately, there is no general term in English that is the equivalent to the German *Karren* and the French *lapiéz*. Though *Karren* will be used occasionally here, the multiplicity of German specific type names will be avoided. Littoral forms will not be discussed at this point.

Factors Affecting Minor Surface Solution Sculpture

Many factors interact to control the nature and pattern of small-scale sculpture on karst rocks. There are passive factors of rock attributes and the presence or absence of covers, active factors of climate, plant growth, etc., and there are historical factors of changes through time of the preceding factors and of human interference.

Lithology may be favourable or unfavourable to *Karren* formation as it is to karst in general. The porous, mechanically weak Cretaceous chalk of south-eastern England and northern France does not provide a sharp interface between soil and rock as is usual with limestones, nor does it crop out in bare exposure except in active cliffs. So these features do not develop on chalk. Where limestone has been turned to coarsely crystalline marble, as in parts of Cooleman Plain and at Wombeyan Caves, NSW, and the White Mountains, California (Lamarche 1967), it weathers to form rounded outcrops, crudely resembling those of glacial abrasion or granite weathering. Joints may find little surface expression, and recesses carry a skeletal soil of coarse calcite gravel and humus. The readiness with which the rock disaggregates into its individual crystals militates against solutional sculpture. In the Chillagoe karst, northern Queensland, where *Karren* are magnificently developed on unmetamorphosed calcarenites, the contact-metamorphosed carbonate rocks, locally called 'sugarstone', produce only rudimentary solution features and exhibit, as do the other karst areas just mentioned, exfoliation, with features such as A-tents and buckles (Jennings 1978a). Greater proportionate expansion of a surface shell in marble compared with granite is due in part to thermal anisotropy of calcite, which responds more to pressure and temperature change along the c-axis.

More obviously still, close-set bedding, joints, cleavage or simply rapid change in lithology mean that there is not enough uniform surface available for characteristic surface features to develop; there may be only differential weathering under structural control.

An increasing percentage of impurities in karst rocks has the effect of producing more rounded solutional forms if these do develop.

The presence or absence of covering soil, superficial deposits, litter and vegetation itself is a most important factor, because solution operates differently on exposed rock and at the cover–bedrock interface. In England there is a big contrast between the karsts of the Peak District and Craven in this respect. The Peak largely escaped the last glaciation of the Pleistocene, and its Carboniferous limestone is covered chiefly by aeolian mantles, so there is sculpture virtually only at the subsoil interfae. On the other hand, Craven suffered much glacial stripping of earlier mantles, so solutional sculpture is much more in evidence on the same geological formation.

Cover need be only a thin surface layer of liverworts, mosses or epilithic lichens, but it stops the movement of films of rainwater and so may inhibit the development of a whole array of forms. The contrast in weathering forms between the upper and lower parts of the crag in plate 1 was formerly thought to be due to the stripping of soil from the lower part as a result of accelerated erosion, but further work in the area makes it more likely that only covers of lower plants of these smoother areas have been lost.

Turning to the active factors, in cold climates thaw–freeze can shatter the rock too much for solutional sculpture to show itself at all. Thus from the treeline on Mount Arthur, NZ, an interesting range of solutional microforms can be traced upwards until, over the last 100 or 200 m to the summit, only angular bedrock shapes and talus are to be seen. At the other extreme, in the tropics, the great length of some downslope features has been attributed by some to the higher rate of chemical reaction in thin water films there.

The nature of precipitation enters into the matter, some forms being best developed in association with snow cover, which must act in some respects like a biologically sterile soil. The duration and intensity of rainfall must also affect bare rock solution and, less markedly, soil water solution at the interface. With precipitation, the most obvious extreme effect is that of aridity, which minimizes and deflects solutional activity; for example, solutional microforms are few on the Nullarbor Plain of Australia, with pans predominating (Lowry and Jennings 1974). The dominant result can be the case-hardening of the exposed rock surface by reprecipitation through evaporation of the modest amount dissolved. This crust development may be accompanied by tafoni breaching it on an impressive scale, as in the Hadhramaut, South Yemen (Wissmann 1957). In the much more humid climate of Canterbury, NZ, Oligocene limestone, chiefly a porous, shelly and foraminiferal biomicrite, also weathers to a rounded, hardened outer surface, broken by large tafoni. This is not found even in more humid West Coast karst in the same geological formation. How far the difference is due to lithological facies change and how much to the climatic gradient is not known.

Historical factors are important in many areas (plate 8). Most important is that of exposure of subsoil surfaces through soil erosion as a result of forest clearance by man and the destruction of many kinds of vegetation by his grazing animals. This process can still be seen in operation today in places where deforestation continues to take place. They are startlingly obvious where dense gardening populations fell and burn tropical rain forest, as in New Guinea. With shifting agriculture, fresh subsurface forms, starkly blanched, emerge from soil and litter each year.

Plate 8 Cavernous weathering through subsoil weathering at Cave Hill, Burrinjuck Reservoir, NSW. The soil was removed from Devonian limestone by wave action.

Only latterly have karst scientists in central and western Europe recognized how much of the variety of microform assemblages depends on this factor of human interference, both now and in the past (Sweeting 1972b). Even the Burren in western Ireland has lost much soil cover as a result of Neolithic–Bronze Age forest clearance (Drew 1983). The story is going full circle in Yugoslavia, where, for example, the bare mountains of Croatia, which under man's destructive hand rose in white expanse skywards from the Adriatic, are now, since goats were banned, becoming clothed once again in oak and hornbeam forest. The story of deforestation of the Dinaric karst is a long and involved one (Gušić 1973), and the consequences were not fully appreciated until recently (Gams 1971).

The effects of past climatic change are much harder to evaluate, but this also may be vital to understanding some karsts. In the limestone Ranges of north-western Australia, with a tropical semi-arid climate (450–750 mm rainfall), and in the north-eastern Queensland karsts of Chillagoe and the Mitchell–Palmer Rivers, with somewhat more rain (1500–1000 mm) but a very long dry season, there are tremendous arrays of bare karst solution microforms. These are so sharp that they must still be developing, yet some have thought that it is unrealistic to attribute them wholly to a short season of a few, if intense, rainfalls, and have suggested that they are an inheritance from former wetter climates. As yet, however, evidence from the Pleistocene points to drier, not wetter, climates, and it is unlikely that these small features have been inherited from the Tertiary.

Types of Minor Surface Solution Forms on Limestone

Though there are transitional and compound forms, it is useful to erect a typology of solutional miroforms; here Bögli (1960, 1961a) will be followed, with some additions.

Forms developed on bare karst

These forms develop with free movement of water uninterrupted by lichens, mosses, liverworts, soil or sediment, though virtually all limestone that has been exposed for some time is subject to attack in some degree by lichens and algae (Jones 1965; Krumbein 1969). Indeed, in the humid tropics algal attack is so vigorous that it produces randomly oriented spongelike surfaces like lacework with a black coating, the *black phytokarst* of Folk *et al.* (1973), where no gravitational control is apparent. The grey colour of most limestone outcrops in temperate climate is due to the action of blue-green algae living in their surface, giving it also a sandpaper roughness.

Additionally, it seems necesary that the surface should not be so overhung with vegetation that the fall of rain on to it is significantly affected. Vegetation is, of course, likely to extend over or on to forms previously created under the free fall of rains, and to degrade them.

With areal wetting. The simplest effect of rain falling on bare rocks is to produce small pitting, each *rainpit* being usually less than 3 cm across

73

and 2 cm deep. Necessarily they occur in fields, whereas pits formed by leaf drips can be single. They form on gentle slopes rather than steep ones (but they can occur there, e.g. interrupting solution flutes). They may be

Plate 9 Solution ripples in Palaeozoic marble, Owen Range, NZ. On the outer surface the ripples are horizontal, but in recesses they are inclined through deflection of wind.

separated by the original surface or become so close as to have only sharp rims between them; then the surface has an irregular, carious appearance. It now seems likely that much of the solution in these pits is biochemical in nature through the metabolism of blue-green algae (cyanobacteria), of both euendolithic and endolithic type (i.e. growing respectively in the top 0.2 and 3mm layer of rock). These tiny organisms breathe out carbon dioxide at night which acidifies rainwater, wetting them and bringing them into activity (Danin and Garty 1983).

Another simple form is the *solution ripple*; this is a wavelike form transverse to downward water movement under gravity, implying a definite rhythm in flow or periodicity of chemical reaction about which nothing is known at present. Two kinds were discussed independently at much the same time. Those described from the tropical humid karst of Sarawak by Wall and Wilford (1966) occur on underhangs, with sharp ribs separating quasi-horizontal, symmetrical hollows about 2 cm across and 1 cm deep. Horizontally they run for a few centimetres or into tens of centimetres. The water passing over them generally has passed over much rock and is likely to have contacted humus and soil. Jennings (1967) illustrated shallower, less symmetrical, ripples on vertical surfaces at Cooleman Plain, NSW, with the edges between them more blunted (plate 9). These can be found on much less steep slopes; then they became wider and more steplike in character. They are much better developed in the alpine karst of the Owen Range, NZ, where they are driven out of the horizontal as much as 30 deg through deflection of water films by winds moving in accord with local rock geometry. This kind of ripple was initially thought to be due to the direct fall of rain only, but at Chillagoe, Queensland, they have been found extending below the present soil surface and down surfaces that have recently been exposed by soil erosion.

More widespread and more striking are *solution flutes* (Ger. *Rillenkarren*), characteristic of steep to nearly vertical surfaces (plate 10), again due to gravity flow but in this case channelled along it. These are longitudinal hollows, running in sets straight down the steepest inclination of the rock, with sharp ribs between. Widths of 2–4 cm and depths of 1–2 cm are strongly predominant, whereas lengths are much more variable, measured in tens of centimetres in temperate climates but often in metres in tropical climates (Jennings 1982b). The cross-sectional shape varies from semicircular to more V-shaped. Where flutes develop on opposite sides of a block, a serrated crest results with a herringbone pattern seen from above.

At Lake Garda, northern Italy, and on the Dachstein Mountains in Austria, Heinemann *et al.* (1977) found that flutes were more frequent, better shaped and longer on south-facing sides than on north-facing; this was associated with greater growth of lichens and algae on the shady northern side and a thicker weathering rind on the sunny side. They also

Plate 10 Solution flutes and bevel in Devonian limestone, Wee Jasper, NSW.

found that the longest flutes occurred at slope angles around 60–65° when they started from ledges and edges, but on the Dachstein another maximum occurred at 25° on rounded bosses of rock that did not possess such steep slopes. In support of this, experimental work with a rain simulator on plaster of paris (gypsum) blocks in the laboratory by Glew and Ford (1980) showed a direct relationship between slope and length of flutes up to 60°. However at Chillagoe, Qld., Lundberg (1977a) and at Wee Jasper and Cooleman Plain, NSW, Dunkerley (1979) found little relationship between length and slope. This led Dunkerley to argue that rainfall intensity and flow hydrodynamics cannot be controlling this flute character. Glew and Ford found that their artificial flutes tended to a parabolic cross-sectional form, as did natural limestone flutes from the Rocky Mountains, Canada. They regard the parabolic form as the most effective shape for concentrating raindrops into the flute axis, explaining the tight packing of flutes separated by sharp ribs only. They also argue for the flutes being localized to a rim zone where the water film does not get too thick for raindrops to reach through to the rock in impact.

On the other hand, Dunkerley finds that flutes that depart from the semicircular form towards a V-shape are approximating to a hyperbola. He thinks that flutes begin on a random pattern influenced by mineral grain boundaries and small surface irregularities and that a process of competition during growth eliminates some so that a closely packed set with similar widths and depths occupies the whole surface width. Semicircular cross-section develops when the chemical reaction rate governs the process, but the deeper hyperbolic ones are a result of flow rate control. Rock textures affect flute forms both broadly and subtly (Dunkerley 1983).

Rippling may occur in combination with flutes to give a netted aspect to the rock.

More frequently associated with flutes are *solution bevels* (Ger. *Ausgleichsflächen*). These are nearly flat, well smoothed elements usually found below the flutes (plate 10), but sometimes occupying the top of blocks, where however there is the possibility that fluted projections have been lost through solution. Flow over them is in the form of a thin sheet. Glew and Ford think that the levels form where the water film gets too thick for raindrops to hit the rock and a different chemistry prevails. The implication seems to be that the steeper fluted surface has retreated to allow a bevel to extend headwards. Bögli (1960) thought that a different, slower part of the solution process was taking over at the junction between flutes and bevel.

In snow climates, e.g. the European calcareous Alps and the marble ranges of the Southern Alps, NZ, the risers at the back of bevels are often smooth and arcuate to produce *solution funnel* or *heelsteps* (Ger. *Trichter-, Tritt-karren*) (plate 11). They have been attributed to solution beneath snow (Bögli 1960). From morphometric analysis, Vincent (1983) argues that elongate bevels backed by crenulate scarplets develop from them.

On vertical surfaces, the ribs between two or three flutes may die out, leaving *rain solution runnels (Regenrinnenkarren)* (type 2 of Bögli 1960). These are two to three times as wide as flutes but, like them, retain the same cross-section along their length.

Plate 11 Trittkarren from north Svartisen, Norway. Photo by P. Vincent.

With concentrations of runoff. Through gathering larger volumes of water, there is generally a downstream increase in width and depth in *solution runnels* (Ger. *Rinnenkaren*). The ribs between runnels are substantial and may be covered partly with flutes and even rain solution runnels. Bögli thinks that runnels are linked to the later stage of limestone solution dependent on diffusion of CO_2 from air to water to maintain the action; this is slow but permits large amounts of solution.

Not only does rain collect to form runnels, but so does water running from moss polsters, snow patches, soil and humus covers. Furthermore, seepage water re-emerging from planes of weakness in bedrock may participate. Therefore runnel formation occurs in a variety of circumstances, giving rise to varieties such as *meandering runnels* (Ger. *Mäanderkarren*), which wind about both flat and inclined surfaces. In contrast are *wall solution runnels* (Ger. *Wandkarren*), which are cut straight in vertical faces by water pouring down. They are deeper than rain solution runnels and they may be separated by untouched surfaces as well as by narrow ribs.

More important and widespread are *grikes* (Ger. *Kluftkarren*), which are solution-widened joints. These inherent planes of weakness canalize flow and promote their own widening. With steep joints on flat surfaces, they form from the merging of lens-like holes in series along a joint. Grikes are straight, long and deep, and often occur in networks formed by conjugate sets of joints, commonly at an angle of about 60°. Enlargement and rounding may take place at intersections of joints, producing cylindrical pits known as *karst wells*. When the bedding is vertical or nearly so, bedding planes are enlarged in the same way as joints; these have been called *bedding grikes* (Ger. *Schichtfugenkarren*).

The blocks between grikes and the strike ribs between bedding grikes may be cut up into isolated projections, which can assume a beehive form or become sharply pointed. The latter may be termed *solution spikes* (Ger. *Spitzkarren*). Alternatively with horizontal bedding, seepage water is likely to open up the uppermost bedding planes and create free tabular blocks called *clints* (Ger. *Flachkarren*). These shift about as solution below disturbs equilibrium and break up into smaller, irregular fragments strewn about. *Shillow* another term from northern England, is appropriate for these clasts (Ger. *Trümmerkarren; Scherbenkarst*). Frost wedging favours this development but is not necessary for its production.

Forms developed on partly covered karst

Some karst areas are patchily covered by soil, sediment, humus, moss polsters and plant litter. This patchiness may result from partial loss of formerly complete cover or from progress towards such a cover. Certain microforms are characteristic of this condition because water retained in the patches of cover, which usually provides a biogenic CO_2 supply, promotes solution beneath. Thus many grikes come into this category also, with soil, humus and living plants along their bottoms.

Solution pans (Slav. *Kamenitsa*) are dish-shaped depressions, usually floored by a thin layer of algal remains, silt or clay. The fine clasts may protect the lowest parts from corrosion, while with CO_2 from organic matter there is a concentration of solution along the waterline round the sides, which extends the flat bottom. Continuous renewal of CO_2 and an absence of protective seal around the pan make this the most favourable place for solution. However, Williams (1968) found higher pH in the muck on pan bottoms in Ireland than in the water above.

Solution flutes may surround pans, and with big ones even solution runnels may run into them. Under forest, solution pans may be formed by water dripping from tree branches, but there they will not be accompanied by flutes. Related but deeper forms are the solution cups in New Zealand of Zotov (1941), who considers that they formed beneath moss polsters since deforestation a century ago.

Undercut solution runnels (Ger. *Hohlkarren*) have a baglike cross-section, and Bögli explains them as solution runnels on gentle slopes that get filled with litter, humus or soil and become recessed within through permanent wetting of their floors and sides.

Solution notches (Ger. *Korrosionskehlen*), larger forms to be measured in decimetres in cross-section and metres in length, are due to particularly

Plate 12 A solution notch in Eocene limestone at Muriraga in the central highlands of PNG, in abandoned agricultural land. Soil erosion has exposed the smooth incut formed beneath the soil.

active solution in the soil against projecting rock. This results in curved incuts, which are best developed in tropical karst. Lowering of the soil surface exposes such features (plate 12); this can be natural or anthropogenic soil removal.

Swamp slots (Wilford and Wall 1965) so far have been reported only from tropical humid karst. They are horizontal, smoothed grooves with flat roofs and floors, a few centimetres to a few decimetres high but up to about a metre or two deep. They are found with swampwater and organic muck in them at the foot of cliffs but also occur high and dry at higher levels, from which it is inferred that they have formed when the swamp surface was higher.

Forms developed on covered karst

Because of surface tension, soil or sediment bears like an acidulated sponge on underlying karst rock and produces an array of special forms – the cryptokarst of Nicod (1976b), who discusses Mediterranean examples, distinguishing active cryptokarst from palaeokarst remnants. Although these forms develop in a wide variety of milieus, not all covers behave in this way. Thus Williams (1966b) found that in Ireland calcareous till may inhibit subsoil sculpture because seepage water become saturated within it (see figure 26). Even glacial striae may survive; ice erosion had removed prior solution sculpture and subsequently the till has protected a scoured limestone pavement (cf. Aubert 1969).

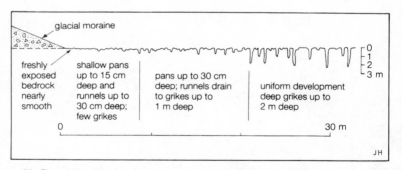

Figure 26   The relationship of surface sculpture to moraine at Clare, Ireland, after Williams (1966a).

Soil water movement is not very free, and it will be guided at the rock surface by structural detail. Thus grikes develop preferentially here; in Craven, many grikes evolved under cover of soil, which has been lost through farming from Neolithic time onwards. In the United States these soil-filled grikes are called 'cutters' (Howard 1963) (plate 13).

Below a certain depth, water movement is so slow that the intimate structure of the rock is delicately etched out on the surfaces of widened

Plate 13 Cutters caused by subsoil solution along vertical joints in Mississippian limestone, Bedford, Indiana. The soil fill was lost after quarrying. Photo by A.N. Palmer.

Plate 14 Grikes and rounded solution runnels formed beneath soil lost through forest clearance in Craven, England. The first row of clints is about 1 m across.

81

joints and bedding planes. Close to the surface, on the other hand, soil movement at times of saturation of the soil is faster and so is solution; here smoothed surfaces result, transecting structural minutiae. When freshly exposed, these surfaces are characteristically bleached white. Hollows gather water to themselves, promoting their own growth. Gravity-controlled features thus develop beneath the cover; they resemble solution runnels except that the ribs between get rounded by the omnipresent acidulated blanket. These *rounded solution runnels* (Ger. *Rundkarren*) become familiar when stripped by erosion. Sweeting (1955) has traced dendritic patterns of such rounded runnels (plate 14) laterally beneath glacial till in Craven, confirming cryptokarstic origin.

The converse process is thought to have happened around Bödmeren, Muototal, Switzerland, as a result of postglacial climatic change; forest has recently extended over bare karst solution runnels and the forest litter has rounded their ribs.

More general in this zone close to the surface are less systematized smoothed and bleached surfaces, with rounded dimpling and perforating tubes. This *cavernous subsoil weathering* (Ger. *kavernosen Karren*) is well exhibited in New Guinea gardens, where there are even dry stone walls made up of fragments of this kind, gathered from the soil, matching those around dolines in Slovenia (Gams 1971, 1974). Detached fragments in the soil are particularly liable to marked rounding (Ger. *Karrennasen*) and must not be confused with fluvial clasts. At Cave Hill in Burrinjuck Reservoir, NSW, wave action over the fluctuating water levels has exposed cryptokarst excellently (see plate 8).

Other subsoil features, which may grow into major forms, are *solution pipes* (Ger. *geologische Orgeln*). In compact and crystalline limestone, they develop in lines along joints. However, in the chalk of north-western Europe (Kirkaldy 1950), and the aeolian calcarenites of Australia (Jennings 1968), such filled conical or cylindrical holes develop unrelated to joints. In the latter rocks they form as part of the induration of calcareous dune sands and often exist as an earth-filled shell of calcite set in unconsolidated sand. The developing pipes are in fact centres of induration. Roots are common in their earth fills and also pass beyond. There is, once more, a positive feedback (autocatalytic) relationship. Root exudates and root respiration help solutional deepening, which in time promotes plant growth. Tap roots may fill the lower parts of pipes. On emerged coral reefs where there have been dense bird colonies, guano may promote pipe development by corroding the limestone.

Root activity is not restricted to pipes. Wall and Wilford (1966) describe root grooves in joint planes in crystalline limestone in Sarawak. In the highlands of New Guinea, roots have been seen penetrating massive Chimbu limestone unrelated to planes of weakness. Often, vertical faces carry vegetation that riddles the surface with grooves and holes (cf. Tricart and Silva 1960 on Brazilian equivalents).

Solution Microforms on Other Karst Rocks

Small solution forms on dolomite are fundamentally similar but generally less elaborate and prolific than on limestone, probably because of its slower solution kinetics. The dominant forms are those structurally controlled, such as grikes, and gravity-controlled forms – e.g. runnels down the walls of grikes – are few. On the Niagara escarpment in Ontario, Pluhar and Ford (1970) describe blunt horizontal ribs along stylolites, with gentle recessing of the more coarsely crystalline and more porous dolomite between. Near Camooweal, in north-western Queensland, close rain pitting of the surface on dolomite outcrops around cave entrances depends on intense storms during the short wet season.

In subhumid to arid climates, intricate patterns of flutes and runnels are to be found on both gypsum and halite, e.g. on rocksalt at Slanic, Roumania (Krejci-Graf 1935) and Djelfa, Algeria (Würm 1953). In humid climate, high solution rates and mechanical weakness cause crumbly surfaces on gypsum (Wigley *et al.* 1973), but subsoil features such as solution pipes can be highly developed (figure 27).

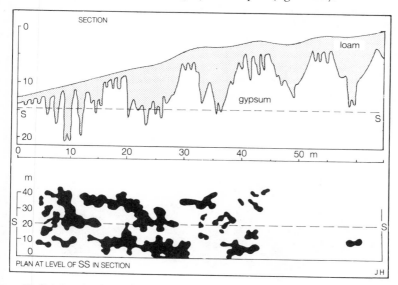

Figure 27   Solution pipes in gypsum, Walkenried, Harz, Germany, after Penck (1924).

Assemblages of Solution Microforms

When outcrop becomes extensive in bare or partly covered karst, various kinds of microform can occur together in systematic fashion. It may be possible to put their development into time sequence through their

83

relationships. Thus, if runnels continue across grikes, the latter are the younger, whereas if the runnels start within a grike-defined clint surface, the runnels are the younger (Williams 1966a).

In Craven, the patterns of forms vary with thickness of beds, their dip and joint spacing (Sweeting 1966). With moderately thick beds and wide joint spacing, clints are well developed and are more likely to carry solution pans and rounded solution runnels than where beds are thinner and joints closer. Increasing dip inhibits pan development and runnels assume parallel, instead of dendritic, courses down clints. Goldie (1973, 1978) has made morphometric analyses in various limestone pavement areas in northern England and Switzerland, based on measures of clint width and length and grike width and depth. These have shown the multiplicity of controlling factors, including intensity of Pleistocene glacial erosion, human removal of clints for garden rockeries, lithology (e.g. sparite content), topographic location and joint densities.

Measurement of Solution At and Close To the Surface

Measurement of solution in the superficial zone in karst has attracted much attention in recent decades. Results should not be subject to close comparison because of differences of method and of circumstance. Details of methods will not be pursued here; Goudie (1981) provides an introduction, with useful references.

In 1947 Sweeting (1966) stripped till from a glaciated pavement in Craven, and by 1960 glacial striae had been removed by corrosion with a surface lowering of up to 3–5 cm. From another area, peat was removed

Figure 28 Glacial erratics of Silurian sandstone on Carboniferous limestone pedestals, Norber Grags, Craven, England. Sketch by C.D. Ollier.

and peaty water directed on to the stripped surface; this cut runnels 7–15 cm deep in the same period. Results of experiments that upset nature to such an extent cannot be extrapolated far.

A method that commands much confidence, if not a great degree of precision, is the use of pedestals that have formed beneath glacial erratics on limestone pavements scoured by ice in the last glacial maximum of the Pleistocene and lowered by solution since, except under their protection (figure 28). Kunaver (1976) has pointed to difficulties arising when this method is applied to the Julian Alps in Slovenia. Table 4 shows only a fourfold range in value over a range of mid-latitude maritime hill, mid-latitude alpine and tropical alpine situations.

Table 4 Surface lowering from limestone pedestals

Area	Average height of pedestals (cm)	Time since ice retreat (a)	Surface lowering (mm ka^{-1})
Mären Mts Switzerland (Bögli 1961a)	15	10 000	15
Craven, England (Sweeting 1966)	50	12 000	42
Clare–Galway, Ireland (Williams 1966a)	15	15 000	10
Mt Jaya, Irian Jaya (Peterson 1982)	30	9 500	30

Basically similar in conception but earlier conceived is the estimation of rates of corrosion from projecting resistant fossils on dressed stone faces, e.g. tombstones; Goodchild appreciated the significance of this situation in 1871 in a graveyard in Kirkby Stephen, Westmoreland, England, and derived a rate-of-surface lowering of 51 mm ka^{-1} (Goodchild 1975).

The micro-erosion meter (MEM) method (Trudgill et al. 1981 Viles and Trudgill 1984) is fundamentally related to the last in that it depends on measuring the level of the surface of limestone with a dial gauge instrument on stainless steel studs fixed in the rock. It can be applied in a variety of circumstances, but replication of sites cannot be indulged very much for several reasons. Some measures obtained in this way are set out in table 5. The indications from the data are that subsoil solution is much more substantial than on rock exposed to the atmosphere, that there is a very great variation within a given climate in accord with limestone lithology, and that hotter tropical climate appears to favour greater loss than do mid-latitude climates.

Another approach is to expose weighed limestone tablets to solution in

Surface Weathering

Table 5   Micro-erosion meter lowering rates from surface sites and sites near the surface

Area	Type of site	Mean erosion rate (mm a^{-1})	Range (mm a^{-1})
Clare, Ireland (Trudgill et al. 1981)	Bare Rock	0.005	
Aldabra Atoll (Trudgill 1976a)	Bare rock in 3 lithologies	0.25	0.09–0.86
Malham, England (Trudgill et al. 1981)	Rock with lichens	0.013	+0.027–0.41
Cooleman Plain, NSW (Spate et al. 1983)	Bare rock	0.017	0.014–0.020
Yarrangobilly (Spate et al. 1983)	Bare rock	0.007	+0.001–0.007
Cooleman Plain (Spate et al. 1983)	Litter on rock	0.009	
Yarrangobilly (Spate et al. 1983)	Litter on rock	0.013	
Cooleman Plain (Spate et al. 1983)	Subsoil	0.029	
Yarrangobilly (Spate et al. 1983)	Subsoil	0.015	
Aldabra Atoll (Trudgill 1967b)	Subsoil (3 soil types)	4.009	+0.1–20.37

[a] The Aldabra data given here have now been supplemented by longer-term data in Viles and Trudgill (1984).

various sites, reweigh them at intervals and derive solutional losses. Table 6 displays some results where local limestone tablets were the subject of the experiments. The striking variation in rate here is related to the acidity and the calcareous content of the soil in which solution is taking place; the more acid the soil and the less $CaCO_3$ it contains, the more it attacks the limestone.

In an attempt to simplify the problem, a single limestone (a micrite from Slovenia) has been exposed in several standard ways in a number of

Table 6   Limestone tablet loss solution rates

Area	Site	Mean erosion rate (mm a^{-1})	Range (mm a^{-1})
Clare, Ireland (Trudgill 1976)	Ranker	-	2.933–5.327
	Peat bog	-	1.817–5.298
	Acid brown earth	-	0.0084–0.025
	Humus rendzina	-	0.00012–0.005
	Calcareous brown earth	-	0.00012–0.001
Cooleman Plain (Jennings 1981a)	Rendzina on flat interfluve	0.010	0.008–0.012
	Rendzina in hollow	0.006	

climates in European countries, Florida and Australia (Gams 1981a). This collaborative experiment has not yet been completely reported. Tablets were exposed in the air, resting on bare rock, lying in grass sward, and buried in soils of different kinds at each site. The results show much difference among the results from each mode of exposure; nevertheless, a direct relation to precipitation is discernible. Subsoil results are on the average greater than those from the surface and the air. Interaction of solution and mechanical action may be involved in high alpine air-exposed tablets.

In a different category to these direct methods is the indirect one of collecting water, measuring its volume and determining its carbonate content. Crowther (1979) did this for 64 solution runnels with and without soil or organic litter cover on a karst tower in western Malaysia during five rainstorms. Their carbonate concentration varied chiefly with the proportion of cover, but it also depended on the proportion of the rain actually touching the rock surface and the duration of the contact time, which are influenced by slope angle and runnel length. During a storm the concentration was greatest at the start, when weathering products created since the last storm were being removed, and at the end, when a thinner film moved more slowly. Applied to the annual rainfall record, rates of loss of 0.033 mm a^{-1} on bare rock and 0.055 mm a^{-1} under soil/litter cover resulted.

Monitoring small artificial catchments, Jennings (1978b) found, from a much broken two-year record, that bare rock (0.009 mm a^{-1}) lost more than soil (0.005 mm a^{-1}) at Cooleman Plain, NSW. The latter result was recognized to be an extreme case, suffering excessive water loss by evaporation.

Results from these different approaches converge to support the view that many surface solution features of the kinds discussed in this chapter can have formed within the Holocene, the climate of which was not drastically different from today's. This accords with the observation of their presence in areas subjected to vigorous glacial erosion during the last glacial maximum of the Pleistocene, e.g. in Ireland (Williams 1966b) and the European Alps (Haserodt 1969). Nevertheless, it is equally evident that many features, such as meshes of deep grikes dissecting scoured limestone pavements, are survivals from the time before that ice intervention.

As will be discussed in chapter 8 a great proportion of the capacity for solution of the water entering the karst surface areally is used up in the top few metres, so that the enlargement of planes of weakness involved in the solution microforms discussed in the present chapter is confined to a zone near the surface. Below this, joints, etc., remain tight and vertical circulation is restricted. As a result, flow is deflected laterally to more favoured points for vertical descent, such as joint intersections and faults. Thus, a subcutaneous zone is created in the hydrological system as a result of surface and near-surface weathering.

D

6   Surface Landforms

Valleys take on special characteristics in karst, but these characteristics are accompanied or replaced to varying degrees by closed depressions, which identify the surface of karst most of all. Usually these are distinguishable from closed depressions formed by other agents such as tectonism, vulcanicity, glaciers, periglacial action and wind. But when karst is subject to these other forces also, problems arise, especially when composite features result.

Gorges

Although gorges (plates 15 and 16) are found in practically all rocks, they are more frequent and bolder in karst, other factors such as general relief and climate being equal. The Grandes Causses of central France are sliced into separate plateaus by the gorges of the Tarn, Jonte, Dourbie and Lot, 300–500 m deep. In young, folded mountain ranges, much larger gorges occur, such as the Verdon Gorge in the southern French Alps, the Vicos Gorge, 1000 m deep but only 1500 m across, which is the 'Grand Canyon' of Greece, the Nahanni Gorge in north-western Canada and the Strickland Gorge in New Guinea. However, they are numerous also in limited available relief, as is the case with the Geikie, Windjana and Galeru Gorges of the limestone ranges of the Kimberleys, WA, where rivers have been superimposed from Mesozoic sandstone covers on to Devonian limestones below.

Narrow canyons form, as with Bungonia Gorge, NSW, which has nearly vertical walls up to 300 m high. But that steepness is often retained with meagre relief. Thus the archaeologically famous Creswell Caves in northern England are developed in cliffs less than 20 m high on both sides of a broad floodplain.

Allogenic drainage is dominantly responsible for karst gorge formation. However, the essential mechanism in this prevalence of gorges in karst is the failure of slope processes to flare back the valley sides. Marked infiltration and reduced runoff minimize slope wash and many kinds of mass movement that tend to widen valleys and moderate their

steepness. River incision, on the other hand, is favoured by the readiness
with which the bedrock river channels may be dissolved and abraded.
Swirlhole action, both mechanical and chemical, is particularly effective

Plate 15 Limestone Gorge, Gordale Scar, Yorkshire. Photo by Tony Waltham.

Plate 16 Limestone Gorge, Vicos Canyon (800 metres deep), north-western Greece. Photo by Tony Waltham.

in karst. Dissolved load is also more easily transported than clastic load. Flatter longitudinal profiles result, and so rivers can run through gorges from their entry into karst to their leaving it.

The sides of the gorges are, of course, not entirely in cliff; a frequent element to be found is a uniform bedrock slope of 25–35° with only thin and patchy covers of talus. These 'Richter slopes of denudation' are more common in karst than elsewhere because of readier removal by solution of talus falling on them from above.

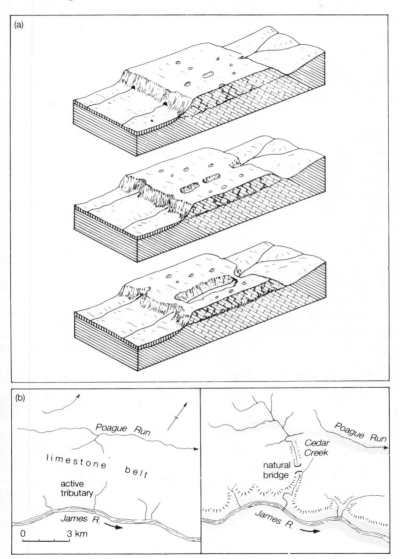

Figure 29 (a) A gorge and natural bridges created by cave roof collapse, after Maximovich (1963); (b) a natural bridge created by river piracy at Natural Bridge, Cedar Creek, Virginia, after Woodward (1936).

91

Cave roof collapse has frequently been offered as an explanation of gorges in karst (figure 29(a)). This certainly applies in some cases, where sections of cave roof survive between unroofed sections, as with the Rak Valley in Slovenia and along the Oparara River, near Karamea, NZ, where three natural bridges come in close succession. However, it has been called upon in many places with no supporting evidence and, indeed, even where there is contradiction in the shape of surface rejuvenation forms along the Cheddar Gorge in Mendip, England (Ford and Stanton 1968). There is the risk of extending too far the significance of a natural bridge, as Sweeting (1972a) has warned for the famous case of Gordale Beck in Craven, England. A collapsed cave may just be one sector of a gorge formed mainly by surface processes.

Although dolomite can stand up in great cliffs, as witness the famous peaks of the Dolomites in the European Alps, this rock usually forms V-shaped valleys rather than the vertically walled gorges favoured by limestone in comparable circumstances. There is also greater readiness to break up into 'ruiniform' relief (Nicod 1972), with castellated tors, etc.

Meander Caves

A contributing factor in maintaining the steepness of valley sides in karst is effective lateral action by rivers. Corrasional undercutting of valley sides encumbers a river with debris, whereas corrosion does so not directly but by rockfall. Rockfall from undercutting is also more readily removed because of its liability to solution as well as to abrasion. In addition, the comparative softness of calcite favours attrition.

Consequently meander caves are typically karst forms, though their frequency must not be exaggerated. A good example is provided by Verandah Cave, Borenore, NSW, which is at the base of an ingrown meander cliff (figure 30). The Verandah itself is a remnant of a higher abandoned meander cave corresponding to a rock terrace upstream.

Natural Bridges

Natural bridges are more common in karst valleys than in others. Cleland (1910) distinguished between a natural bridge, through which a river runs or has run, and a natural arch, where the span has never bridged a river but perforates spurs as a consequence of weathering, e.g. Porta di Prada, La Grigna, Italy. When a feature should be called a bridge or regarded simply as a cave is bound to be arbitrary. As good a criterion as any is that daylight reaches through a bridge. The larger and straighter the penetrating passage, the greater the length that can be lit from outside. On this basis the 180 m long Arch Cave at Abercrombie, NSW,

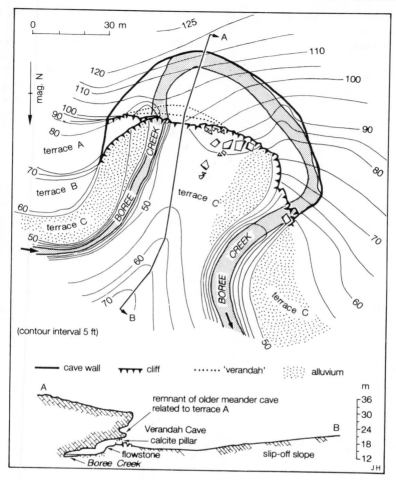

Figure 30 A meander cave on Boree Creek, Borenore, NSW.

is probably close to the limit. Where a stream crosses a narrow band of limestone, a cave may become nothing more than a bridge. Steeply dipping beds favour such narrowness of outcrop as at Jenolan, NSW: here the Grand Arch is about 140 m long in an outcrop only 180 m wide. Its greatest span is 50 m and its maximum height 20 m above Harry Creek flowing through it.

Other bridges are surviving parts of much longer cave roofs (figure 29(a)), as with the Rak Valley mentioned above. Some natural bridges of this type are associated with underground river capture, with the valley below the bridge more deeply entrenched by the work of the capturing stream. This is thought to be the situation at Natural Bridge, Cedar

93

Creek, near Lexington, and at Natural Tunnel on Stock Creek near Clinchport, both in Virginia (figure 29(b)).

Self-capture is a common cause of natural bridges. Meander caves on one or both sides of a meander spur can breach the limestone through edge plane action of the whole stream, but generally water escaping from the river by solution along joints or bedding planes will have pierced the spur before that. London Bridge, Burra Creek, NSW, provides a good example of a bridge formed this way. Here a meander spur includes a narrow band of nearly vertical limestone. The long bend was cut off by cave development across the neck of the spur where the limestone lies. An alluvial fan has partly filled the old meander and its construction may have been a final trigger to abandonment of the surface course (Jennings *et al.* 1976).

Bridges also develop without meandering by self-capture at rejuvenation heads. Where waterfalls cascade down the steep drop in the river profile, joints may open up behind and engulf more and more of the flow to leave a span of rock over the degenerating fall. Cleland (1910) suggested this was involved at the Natural Bridge near Lexington.

Other bridges form from karst river deposition (see below).

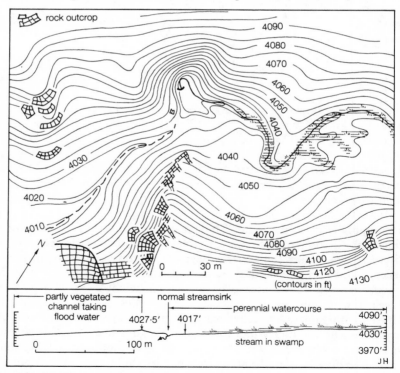

Figure 31 A half-blind valley on Cooleman Plain, NSW.

94

Half-blind Valleys

Persistent sinking of water at a point on a river's course lowers the bed there through solution of bedrock and transport of bedload underground. Below this point of engulfment, the river has less power for mechanical action and for solution. Gradually an upward step or threshold develops. The underground course enlarges its capacity to take in water and eventually it can accept the base flow. Flow continues beyond only after heavy rains or snow melt when the streamsink cannot accept the flood discharge. Water banks up the counterslope to the threshold level and flows over it. The bed beyond the threshold becomes vegetated progressively and the channel and its gravels become more weathered as the frequency of use of this continuation gets less. This is the condition of the *half-blind valley*. Figure 31 presents an instance from Cooleman Plain, NSW, where a small stream flows from igneous rocks only about 150 m over limestone outcrop before sinking at a small alluvial flat. At the time of mapping it entered a small earth hole in that flat, but now it enters fissures in the bedrock at its north-west side. A low, grassy threshold, about 3 m high along a felsite dyke, separates this depression from a gravel stream bed which is only rarely followed by overflow.

Blind Valleys

Eventually a sinking stream cuts its bed so far below the threshold that it always goes underground and never flows beyond. Thus a blind valley is produced, closed off at its downstream end. (Note that, while Fr. *vallée aveugle* is equivalent, Ger. *Blindtal* is not – (Trimmel 1965.) The reversed slope may be only a few metres high or may range into hundreds of metres. The larger the disappearing stream the more likely is it to enter an open cave. The example of figure 32 is one of many at Yarrangobilly, NSW, where a strike belt of limestone forms a strath terrace between the Yarrangobilly River gorge and the steep slopes of an igneous range. The blind valley closes off only 45 m within the limestone and the stream enters a cave at the foot of crags in the 15 m counterslope. Beyond, a valley about 8 m deep is interrupted by small dolines; this is the much modified former onward course of the stream.

Sometimes blind valleys possess a series of closed depressions into which the stream spills successively as it banks up in flood, each one providing entry into the underground conduit. Temporary ponds or small lakes form in this way as they do also with half-blind valleys. With a high threshold, a vertical sequence of entries may be left by a deepening of the blind valley.

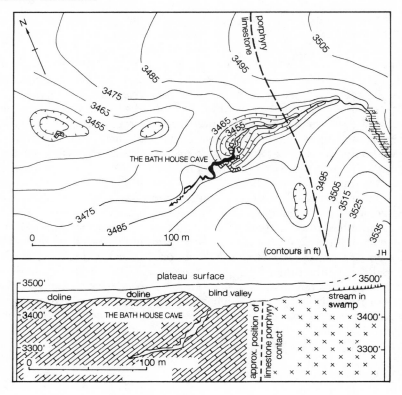

Figure 32 A blind valley at Yarrangobilly, NSW.

How far blind valleys reach into the karst and how big they become depend on various factors. Studying some large blind valleys in the classical karst of Slovenia, Gams (1962) found that their form was related to the carbonate content of the stream waters where they entered the karst. With high concentrations there, the blind valleys are narrow and short, whereas where they are low, long and wide, blind valleys are found.

At Yarrangobilly, NSW, the dimensions of blind valleys were compared with those of their catchments outside the limestone to test the hypothesis that the bigger the catchment (and therefore its discharge), the bigger would be the blind valley that resulted. In fact, only a partial explanation was provided in this way because the time since underground capture varied (Jennings *et al.* 1980). The older a blind valley, the larger it is likely to be.

The shape of blind valleys will also vary with the nature of the alluvium accumulating in them. If this is impervious, it will tend to seal off the floor and favour widening by lateral erosion of the sides. With pervious alluvium, as with much Pleistocene cold climate gravel in the Yugoslavian karst, solution can still go on beneath the openwork fill, continuing to deepen the valley without widening it much.

Steepheads

Springs of both exsurgence and resurgence type are frequently found at the heads of valleys, which begin very abruptly (plate 17) and are steep-walled, sometimes like gorges. They are usually short valleys in the margins of plateaus or in the flanks of mountain ranges. The Fontaine de Vaucluse in Provence arises beneath a 200 m cliff at the head of such a valley; this is implied in the origin of the name – *val clos*. In several languages the popular name for these cul-de-sacs is 'World's End', but in English the American term *steephead* is becoming customary for them in scientific writing. A distinction is sometimes made between steepheads incised to an impervious basement and pocket valleys where the floor of the valley is still within the karst outcrop.

These features may be due to spring sapping. A spring undermines the cliff or slope above it; rock and soil gravitate into it and are removed by the stream. In this way there is headward retreat of the valley, an evolution implied in the French term for them – *reculées*. However, the gorge may be due to collapse of substantial lengths of cave roof, which has happened in several sections united later by further collapse. Natural bridges may survive to prove this second mode of origin, but if the valley formed a long time ago, such distinguishing evidence may now be lacking.

Whatever the manner of formation of a steephead, when the waters emerging are autogenic, both stream and valley are 'old at birth'.

Dry Valleys

Dry valleys lack stream channels in their floors (plate 18). Defined thus simply, they are not confined to karst. In normal fluvial relief, streams often have short dry valleys at their heads and their minor tributary valleys may be entirely of this nature. In them, surface flow (whether infiltration excess overland flow, saturated overland flow or return flow) is not sufficiently large or frequent to gather into linear threads capable of cutting a channel. Longer and branching dry valleys form on pervious rocks such as sandstone and pumice, but dry valleys are most characteristic in karst.

Some of the most spectacular dry valleys in karst are the easiest to explain. Allogenic river valleys often continue through karst beyond their sinking points in dry valleys. In the Istrian Plateau, three rivers have

97

Plate 17 Steephead at Sogoksu, Turkey, with a spring.

eroded wide valleys in impervious rocks in which they rise and then drain south-west into limestone (figure 33) (Roglić 1964a). Two of them, the Mirna and Rasa, cross the karst to reach the sea along canyons. Between them, a third river sinks at the limestone but its former course is continued along the Pazinksi Potok, a dry valley of canyon form.

River capture is involved in the case of the Sadeng dry valley, which winds through the Gunung Sewu conekarst of south-central Java to the

Plate 18 A dry valley at Cooleman Plain, NSW, cut in the corrosion surface and truncating Silurian limestone. The stream now sinks at the foot of an igneous range in the background.

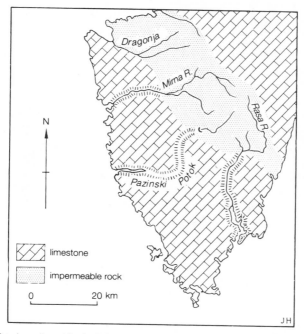

Figure 33 The dry valley of Pazinski Potok, Istria, Yugoslavia, after Roglić (1964a).

99

south coast (figure 34). It is the former course of the Solo River that now drains northwards (Lehmann 1936). The dry valley is 250–300 m wide and 150 m deep; its long profile is interrupted by shallow lakes or *telagas* with gentle saddles between as much as 30 m high.

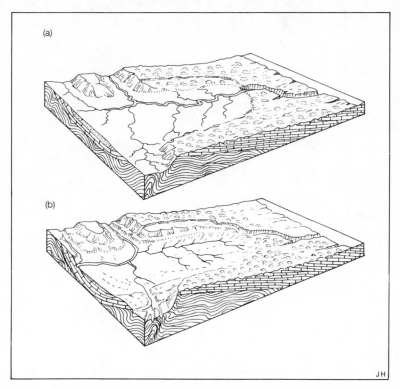

Figure 34 The Sadeng dry valley through Gunung Sewu conekarst, Java, caused by reversal of River Solo, after Lehmann (1936).

Dry valleys of this kind can be correlated in their long profiles with river terraces and the present surface river profile of the drainage line that formerly flowed along them (White and White 1983).

More problematic are branching systems of dry valleys within karsts where there is a general absence of stream channels. Most of the Peak District limestone is covered by such systems (figure 35). These dry valleys often begin in shallow, bowl-like basins, which lead into rock-walled valleys. Smaller dry valleys often hang above major dry valleys and the allogenic river valleys of the Wye, Dove, Manifold and Derwent River. Warwick (1964) found that nickpoints along dry valley tributaries of the Manifold could be related to phases of rejuvenation found in the main valley. Therefore he thought that the dry valleys are inherited features that originated on former overlying shales. After this cover was stripped, the rivers cut down into the limestone until solution created secondary permeability, permitting drainage to go underground. The hanging valleys arise because main valleys had a surface flow lasting

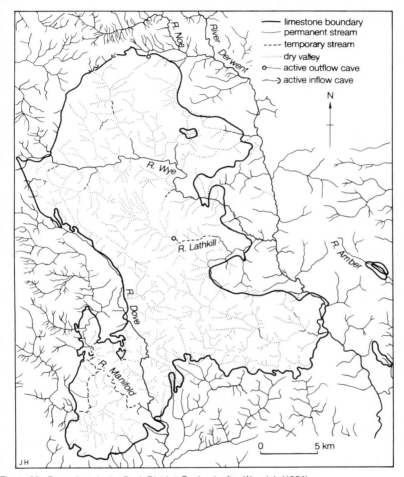

Figure 35 Dry valleys in the Peak District, England, after Warwick (1964).

longer, during which time they continued to cut their valleys down. They lack streams where they hang, in contrast to hanging valleys arising from other causes, such as glacial erosion.

The dry valleys of the Cretaceous chalk of south-eastern England and northern France have caused more study than any others. Apart from allogenic rivers passing through the chalk cuestas in water gaps, only the lower parts of the autogenic valleys have stream channels, usually over

101

alluvial floodplains. Convexo-concave profiles characterize the dry valley cross-sections, and in plan some exhibit rectangular patterns suggestive of joint control. Exceptionally wet winters cause surface flow over their grassy floors.

It is difficult to attribute these dry valleys as a whole to an inheritance from surface drainage on impervious cover, though some have this nature near the dipslope contacts with Tertiary covers. Dry valleys are found in parts of the English chalk country that were planed off in an Early Pleistocene marine transgression. These have sometimes been thought to be the product of glacial meltwater streams. Though there are some of this origin, however, the dendritic patterns of dry valleys do not fit any conceivable pattern of ice retreat margins and much of the chalk was too far from glaciation.

Periglacial conditions in the past have been called upon, to explain their origin with permafrost inducing surface flow from snow melt and summer rain (Reid 1887). Dry valleys commonly have deposits of angular chalk rubble with a mud matrix, which are at least in part periglacial gelifluction materials, and the rounded forms of the chalk country have been interpreted by some as being due to periglacial mass-wasting. There is no doubt that many chalk dry valleys have been modified in Pleistocene periglacial phases (Kerney et al. 1964). However, it is unrealistic to think that the chalk terrain was undissected prior to Pleistocene cold periods.

Changes in water table level have been used to explain the dry valleys by many authorities. Sparks and Lewis (1957) thought that some of the scarp dry valleys were formed by spring sapping, followed by a lowering of the water table with a downvalley shift in springs, which are now countersunk into the dry valley floors well below their heads. Since springs are considered to be fed along joints, which will therefore govern their migration, lack of statistical correlation between joint and dry valley directions caused Brown (1969) to argue against spring sapping as the mechanism of scarp dry valley formation.

Chandler (1909) and Fagg (1954) explained the dipslope dry valleys of the chalk Downs of south-east England by scarp retreat, which lowered the scarpfoot springline at the contact with underlying clay and thus also the water table, causing drainage to go underground in the dry valleys on the dipslope. This hypothesis implies that the scarp dry valleys must be a separate later generation, for which there is no evidence. Moreover, erosion surface remnants at the foot of the North Downs scarp show that it has not retreated much for a long time. However, Sparks (1961) points out that erosion surface remnants in the clay vales are evidence that there must have been lowering of water tables in the cuestas of chalk even without scarp retreat, and so this could have dried out both scarp and dipslope valleys.

Alternating graded reaches and nickpoints along the Chiltern dry valleys also indicate successive rejuvenations. C. D. Ollier and A. J. Thomasson (personal communication) think that this is incompatible with a genesis by meltwater over frozen ground but support the idea of headward sapping from springs shifted downvalley by falls of base level drying out the higher reaches of the valleys. Similarly, Pinchemel (1954) relies on valley deepening over a long period to dry out tributary valleys in the French chalk country. Springs would shift down tributary valleys as each incision of a major river lowered the water table. He terms this process one of auto-desiccation and calculates an index of desiccation, which is the ratio of valley density to stream channel density. Chalk terrain near Amiens gave a much greater ratio than he obtained for other rocks.

In discussing the role of subcutaneous lateral water movement from a perched storage, Williams (1983) suggests that a lowering of this zone with time through improvement in vertical circulation as more planes of weakness are enlarged by solution may be the cause of dry valleys, which previously received more water from the erstwhile near-surface, weathered zone.

Constructional Action of Rivers

Because of the high concentration of carbonate they carry, karst rivers have a special capacity for constructional activity through the precipitation of part of their chemical load. The most important cause of such precipitation is diffusion of carbon dioxide to the atmosphere, which will be particularly important where water emerges from caves or soil with a higher P_{CO_2} than that of the open air. In conditions of high temperature and slow flow, evaporation may also bring about supersaturation. Plants also intervene. Some plants, such as Characeae — stoneworts is their revealing common name — secrete limey skeletons. Others cause deposition around their organic tissues, in part because of their requirement for CO_2 for photosynthesis. At Plitvice on the River Korana in Yugoslavia, Pevalek (1935) distinguished four kinds of precipitate, formed in and around plant remains, and associated each with particular microrelief and flow conditions. One is formed by the blue-green alga *Schizothrix*, two dominantly formed by mosses *Cratoneuron* and *Bryum*, and another depends on a grass *(Agrostis)* together with *Schizothrix*. Organic debris — leaves and twigs — may be incorporated, as well as sand and silt. Modern work, e.g. Casanova (1981), stresses the importance of algal and bacterial activity producing stromatolitic structures.

Where the result is a porous mass it is called *tufa*, but where the product is solid and crystalline it is called *travertine* and is not readily distinguished from flowstone of caves.

Plant growth, evaporation and CO_2 diffusion are all promoted by aeration accompanying vigorous turbulence. Therefore deposition will take place preferentially where the water flows over any initial irregularity and a barrier or dam gradually builds up (plate 19). This in turn favours further accumulation on the front where the steep slope involves frothing and bubbling, and the thinner layer passing over the top is also conducive to precipitation. Any lower point in the rim will have faster flow and greater turbulence; this accelerates deposition there, tending to produce a flat top. The features are generally arcuate in plan, with the ends presumably the initial points of deposition. In section they may be nearly vertical or inclined downstream.

Plate 19 Tufa dam formation in McKittricks Canyon, Guadalupe Range, New Mexico.

So barriers and waterfalls develop across karst rivers through their own action. These *constructive waterfalls* (Gregory 1911) may advance downvalley leaving a broad fill of tufa or travertine behind. The barriers may become overhanging, and curtains of tufa may envelop caves behind them.

Alluviation may take place above growing barriers, as on the River Krka near Knin in Yugoslavia, where there is an alluvial plain above the 20 m high Topolje Falls. However, barrier growth may be so rapid as to cause pools or even lakes to form. This is true along 6 km of the Korana valley (figure 36), where the two largest of a series of lakes together have an area of 1.5 km² and the greatest depth is 50 m. Two barriers were drowned by a lower one growing faster, thus merging three lakes.

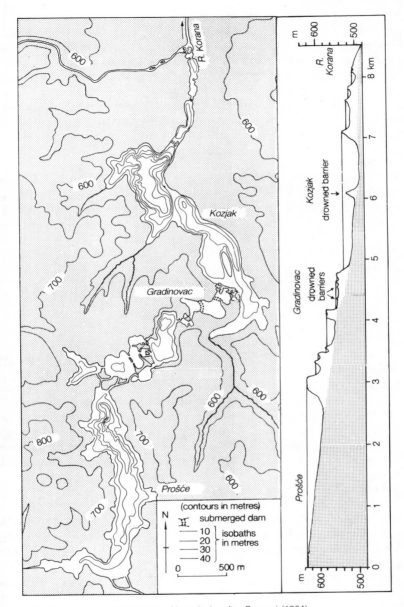

Figure 36 Plitvice Lakes, River Korana, Yugoslavia, after Gavazzi (1904).

Phases of deposition may alternate with phases of erosion. Thus, there are three phases of travertine formation in the Arbuckle Mountains, Oklahoma (Emig 1917), with the first period of deposition giving rise to higher and wider falls than the present Turner Falls on Honey Creek and Prices Falls on Falls Creek. The travertines of Millau in the Grandes Causses, France, fall into five age-groups, which range back to the Lower Pleistocene (Ambert 1981) and are closely related to the River Tarn terraces. The climatic significance of the alternations of construction and erosion to be found with various localities of these kinds awaits careful investigation with the resources of modern isotope chemistry; Thorpe *et al.* (1980) show that the combination of radiocarbon dating and oxygen palaeotemperatures has potential in this kind of context.

The largest primary travertine caves in Europe are at Lillafured, Hungary, where a spring formerly emerged at the base of a hill of travertine built by the Szinva Brook in the past. The biggest natural chamber is about 10 m long, 5 m wide and 8 m high, but there are artificial cuts linking the chambers as well as natural passages. Pine branches and leaves indicate a Pleistocene age for the deposition and so of the caves also.

Natural bridges occur in travertine (Cleland 1910). Some are due to construction of travertine by splash and spray above a stream until it meets, e.g. on Pine Creek, Arizona, but others are left in the air by subsequent removal of gravel on which the travertine was built up.

Dolines

Closed depressions of simple form are exceedingly common and important in karst. Since the Anglo-American words 'sinkhole', 'swallow hole' and 'swallet' have been used very loosely and extended beyond such features, for more clarity the word *doline* has been preferred by many. This has come from the south Slav languages through German. It is unfortunately a bad choice as far as the Yugoslavs are concerned, because that word has even wider meaning for them (Gams 1973). Nevertheless it will be retained here. Dolines are generally circular or oval in plan, with a range of forms – dish and bowl-shaped, conical and cylindrical.

In bedrock, with small area and great depth, there is transition to the open shaft which is best considered with caves. When they are elongated in plan, there is transition to the karst corridor. If a stream runs into the depression, there is a gradation to the blind valley.

In size dolines vary from a few metres in their dimensions to more than a hundred metres in depth and to several hundreds of metres in horizontal dimensions. Increasing size is usually accompanied by complexity of form, which takes them into other categories of closed depression.

Bedrock crops out on the sides and floors of some dolines when there is often angularity of general form as well as in detail. Others are surfaced largely or entirely by soil or superficial deposits. Still others are in bedrock formations overlying the karst rock. If there is a flat floor, this consists of detrital materials, often impervious, including insoluble clay residues. These impervious seals can cause swamps or ponds, but the latter occur also in bedrock dolines through intersection with water rest levels. In other dolines there are cave entrances or open shafts.

With such variety, it is not surprising that a number of processes are operative in dolines, including solution at and near the surface, cave collapse, piping and subsidence. Though these often work in combination or in sequence, it is useful to consider them initially in a simple division on the basis of dominant mechanisms (Cramer 1941). A more complex classification is given by Quinlan (1972).

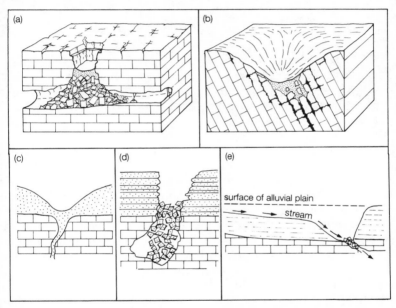

Figure 37 Major types of dolines: (a) collapse doline; (b) solution doline; (c) subsidence doline; (d) subjacent karst collapse doline; (e) alluvial streamsink doline.

Solution doline

Some favourable point such as a joint intersection leads to a concentration of surface solution. The solutes and some of the insoluble residues are removed down solution-widened joints and bedding-planes, though once these are enlarged somewhat rock fragments as well as residues will slide and fall down them. Such a focus of solution and downward percolation gathers drainage to itself and the embryonic doline furthers its own growth (figure 37(b)). In uniform rock, solution, mechanical slope wash and mass movements of material can result in uniform slopes

Plate 20 A solution doline with bedrock exposed over its floor and sides, Velebit Mountains, Yugoslavia.

in dynamic equilibrium, resulting in a conical shape. However, if residues accumulate too quickly for removal down enlarged bedrock planes of weakness, the doline may become bowl-shaped and even flat-floored, with swamps or pools. Around such floors, the slopes may maintain characteristic uniform slopes, often in the 30–40° range. But if impervious clay residues accumulate, water may be deflected laterally to sap slope bottoms and so uniform angle of sideslopes may be lost (Aubert 1969). The character of a doline thus may depend on two ratios: (a) vertical solution to lateral solution, and (b) evacuation of solutes and clasts to accumulation of clastic fill.

If bedrock is exposed over much or all of a doline's surface, an origin through surface solution will be apparent; this condition is found in high mountains, dry climate, or as a result of accelerated soil erosion (see plate 20). If a doline is covered by soil or waste mantle, a shaft in undisturbed bedrock in the bottom of the depression will still reveal its nature. Aubert (1966) sectioned a solution doline at Grandes-Chaumilles in the Swiss Jura, revealing a bedrock solution pipe into which the doline fill descends. In figure 38(a), frost-shattered rock (1) and residual clay soil (2) underlie clay soils containing Würm glacial erratics (3) and stone-free clays above (4). Part of the fill was evacuated causing an inner doline. This is partly refilled with rendzinas containing talus from the doline wall, bones and wood (5). This whole fill is interpreted as registering the history of the doline from the pre-Würm interglacial or a Würm interstadial.

An even greater proportion of the fill of dolines of the Mitchell Plain, Indiana, appears to be foreign, washed in from beyond the limits of the depressions (Hall 1976). Apart from reworked loess, the bulk of the fill, formerly thought to be residual 'terra rossa', is now regarded as having been transported from surrounding upland areas (figure 38(b)). Magaldi and Sauro (1982) discuss more complicated doline histories in the Italian Alps.

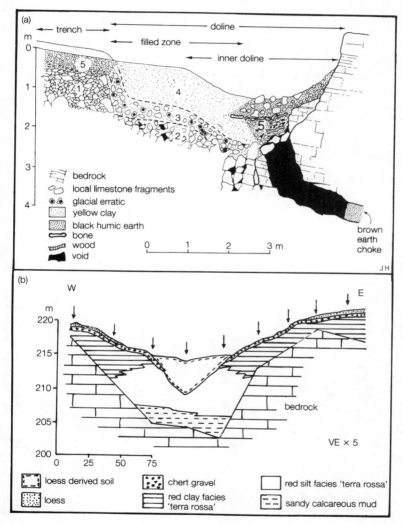

Figure 38 Sections through solution dolines: (a) at Grandes-Chaumilles, Swiss Jura, after Aubert (1966) (numbers explained in text); (b) in Indiana, after Hall (1976).

In Williams (1982a), the processes at work in solution dolines in the King Country, NZ, are related afresh to the morphology. Convergent lateral flow in the subcutaneous zone and through the soil to a lesser extent combines with vertical flow at the centre to remove more limestone there than from the sides and so promotes their bowl shape. Since the 'capillary barrier' of tight joints below the subcutaneous zone is punctured only at intervals, this accounts for the development of the doline pattern. This view is elaborated on a broader regional basis in Williams (1983).

Asymmetry can result from steep dip of the beds, with the gentle side downdip and the steep side in joint planes on the anti-dip side. Even without such dip, if dolines are on a steep slope the uphill side is reduced to lesser angle than the downhill side. In bare karst, snow drifting under prevalent winds may fashion gentler slopes beneath persistent snow-banks. Where there is soil cover, it may be thinner and less rich in humus on the snowbank side, reducing solution there.

Collapse doline

The prime cause of a doline can be the collapse of the roof of a cave formed by underground solution (see figure 37(a)). To begin with, it will be vertically walled and may be angular in plan through joint guidance. The depth–width ratio may exceed the maximum likely in solution dolines of 1 to 3.5.

Unless there is further collapse, these dolines will change progressively to a conical or bowl shape through a wearing down of the sides and

Plate 21 A cenote near Konya, Turkey; a collapse doline intersecting the water rest level and thus giving rise to a permanent lake.

filling of the bottom (by solution, rockfall, frost shattering and salt wedging according to climate) and, once a soil cover forms, through soil creep and other mass movements. In time, overt evidence of collapse is concealed and a superficial similarity to other dolines prevails.

Where collapse has been into water-filled caves or where the water level has risen subsequently, the collapse doline may have a lake in it. Such are the cenotes of Yucatan, the 'obruk' lakes of the Anatolian Plateau (plate 21) and similar features in south-eastern South Australia (Marker 1976), where several have more than 50 m of water depth.

Subsidence doline

Where thick soils or superficial deposits cover karst rocks, dolines can develop through spasmodic subsidence and more continuous piping of these materials into widened joints and solution pipes in the bedrock beneath (figure 37(c)). They vary much in size and shape. A quick movement of subsidence may temporarily produce a cylindrical hole (plate 22), which rapidly weathers into a gentler conical or bowl shape. The latter shape, however, can also be the consequence of more or less continuous small-scale movements only.

The 'shakeholes' of Craven are conical subsidence dolines in the glacial moraine left on limestone by the last Pleistocene glaciation (Sweeting 1950). At Mole Creek, Tasmania, many dolines occur in Pleistocene gravel fans and terraces, of glaciofluvial and periglacial-fluvial origin, resting on Ordovician limestone (Jennings 1967). Some are full of water, forming circular ponds. Lowry (1967) has shown that the conical doline

Plate 22 A subsidence doline in alluvium over limestone behind the May River dam near Konya, Turkey, formed after a reservoir was created.

111

feeding into open solution pipes above Easter Cave, Augusta, WA, is a subsidence doline in thick residual soils above aeolian calcarenite of at least the last Interglacial age (figure 8).

Subjacent karst doline

Closed depressions of wide-ranging shape and size, many falling into the doline category, are found in other rock formations overlying karst rocks (figure 37(d)). Thus, in South Wales there are more and larger dolines on a conglomeratic sandstone above limestone (both in the Carboniferous sequence) than on the limestone outcrop itself (Thomas 1974).

Some of these subjacent karst dolines are undoubtedly due to the collapse of a cave roof. This is the likely explanation of the Big Hole at Braidwood, NSW. Entirely cliffed to its 115 m bottom, it is twice as deep as it is wide at the surface. Silurian limestone is inferred to underlie the Devonian quartz sandstone of the walls. Nearby in Wyanbene Cave, the Gunbarrel is a shaft reaching up to the Devonian–Silurian unconformity from a very large chamber capable of accepting as much rock as has been lost down the Big Hole.

This mode of origin certainly applies to some of the South Wales gritstone dolines but probably not to small dolines occurring in fields, because collapses in caves do not occur in such patterns. Likewise, it is difficult to apply it to a few extremely large but shallow depressions, because cave chambers large enough to form them are not known in South Wales caves. Progressive removal of overlying rock down widened joints in the limestone, as with subsidence dolines, is a more likely mechanism for the small ones; areal solution at the top of the limestone is more compatible with the large shallow dolines. The latter is characteris-

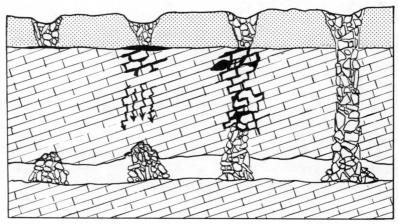

Figure 39 The solution-shuffle hypothesis for subjacent karst doline formation in Wales. Four possible relationships of doline and cave are portrayed after Bull (1977).

tic of the subjacent evaporite karst of central Germany (Cramer 1941; Hundt 1950), though the karst rock there is much more soluble and the overlying rock formations weaker than in the South Wales area.

Study of quartz sand sediment in relation to limestone boulder chokes in the South Wales cave, Agen Allwedd, leads Bull (1977) to postulate a 'solution-shuffle' hypothesis, which links the two extremes in mode of origin discussed above (see figure 39). Percolation through the gritstone leads both to subsidence at the top and cave roof collapse at depth with initially undisturbed rock between. Eventually the intervening rock mass between is weakened so that it shuffles down progressively to link the two seats of action.

Alluvial streamsink dolines

Cramer (1941) distinguished this kind of doline, in which streams sink through alluvium into underlying karst rock (figure 37(e)). They occur frequently in polje floors. Processes that create subsidence dolines operate here, but in addition the sinking stream helps with the mechanical removal of insoluble alluvium. Stream-cut trenches lead into the side of conical or basin-shaped depressions. This kind of doline is frequently partially blocked with detritus, and much of the time no bedrock will be visible.

Origins of dolines

Determining the mode of origin of dolines can be difficult. Where study of a cave beneath can be combined with close examination of the surface, positive answers can sometimes be obtained, as with three dolines over Murray Cave, Cooleman Plain, NSW (Jennings and Bao 1980); two were solution dolines and one was of collapse origin, though they are close together in an isolated group. The subsidence doline of figure 8 required, in addition to surface and underground survey, deep augering before the true mode of origin was proven by Lowry.

Where quarrying reveals the stratigraphy of doline fills, the sedimentary structures may provide valuable clues as to the mechanism of enlargement and emplacement. In doline fills in Missouri, Bretz (1950) found compressional rather than tensional features characteristic and pressure solution effects, pointing to a long progressive development of the cavities. Subjacent karst dolines in the Peak District of England provide similar evidence, and Walsh et al. (1972) used laboratory models to simulate them. They found that the progressive removal of small parts of the bottom of the model doline, rather than a sudden large-scale lowering of it, yielded a structure most like those revealed in the quarries. Thus, cave roof collapse does not appear to explain the facts as well as surface solution or Bull's 'solution-shuffle'.

Doline Morphometry

Such intensive attacks are not practical where there are many problematic dolines. Because dolines often occur in large numbers close together (see figure 40 and plate 23,) geomorphologists were early led to adopt morphometric methods in their study (e.g. Cvijić 1893; Lozinski 1907; Cramer 1941). Even if morphometry may not point decisively to a given mode of origin, it may at least exclude some and indicate whether the result of a detailed examination of one doline or a few can be applied to many around them.

One of the first of modern doline morphometric studies was that by Coleman and Balchin (1959) of small depressions on part of the Mendip plateau. They argued that, if these were of surface solutional origin, there should be a tendency to dynamic equilibrium in their slopes; as they get wider, they deepen proportionately. Therefore a depth/diameter plot should give a cluster along a straight line. Collapse dolines, in contrast, would be variable in depth/diameter ratio and there should result a wide scatter in the graph. A plot of 140 measured Mendip depressions gave such a wide scatter, and this with other evidence was used to argue for collapse origin. However, the data included many artificial mining holes, and when Ford (1964a) dealt with a larger sample of 566 definitely natural hollows he came to a different conclusion. Eighty per cent of them lay in dry valleys where their long profile had less than a certain

Plate 23 A doline field on Mt Cookson, North Canterbury, NZ. in Oligocene limestone with a loess cover.

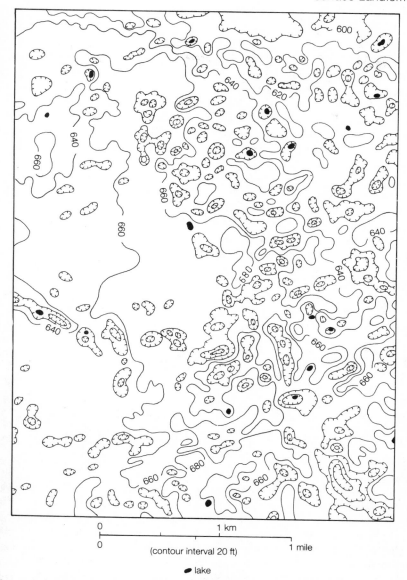

0

0

1 km

1 mile

(contour interval 20 ft)

🕭 lake

Figure 40 Doline karst in Sinkhole Plain, Kentucky, from US Geological Survey map.

gradient. Mapping of the caves in the area showed that they did not underlie the dry valleys, and collapses in them did not correspond with surface depressions. Therefore he argued that the latter had been formed by surface solution where much surface water was gathered together but where the slope was not steep enough to allow fast surface runoff.

115

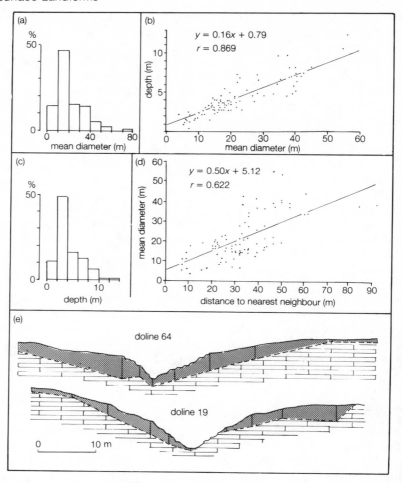

Figure 41 Doline field, Craigmore, Canterbury, NZ: (a)–(d) doline morphometry; (e) augered profiles of representative dolines.

Measurement of a field of 90 dolines on the Craigmore plateau, Canterbury, NZ (Jennings 1975), showed strong modality in diameter and depth (figure 41), with a strong correlation between depth and mean diameter ($r = 0.87$, significant at 0.001 level of probability). These shape characteristics argue against a collapse origin and point to parallel slope retreat; this is compatible with either solutional origin or subsidence. Lines of auger holes across several of them indicated composite origin, with younger subsidence dolines in a loess cover overlying bedrock dolines beneath. Various lines of argument pointed to surface solution for the buried dolines, including nearest neighbour analysis, which revealed a tendency towards a uniform distribution unlikely with collapsed cave origins and a further tendency for neighbouring dolines to hold back one another's growth. A basically similar doline field on Mt Cookson in the same New Zealand province of Canterbury was not so uniformly buried in loess, and direct observation of shafts in the doline bottoms showed that undisturbed bedrock underlies them.

The large areas of 'sinkhole plain' in the Midwest of the United States, where good topographical, geological and pedological maps are commonly available and structures are comparatively simple, lend themselves to statistical morphometric studies of large areas on a unit area sampling basis, with multi-variable regression, nearest neighbour and factor analyses, among other techniques.

One of the earliest efforts, however, relied on a simpler procedure. For the central Kentucky karst, Howard (1968) employed histograms of the frequency of doline bottom against stratigraphic elevation and also of hilltop summits against stratigraphic elevation. A third plot was of the difference in numbers of doline bottoms and of doline rims in each stratigraphic elevation class, which indirectly indicates the frequency distribution of doline depths. These showed that the frequency and depth of dolines are closely related to the lithology of the rocks. In particular, they were of high frequency and greater depth in the middle of the St Louis limestone and around the contact of that limestone with the overlying Ste Genevieve limestone, both of Mississippian age. These are horizons rich in bedded chert, which makes them resistant. They form low escarpments, with dolines frequent in an updip location close behind them.

For the same area, Lavalle (1968) attempted to explain the depth, area and slope of dolines by multiple regression against a wider range of controlling factors related to the general hydrology, bedrock lithology and structure. Of the geological factors, he considered that the most important were joints and faults; the more the dolines corresponded with them in direction and the more elongated they were in this sense, the deeper, larger and steeper they were as well. These dimensions were also directly related, but much less closely, to the density and purity of the limestones. Three measures related to the hydrology were employed: (a) karst relief ratio (height difference between the highest point on the surface and the lowest point on the water table per unit area, divided by distance from nearest underground divide); (b) percentage of unit area with underground drainage; and (c) distance from outflow points. All three operated in the sense hypothesized: the greater the potential hydraulic gradient (a) and the greater the development of caves (b), the greater the doline development, whereas the farther from the springs, the less it is. The underground divides were located without the help of water tracing, which has since shown a more complicated pattern than was relied upon, and others would hypothesize that nearness to streamsinks also favours doline development. However, this pioneering approach fostered more realistic analyses.

White and White (1979) included doline analysis in their study of more widely varying carbonate rocks in the Appalachian Plateau and Appalachian Valley and Ridge physiographic provinces to the east. They calculated: (a) area draining into dolines, (b) number of dolines per unit area of carbonate rock, and (c) doline depth.

As might be expected, the more the dolines, the bigger the area drained in this way. However, the horizontal Mississippian limestones of the Plateau gave rise to larger dolines on average than the highly inclined Ordovician limestones and dolomites of the Valley and Ridge province, and the same relationship holds for the proportion of the karst rocks draining into dolines. Dolines are more frequent per unit area and are larger on limestones than on the less quickly soluble dolomites (cf. W. B. White 1984). However, the frequency distribution of doline depth shows no relationship to this lithological factor or to dip of the rocks. Depth seems to be a function of doline evolution itself. Dip may be influential only through the differing lithology of the pure horizontal Mississippian limestones and the less pure dipping Ordovician limestones.

Kemmerly (1976) dealt with doline karst in Tennessee in basically the same geological context as the Kentucky studies. He found that a power function ($L = 1.656$, $W = 1.024$) described a fairly strong relationship between the length (L) and width (W) of the dolines he sampled. The dolines get more elongated as they grow larger, one kind of heterogonic allometry. The exponent is very close to unity so it is not a marked tendency. The question of change in shape over time was taken further by Kemmerly and Towe (1978) by comparing the shape of a doline sample in air photographs taken in 1937 and 1972, and this confirmed different rates of change in the two dimensions, DW/dT. This is expressive of structure, material being removed more easily parallel to the major joint systems. However, there was variety among the dolines in their surface mantles of residual clay, loess and silty colluvium. The last group were elongating fastest as a result of greater permeability which gave greater effect to joint control of shape.

Compared with Kentucky and Tennessee, more of Iowa's karst rocks are mantled with transported, unconsolidated sediments, even the 'Driftless Area' carrying remnants of Nebraskan till and a loess blanket; Palmquist et al. (1976) evaluated this factor in doline development along with other factors such as have been assessed elsewhere. Three areas with mantles of different age and character were subjected to morphometry, in particular of doline density. Correlation of density with mantle thickness showed that too thick a cover reduces or inhibits the genesis of dolines. The ages of the mantles permit the conclusion that doline density increases over time but at a decreasing rate. Doline enlargement eventually replaces doline initiation. However, the ratio of variance to the mean density on different mantles points to an increasing tendency to clustering with age of surface. This is particularly true along valleys where mantle thickness is most appropriate for doline development; here the growth of one doline appears to favour the development of others nearby. Drake and Ford (1972) had earlier tested, by nearest neighbour analysis, this concept of mother and daughters on the Mendip plateau and came to the conclusion that each 'mother' tended to cause about four 'daughter' dolines to form around it. On the other hand a contrary finding was mentioned above about the relations between dolines, namely that dolines tended to hinder the growth of other dolines near them (Jennings 1975).

Palmquist (1979) made a fuller analysis of density and size of dolines in the Driftless Area of Iowa, the oldest surface of the three studied before, regressing doline dimensions against various parameters, which were surrogates for a range of postulated controlling factors. This confirmed that local factors, including mantle thickness, local topography in its effect on groundwater recharge, and percentage of surface drainage, which is taken to be inversely related to local secondary permeability (including cave development), govern doline initiation and enlargement more than regional factors such as location within regional groundwater basins.

The Mitchell Plain in Indiana is another Midwest doline karst that has attracted attention along the lines under discussion. McConnell and Horn (1972) subjected the frequency distribution of densities of dolines in sample areas to statistical comparison with Poisson, negative binomomial and double Poisson probability distributions. The variances were greater than the means, implying a geographical pattern more clustered than random, and the frequency distribution fitted the double Poisson best. This is interpreted as reflecting the operation of two mechanisms of doline formation: surface solution, forming many small depressions, and cave roof collapse, creating fewer but larger units. Both were regarded as random in their likely pattern.

Another investigation of the Mitchell Plain dolines is distinguished from all other Midwest doline studies discussed above in that it relates the surface features concretely to the underground drainage. Palmer and Palmer (1975) showed density to be in part dependent on bedrock lithology, being highest in chert-bearing parts of the Ste Genevieve and St Louis limestones; and Howard (1968), in his study of the continuation of this terrain southwards into Kentucky, obtained similar findings. But dolines are also concentrated in the lowest downdip exposure of these beds, and are most frequent near deeply entrenched river valleys but on gentle slopes, round the margins of unconsolidated covers and in lines prolonging the course of sinking streams that flow from the covers.

Very large cave systems have been mapped under parts of the Mitchell

E

Plain, including Blue Spring Cave with nearly 31 km of passage. The deeper dolines are preferentially located over or close to cave passages, and contouring of the absolute levels of doline bottoms showed low zones over the dendritic cave systems. On the other hand, maps of doline density do not correspond closely with cave passage pattern but are linked to the known caves only in a general way (figure 42). All this suggests a mutual interdependence of doline and cave development but with only a small proportion of the dolines being directly connected with underground passages by collapse.

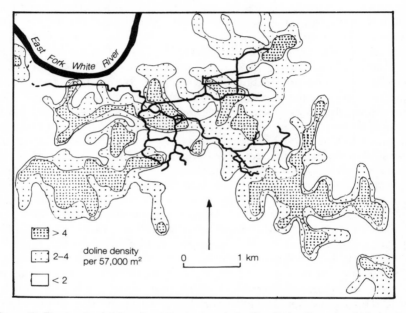

Figure 42 The density of dolines in relation to caves in the Blue Spring Cave area, Indiana, after Palmer and Palmer (1975).

Although there is much agreement between the results of these morphometric studies, there are also divergences, which are probably due less to differences in method than to real variation in static contexts, active mechanisms and historical inheritances.

Cockpits

In tropical humid karst, there are many simple closed depressions which differ in important ways from those discussed so far (figure 43). They have sides lobed convexly inwards, making them star-shaped, with gullies carrying streams after heavy rains, as Lehmann (1936) described for south-central Java. Moreover, they do not perforate a fairly simple surface but are set among steep residual hills. The Jamaican name 'cockpit' has come to be applied to this kind of closed depression. Aub (1969) found that 60 per cent of the cockpits in the Crofts River area of Jamaica have bedrock shafts at or near their lowest points, so that here the cockpits are due to surface solution.

To study their morphometry, Williams (1972a, b) draws their boundaries round the hilltops and cols so that all the slopes draining into the cockpits are included. Using such limits mapped from air photographs for a number of New Guinea karsts, he ordered the depressions on the basis of their gully systems as if they were normal drainage basins. Analysis of various plan dimensions, shown in figure 43, revealed a system in relief previously described as chaotic. For example, the frequency of depressions is greater in an intermediate order than in the simplest and most complex orders. Their area, however, increases with order, as does the number of residual hills on their boundary. There is not much change in elongation with order or in distance to nearest neighbour of the same order. On the other hand, the product of symmetry, a measure of departure of the lowest point from a central position, increases with order. There is a general but unequal tendency to a more uniform pattern than random. All these characteristics Williams interprets as being due to the development of small centripetal drainage systems in the cockpits, together with competition between them.

Day (1976) applied the depression ordering method of Williams to a karst area of northern Jamaica and arrived at results that differed in some respects from those of Williams; for example, frequency declined consistently with increasing order. However, Day had none of Williams's order 0 (having no channels) and recognized that, despite this, he was dealing with depressions much more like normal dolines than cockpits in the sense defined above.

Tower Karst

Tower karst has been recognized as a distinctive landform for many years. The flat plain with near vertical stacks of limestone, producing the characteristic tower scenery so often portrayed in classical Chinese landscape paintings has, however a problematic origin. Brook and Ford (1976, 1978) have identified tower karst as forming in the subarctic climate of the North West Territories of Canada, whereas the more conventional approach has been to see these features as characteristic of humid tropical karst processes. This traditional climatic geomorphological approach has therefore had to be re-examined and it is becoming increasingly evident that tower karst formation is controlled more by structure than was ever thought before (Jennings 1982b). Indeed Yuan

121

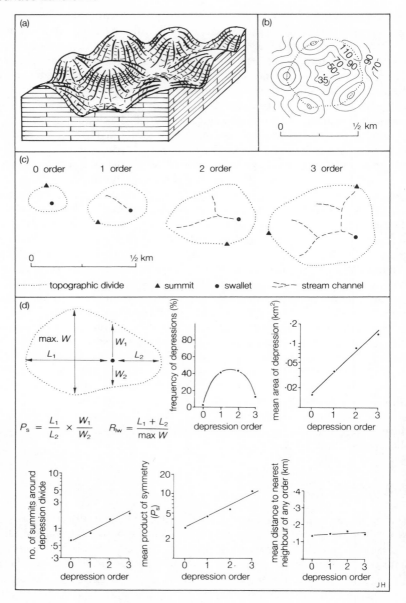

Figure 43 Tropical cockpits after Williams (1972a) (a)–(b) characteristics; (c) system of ordering; (d) dimensional analysis of set from Mt Kaijende, PNG.

Daoxian from the Institute of Karst Studies in Guilin (Southern China) reports tower karst, in its most traditional form, being produced in quartzites! Here structure may predominate even over lithology and hence even over specific solutional processes (Yuan 1981).

Uvala

'Uvala' is another term of south Slav origin now used internationally for closed depressions; it refers to more complex ones, having uneven floors with more than one low point but no extensive flat areas. Often they are due to the intersection of dolines or to smaller dolines forming within one large one. Where rocks dip steeply, uvalas are often elongated along the strike with a chain of constituent depressions along that trend, e.g. Ceteniste uvala along the strike of Triassic limestone in south-west Serbia (Cvijić 1960). Haggas Hole, in the upper Waitomo Valley, NZ, is a uvala elongated along a fault. Where there are no such structural controls, uvalas are more lobate in plan, e.g. at the Lost World, King Country, NZ (plate 24).

Cvijić (1960) attributes uvalas to surface solution, but this does not apply in all cases. North-east of Mole Creek, Tasmania, there is a uvala 250–300 m in diameter and 25 m deep, with 14 hollows of various sizes within it (Jennings 1967). It is in Ordovician limestone but breaches a cover of Tertiary basalt. A small stream drains into the deepest hollow and gullies its flank. Here the solution has taken place beneath the lava at the top of the limestone, where a shallow cave may have formed. The

Plate 24 A uvala in the King Country, NZ, with, at its centre, a large collapsed entrance into the Lost World, a cave along the underground course of the River Mangapu.

basalt has largely been removed as clasts through Mersey Hill Cave at greater depth below. Uvalas in the central parts of the Middle Atlas of Morocco (Martin 1981) lie in Liassic dolomite but have formed as a result of solution of Triassic salt below.

Poljes

In the Yugoslavian karst there are many large closed depressions with flat floors across which streams flow (figure 44). The flat floors often provide the only agricultural land around, and the name for a field – *polje* – has come to be applied to this kind of closed depression internationally. A sharp break of slope with parts of the steep slopes of the surrounding rim is also regarded as an essential attribute. To avoid confusion, Gams (1978) suggests that the flat floor must be at least 400 m across for classification as a polje. However, the term is in common usage in Yugoslavia in ways that disagree with this scientific definition; in particular, it is used for wide, alluvial plains along rivers that enter and leave the plain in narrow valleys or gorges, such as along the Neretva River. These are the 'open poljes' of Cvijić (1960). Williams (1982a) describes a structurally controlled case along Bullock Creek near Punakaiki, NZ.

Poljes are found in other parts of the world, where they have often generated local names just as dolines have – 'plans' in Provence, 'piano' in parts of Italy, 'wangs' in Malaysia, 'interior valleys' in Jamaica and 'hojos' in Cuba.

They are usually elongated along the strike of the rocks; e.g. Glamoč Polje in Croatia is 26 times as long as it is wide. They can also be compact or irregular in plain; Lož Polje in Slovenia is practically as wide as it is long. Lika Polje is over 80 km long, but Imotski Polje has the largest flat floor (385 km^2); both of these are in Croatia.

Parts of the sides may be in impervious rocks from which streams flow down on to the floors. Along the margins in limestone, springs arise. The streams flow over alluvial fans or plains to low points where they sink. These streamsinks are called *ponors*, which vary from cave entrances at the foot of limestone slopes to alluvial streamsink dolines. A stream may branch to several ponors or there may be a sequence along the one channel. There may be flood ponors at higher levels than the normal place of engulfment. Old abandoned ponors are found higher still. Small poljes may have only one alluvial plain and one stream; others have several and there may be low, doline-riddled limestone areas between them.

In many poljes, the ponors cannot dispose of the runoff fast enough after rainy weather, even when higher-lying ones come into action. Then shallow lakes form over part or even the whole of the polje floor (plate

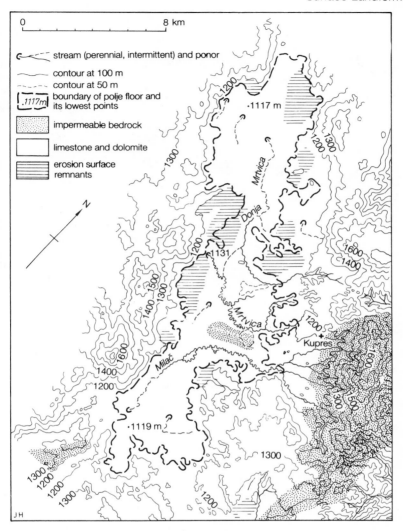

Figure 44 Kupres Polje, Bosnia, Yugoslavia, after Roglić (1939).

25). Thus Popovo Polje, Herzegovina, Yugoslavia, was inundated over three-quarters of its floor in each of seven years between 1891 and 1900, with depths of more than 30 m at its lower end. These circumstances are conducive to the occurrence of estavelles; with rising water levels, these spew out water to fill the periodic lake but afterwards help to drain it into the ground beneath. Popovo Polje has three sections to it, hydrologically. At its eastern end springs emerge from the higher plateau to the north-east and there are ponors along the Tresbisnjica River, which enters at

Surface Landforms

Plate 25 Planina Polje, Slovenia, under winter floods, which recur for several weeks each year. Photo by I. Gams.

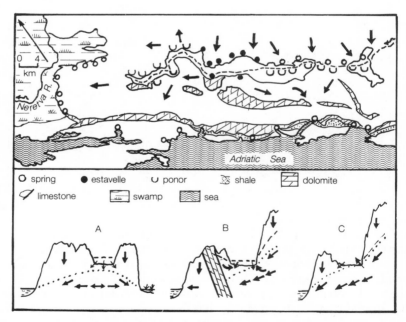

Figure 45 Hydrological zones of Popovo Polje, Herzegovina, Yugoslavia, after Milanović (1979); A, zone of ponors; B, zone of estavelles; C, zone of springs and ponors.

this end. In a middle section there are estavelles on both sides of the polje floor, while at the western end there are ponors on both sides, feeding water to both the Neretva Valley and the Adriatic (figure 45). During the dry summer season polje lakes recede, by both evaporative loss and underground drainage, but there are permanent lakes over parts of some polje floors, e.g. Cerknica Polje, Slovenia.

The Poljes of the north Nahanni karst, north-western Canada (Brook 1983) are liable to flood from two causes. Snow meltwater in spring combined with ice blockage of ponors is responsible for lesser floods, while heavy rainstorms in summer cause greater flooding, though this may not occur every year. The floors become dry in winter.

Residual hills of limestone, or *hums*, in some cases protrude through the alluvial plains of poljes or rise from slightly higher bedrock floors of limestone. In Yugoslavia they vary from 15 to 90 m in height and have a sharp break of slope at their foot. They are often conical or pyramidal in shape with uniform slopes, but those in the alluvium tend to more convex profiles with a basal steepening of their sides (Klaer 1957).

Early debate on the formation of Yugoslavian poljes was confused by their close relationship to the mid-Tertiary folding and faulting of the Dinaric Mountains and by the presence of late-Tertiary lacustrine beds in some of them. This led to the idea that they are of tectonic origin, occupying fault-angle depressions (figure 46(b)), fault troughs and synclines. Poljes of basically primary tectonic origin are to be expected, because of the strong likelihood that a closed basin, created by earth movements, will be preserved as such by the development of underground drainage, especially in the case of fault depressions (Birot 1966). Nevertheless, it is hard to find well attested examples in the literature; it is possible that Lake Tibera in the highlands of New Guinea occupies a closed tectonic depression as a result of high-angle reverse faulting in the Pliocene–Pleistocene orogeny which created the mountains.

However, there is much evidence in Yugoslavia against so simple an origin. There are high-lying erosion surfaces precluding the survival of tectonic relief. The Tertiary lacustrine beds are themselves highly deformed. Some poljes are in tectonic highs – anticlines and horsts. Moreover, poljes in synclines and fault troughs often have irregular margins, which transgress the faultlines, and synclinal axes, which broadly define the polje floor. Structures in the limestone are sometimes truncated by the floors (figure 46(a)). In the Dinaric karst it seems to be a question of structurally guided relief, not tectonic. In the central Middle Atlas, Morocco, although all poljes occupy tectonic lows of Miocene orogeny – fault angles, rifts and synclines – they were all evacuated by solution mainly in the Pliocene and are related to a particular hydrological belt where water rested at a favourable level for this (Martin 1981).

Thus, poljes have come to be regarded as features excavated predominantly through solution of the carbonate rocks. Roglić (1939, 1940)

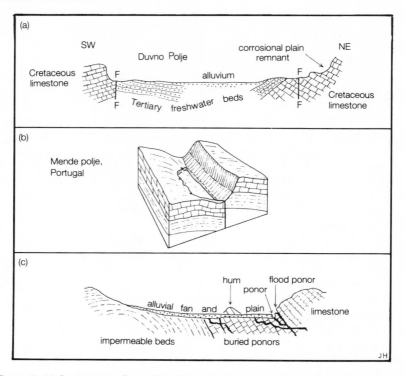

Figure 46 (a) Section across Duvno Polje, Bosnia, Yugoslavia, after Roglić (1940); (b) Mende Polje, Portugal, after Birot (1966); (c) polje formation by lateral corrosion from the alluvial floor, after Roglić (1964b).

stressed the role of lateral solutional undercutting, a mechanism applied elsewhere by others (e.g. in Turkey (Louis 1956) and in Italy (Lehmann 1959)). Parts of the walls and floors of the poljes that Roglić studied are developed on impervious Mesozoic and Tertiary beds, and this is where they began to form (figure 46(a)). Surface streams from them carried detritus to streamsinks in the surrounding limestone where alluvium accumulated (figure 46(c)). Because dolomite is less permeable than limestone, some poljes have developed along the contact of these rocks in a similar way (Gams 1969). The surface of the alluvial flat formed in this way was periodically flooded and aggressive water, enriched in CO_2 by rotting organic matter, attacked the limestone margins. In this way a flat floor extended into the limestone, and simultaneously an alluvial seal spread over it. The seal protected the limestone but promoted lateral extension. Poljes created in this way represent a development from blind valleys. Sweeting (1958) thinks that all the interior valleys of Jamaica form where lithology, structure or relief allow floodwaters to collect and prevent rapid drainage.

At certain junctures, ponors may open sufficiently for the sinking streams to incise the alluvium; subsequent partial blocking results in fresh lateral planation at a lower level, countersinking the floor. Rock terraces along the polje margins support such a history (figure 46(a)).

Other questions relate to the imperviousness of the alluvium. Melik (1955) presented evidence for the accumulation of alluvium, mass movement materials and even lake deposits in Slovenian poljes during Pleistocene cold periods. In high-lying poljes in the southern Yugoslavian karst, glaciofluvial fans were also laid down (Rathjens 1960; Roglić 1964b). All thought that these aggradation phases arrested the development of the poljes. However, Gams (1965, 1974) argues that many of these deposits are pervious and do not seal off the bottoms of the poljes. In his view, solution persisted beneath these covers and the poljes continued to deepen as well as extend laterally during Quaternary climatic oscillations.

There is also disagreement on what controls the level of planation of the floors of poljes. Lehmann and others have stressed control by the level of the outflow (*Vorfluter*) of the underground drains of the polje. Where these outlets have a common level through entering the sea or debouching at the back of a coastal plain, several poljes may have a common level. Another school of thought led by Roglić emphasizes control by ponor level within the polje whereby each one can have an independent level. Cave systems between ponors and outflows vary so much, for example between the cases of Yugoslavian poljes and Cuban hojos, that both conditions may apply.

From Cuban tropical humid karst, Lehmann et al. (1956) described karst margin poljes where the flat floor is surrounded largely by impervious rocks with a limestone wall on the outflow flank only. However, Panoš and Stelcl (1968) deny that linestone has been stripped from the floor as Lehmann thought. In the case of the karst margin polje that drains out through Tunnel Cave in the Napier Range, WA, the back-reef facies of a Devonian reef has certainly been lost mainly in this way.

Other Closed Depressions

There are closed depressions that do not fit readily into the threefold classification of doline, uvala and polje, and there are clearly transitional forms also. The old idea that poljes represent the endpoint of an evolution from dolines through uvalas no longer carries conviction, however. On the other hand, it can be hard to decide whether a particular depression is a kind of polje or simply a large blind valley. Uvalas are generally thought to develop by inosculation of dolines or by smaller dolines developing within large ones.

In the American Midwest a particular kind of closed depression is

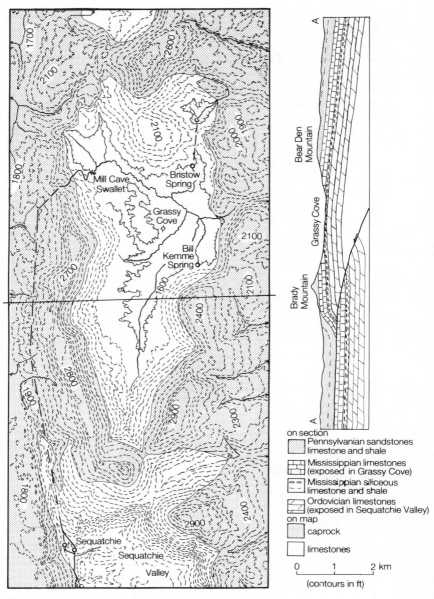

Figure 47 Grassy Cove, Tennessee, after Crawford (1984).

called a *karst valley* because it is not readily allocated to any of the three basic categories. These are wide valley floors developed on limestone which are riddled with dolines but as a whole form large elongated closed depressions. They are largely surrounded by scarps capped by impervious rocks, sandstones and siltstones, which are more resistant. Typical are the Houchins and Doyel Valleys, in Mississippian limestone, between the Flint, Mammoth Cave and Joppa Ridges, which are flat-topped residuals of Pennsylvanian sandstone. These ridges and valleys house the largest cave system in the world.

However, the name has also been applied to Grassy Cove in eastern Tennessee, which is completely rimmed by sandstone but has a flat alluviated floor of several kilometres square, across which Grassy Cove Creek wanders from Bill Kemme Spring to Mill Cave Swallet, and which is liable to be drowned by a temporary lake. Thence it goes underground 11 km to springs at the head of the Sequatchie Valley. The cove is in fact a breached anticline (figure 47). It fully satisfies the definition of an anticlinal polje though it retains the characteristic sandstone-capped rim of the karst valley (Crawford 1984).

There are also closed depressions that, apart from having too small a flat floor, satisfy the definition of a polje so closely that there is no possibility of confusing them with uvalas, the chief reason for this criterion. It is hard to escape calling them 'mini-poljes' (plate 26).

The American term *gulf* is used for a large collapse doline with cliffed walls but with an alluviated floor of some size (Malott 1932). Wesley Chapel Gulf in Indiana lies on the underground course of the Lost River (figure 48). It has a floor of 3.4 ha, 10–20 m below its rim. The Lost

Plate 26   A flat-floored closed depression in Devonian limestone at Lawford Range north-western Australia. Mimbi Creek crosses the floor from cave to cave.

River emerges in flood from a rise pit at one end and sinks into many points round the far side of the flat, which in extreme flood is drowned entirely. Gulfs differ from poljes in that they depend essentially on cave collapse and so belong fundamentally to the class of collapse doline.

Karst windows are closely related to gulfs. They are elongated collapse dolines that reveal the cave stream for a short distance, but here there is

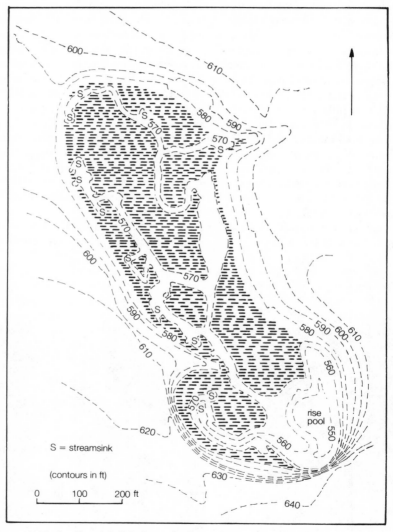

Figure 48 Wesley Chapel Gulf, Indiana, after Palmer (1981).

no alluviated flat. A good example is provided in Pleistocene aeolian calcarenite between the First and Second Stockyard Gully Caves south of Dongara, WA.

Karst Plains

The planed bedrock surfaces that floor poljes partly or wholly are found also along rivers through karsts and along their outer margins (including the coastal fringe) where there is surface external drainage. Thus, along the lower Neretva Valley, Yugoslavia, a plain only 4–6 m above sea level extends 20–30 km inland (Morawetz 1967). It is a bedrock plain; hums project from it and steepheads embay its margin. This a *karst margin plain* (Kayser 1934), being actively extended by spring sapping and also by general flooding by the river in winter and springtime.

Pfeffer (1973) describes the basically similar Black River plain in Jamaica and points to solution notches round its margin and residual hills where inundation occurs. The humid tropical karsts, with their regular heavy storms, provide the best examples of corrosional plains of this type extended by lateral solution undercutting, e.g. in the Celebes (Sunartadirdja and Lehmann 1960) and in Tabasco, Mexico (Gerstenhauer 1960).

Extensive opencast workings for tin in the wide alluvial plain of the Kinta River in Perak, Malaysia, reveal intricately corroded limestone beneath coarse granite gravels. This subsurface relief of an amplitude of 10 m is nevertheless sharply truncated horizontally at a level matching well developed notches and caves round the feet of the limestone towers rising as much as 500 m higher. Downward solution is involved as well as lateral extension, and mechanical abrasion by the river gravels must also have played a part in the fashioning of the plain.

This last process assumes greater importance with some of the active pediments around the limestone ranges of north-west Australia (Jennings and Sweeting 1963) in a tropical semi-arid climate with, however, a short season of intense rainstorms. Some of these pediments carry veneers of coarse gravel, even of cobbles, and are subject to mechanical erosion by sheetfloods and stream distributaries from inliers of impervious rocks including quartzite and granite. Nevertheless, many of the pediments here escape such allogenic interference and are flatter and more planated, with solution dominant through poverty in abrasive tools. Rock fans where streams emerge from the wall-like fronts of the limestone ranges also occur; these have been especially linked to mechanical fluvial action in the past (Johnson 1932).

Corrosional plains tend to greater perfection in their overall form than most other kinds of degradational plain. They are the end member at the larger end of a range of karst forms of which the solution pan is at the smaller end and which shows that the crucial karst process of solution operates most effectively at opposite extremes, in the vertical and the horizontal directions. Though surprisingly abrupt hills and hollows come to mind when karst is invoked, planed surfaces that approximate most closely to the geometrical ideal are in fact equally characteristic.

7 Caves

A cave is usually defined anthropocentrically as an underground space into which one can get. Although this size limit governs the way in which we learn about caves, it has no significance as regards natural processes. A significant natural limit is the diameter of around 1 cm for tubes, separating smaller ones, in which water flows with laminar motion only, from larger ones, in which flow may be turbulent. Thus, although the common idea about what constitutes a cave is the practical one to adopt, it is important to remember that accessible passages connect with larger volumes of impenetrable fissures and small tubes which function in much the same way (Wigley 1967).

Karst processes are the most effective of geomorphic actions making caves, though others such as volcanicity, weathering, various slope processes, glaciers and marine erosion also do so. The karst rock must be pure enough not to yield insoluble residues in such quantities and of such nature as to block incipient cave passages. It must also be strong enough to support cave roofs. Evaporites are not mechanically strong and so large cross-sections cannot be supported. Although planes of weakness are necessary to promote secondary permeability, bedding planes, joints and cleavage may be too close together for cave development to be favoured. Water in a liquid state must be supplied for the solution of rock and some available relief is needed to provide a hydraulic gradient to move it about. As a general rule, the water for this is meteoric. Locally hydrothermal water may form caves, as with Zbrasovska Cave at Hranice in Moravia (Kunsky 1958). Also, waters of connate origin from considerable depths are regarded by some as responsible for even large caves like Carlsbad Caverns, New Mexico (Palmer *et al.* 1977a).

General Characteristics

The variety of caves in karst is immense, both in size and nature. In the Flint Ridge–Mammoth Cave system in Kentucky, more than 350 km of passages have been surveyed and exploration will yield more. The current depth record rests at 1494 m in Gouffre St Bernard in the French

Alps. Measures of total cave area and volume are few, though there is no doubt about which is the largest cave chamber — Sarawak Chamber in Good Luck Cave (Lubang Nasib Bagus), Sarawak, which is 700 m long, 400 m wide and 280 m high.

In complexity caves vary from single rooms, short passages and open shafts (potholes) to intricate, three dimensional systems of passages linking rooms, shafts, chambers and halls of all manner of shapes and sizes. Hölloch Cave in Switzerland, for decades the longest known cave in the world, has more than 15 km of passage for each square kilometre of the area it underlies. The density of cave occurrence reaches from the single small cave in great isolation to residual hills that seem to be mere shells, riddled with large and small cavities. Sober assessment of apparently extreme cases such as Mt Etna, in Rockhampton, Queensland, proves that much more rock remains than voids.

Caves may be completely dry or totally filled with water. In Padirac Cave, Causse de Gramat, France, there are more than 10 km of canal-like 'lakes'. More truly a lake is the Lost Sea in Tennessee, 244 m by 67 m in extent, with a maximum depth of 18 m beneath a 10 m air space. The Shaft near Mt Gambier, SA, is almost entirely filled with water at least 65 m deep. Cocklebiddy Cave in the Nullarbor Plain is virtually a single large passage over 6 km long, of which about 5 km is filled to the roof with water. An excellent review of this and other caves totally filled with water can be found in Martyn Farr's book *The Darkness Beckons* (Farr 1980).

Bedrock is exposed over all of some caves, but most have deposits covering parts of their surfaces. These may accumulate to fill the void completely when the cave becomes fossil.

Caves are found all the way from the tops of mountains to valley bottoms and coastal plains, and even well beneath the sea. High, steep ridges can be rare in caves because they shed water easily and little of it infiltrates (Grund 1910). In high plateaus and ranges, deep potholes and caves can occur, but most are much more extensive in horizontal dimensions than vertical. Caves beneath valley bottoms and plains are mainly water-filled, and only recently has cave diving enabled a knowledge of them and of submarine caves to be acquired by direct observation.

Entrances to caves vary from vertical shafts and fissures to lateral openings in hillslopes and cliffs. When small the entrance may be smoothly erosional, but large ones usually owe some of their size to rockfall, though weathering may even then round off large arches. Tiny entrances can lead into large systems. Indeed, many caves have only artificial entrances. These are usually made through the removal of rockfall and other deposits blocking a former natural aperture; however, quarrying and mining have opened up caves that apparently lacked natural entrances altogether (Warwick 1968). The Ochtinska Aragonite Cave in Slovakia is one such example.

The relationship of caves to streams forms a useful descriptive classification (Grund 1910). An *inflow cave* is entered by a stream that can be followed from its engulfment to some downstream limit to exploration (see front dust cover). In an *outflow cave*, a stream is traceable upstream to an impassable obstacle, e.g. Wookey Hole, in Mendip, England. The stream in a *through-cave* can be accompanied from its sinking to its rising, perhaps through water-filled sections (figure 49(a)). Nowadays diving is turning what were formerly a pair of an inflow and an outflow cave into one through cave, e.g. Gaping Gill Hole and Ingleborough Cave, Craven, England. With a *between-cave*, a stream passage is entered by a tributary from the side or from above but the stream cannot be followed to the surface either upstream or downstream.

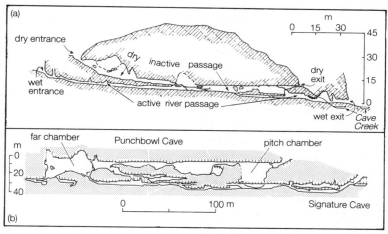

Figure 49 Long profiles: (a) Barber Cave, Cooleman Plain, NSW. The abandoned passage shows upstream river concavity of vadose section, downstream nearly horizontal roof of dynamic phreatic passage; (b) Punchbowl and Signature Caves, Wee Jasper, NSW: four levels of development with nearly horizontal solution roofs in vertical beds.

Active river caves of any of these kinds may lose their streams without any change in external conditions, simply because there is a perpetual tendency for water to find lower routes through karst rocks. This may be through the stream capturing itself or through piracy of a stream by a neighbour. Often caves consist of abandoned passages at successively lower levels, with the lowest one still active (figure 49(b)). In the case of the King Country, NZ, Williams (1982a) has inferred that such successions of passages may decline in size through multiplication of streamsinks or may increase as a result of adjustment to changing discharges from competing underground catchments (see figure 49 above).

Caves

The stream-abandoned passages help the geomorphologist, in that here both erosioñal forms and deposits tend to be preserved longer with less alteration than surface features. They are immunized from most erosional forces, and stable cave atmospheres minimize weathering as a rule. In karst caves, there is a great array of bedrock forms resulting from the interaction of various processes with different rock types and structures (Bögli 1956; Renault 1958). Some of these *speleogens* will be discussed at appropriate junctures below.

Cave Formation

Great controversies have raged in the past about karst cave formation, and new ones continue to emerge. Space forbids anything but a broad outline of the subject.

Earlier, there was an understandable tendency to attribute these often gaping holes in the crust to earth movements, an almost catastrophist standpoint. Now, few caves are thought to be due directly to tectonics, though structural guidance of the form and location of caves – which may have confused the issue – is of great importance. The slicken-sided, inclined roof of Terrace Chamber, Marakoopa Cave, Tasmania, tells us not that the cavity has been dragged open by the fault, but that the faultplane has controlled cave breakdown.

Arnberger's resuscitation of tectonic origin for some Dachstein caves by thrust fault displacement of rock masses by different amounts (cf. Groom and Coleman 1958) has not persuaded Austrian speleologists. Tensional forces near high rock faces, however, create vertical fissure caves through outward movement in limestone as well as in other rocks, e.g. the 90 m deep Igue des Landes in Tarn, France (Gèze 1953); see figure 50(a).

Renault (1967–8, 1970) argues that residual tectonic stresses released by both surface and underground erosion influence cave development, as revealed for example by geophysical exploration around the Grotte di Castellana, Bari, Italy. The way in which caves sometimes turn parallel to a valley wall as they get near it, or form a distributary pattern influenced by the orientation of the wall, may be due to such tectonic stress or more simply to release of lithostatic load by erosional offloading. (Palmer (1984) alternatively explains this pattern by pressure head behind the outflow in floods, forcing water into originally small openings here.)

Late in the nineteenth century, a controversy completely within the bounds of uniformitarianism arose about the relative importance of corrasion and corrosion by underground rivers. In caves, the noise of waterfalls and of boulders being ground against one another by streams flowing at speeds like those of surface streams is so impressive as to lead to the idea that caves are primarily the product of the enlargement of

138

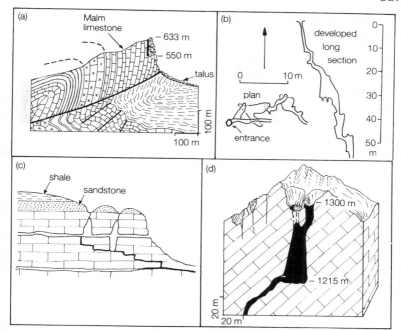

Figure 50 (a) Avens du Pic St Loup, Montpellier, France, after Gèze (1953). Fissure caves have been caused by the spread under gravity of vertical beds near a cliff; (b) Putrid Pit, Bungonia, NSW. An open shaft in successive joint planes has been caused by seepage solution, after Sydney Speleological Society survey; (c) blind shafts or 'domepits' in limestone caves under sandstone caprock, Kentucky, after Pohl (1955); (d) the upper part of Gouffre Henne Morte, Pyrenees, France. An open vadose shaft fed from small dolines, after Gèze (1953).

plunge pools and swirlholes (i.e. river potholes) as well described by Ford (1965a) (see frontispiece). The less patent case for unobtrusive chemical solution had to be argued. Where karst is extensive, rivers may lack tools for mechanical action, and, regardless of this, solution must first fashion thoroughfares large enough for the velocities needed for impact, abrasion, attrition and cavitation. Delicate projections arising from differential solution indicate in some caves that mechanical attack must be subordinate to the chemical – e.g., chert shelves in the caves of Clare, Ireland (Ollier and Tratman 1969).

The great French speleologist, Édouard Martel (1921), who earlier was involved in this debate, properly stressed that the relative roles of the two modes of erosion are modulated by geological contexts and hydrodynamic circumstances. The caves of the Muller Range, PNG, are rich in clastic sediment from clastic interbeds in the host carbonate formation, which supply angular quartz and limonite sands for corrasion (Gillieson, 1984). The finer clastic products coat much surface, tending to insulate the limestone from solution except where motion is greatest and mechanical action concentrated. Huge swirlholes have been found in

New Guinea caves, cf. Maire (1981), which testify to the importance of mechanical action there.

In this century conflict has centred chiefly on the favourability of different parts of the karst hydrologic system for the making of caves. In particular, it developed into argument between protagonists of action in the vadose zone and those of action in the phreatic zone, stemming from the seminal 1930 paper by William Morris Davis. Again, it has come to be recognized that over space and time there will be variation in the relative importance of the different hydrodynamic domains.

Vadose Seepage

Water infiltrates into the bedrock either directly on outcrop or through soil and superficial deposits. If the limestone has much intergranular porosity, percolation can take place over the whole surface. Nevertheless, even with dune limestones, which are largely joint-free, preferential seepage soon develops, probably because of stemflow and root guidance, and soil-filled pipes begin to diversify the soil–rock interface. With most karst rocks, seepage takes the steepest descent available down joint planes and bedding planes where the rocks are dipping, or at points such as joint intersections. In consequence, fissures and shafts are formed in both bare and covered karst (figure 50(b)). With the latter, they tend to be filled with detritus, but as dolines develop, which concentrate water at their low points, the enlarged joints may be kept open.

Initially flow will be laminar, filling the tight joint or running down its two faces as it widens. However, as inputs become more concentrated into them and as the routes enlarge, turbulent flow will take over. Since the CO_2 from soil and atmosphere is commonly used up quickly, the vertical features should narrow downwards. This should be so even if organic matter washed down from the surface renews the corrosive power of the water.

Despite this consideration, many shafts and fissures widen downwards. It has therefore been argued, e.g. Maucci (1960), that these developed from below upwards, by water that first percolatd through a tight joint before beginning to enlarge its way down. If a fissure or shaft develops upwards, it is likely to narrow in that direction because the lower surfaces will have been corroded longer. This manner of development must apply, of course, in blind shafts and fissures, which reach upwards near to but not right to the surface (plate 27). The walls of both open and blind shafts may be gouged by spray falling on them into vertical cave runnels (Ger. *Höhlenrinnen*) separated by sharp ribs.

Burke and Bird (1966) have described blind shafts in Carboniferous limestone beneath the margin of overlying Millstone Grit in South Wales. This coarse sandstone carries acid peats, and humus from them

Plate 27 A vadose shaft at Midnight Hole, Tasmania. Photo by A. T. Warild.

percolates down joints, making the water especially aggressive. Similar features, called 'domepits', are found near the head of recesses in the flanks of the sandstone-capped ridges of the central Kentucky karst (Pohl 1955) (figure 50(c)).

Very much larger shafts, often of inverted conical form, such as Gouffre Henne Morte, 466 m deep, in the French Pyrenees, are attributable to seepage water since they are fed only from small dolines in mountain tops (figure 50(d)). These are the absorption potholes of Gèze (1953) and may depend on a steady release of water from banks of snow drifted into them, an autocatalytic effect. In summer, descending air currents of thermodynamic origin will be cooled to dewpoint in these shafts and the water condensing on the walls will be corrosive.

Beginnings of Caves and Nothephreatic Solution

Since only in rare circumstances will tectonic activity or erosional offloading provide initial throughways for water, the beginning of cave development is attributed in general to a state of water saturation in which slow laminar motion creates interconnecting patterns of tiny tubes that fork and rejoin endlessly. These *anastomoses* (Bretz 1942) usually lie in bedding planes and joints (plate 28), but in rocks of high primary porosity they may develop in all directions, well seen, for example, in White Wells Cave, Nullarbor Plain, because of subsequent infilling with

141

Caves

black calcite. (See Palmer (1984) for a different view on the origin of anastomoses.)

Insolubles may accumulate on the lower side of a plane of weakness, inhibiting further solution on that side, so that half-tubes rather than complete tubes develop. To initiate movement through these tiny ways, earth tides may pump water as a result of dilation and contraction of

Plate 28 Anastomosing half-tubes in the roof of Junction Cave, Wombeyan, NSW.

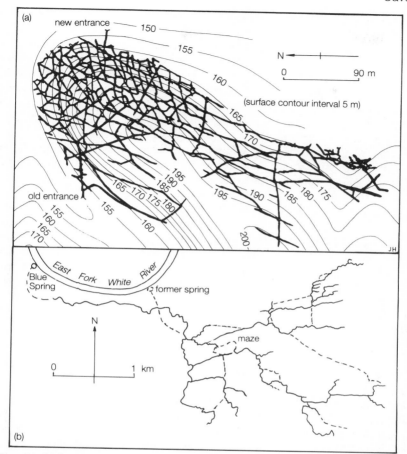

Figure 51 (a) Cameron Cave, Missouri, after Missouri Speleological Society survey: a maze cave of nothephreatic origin; (b) Blue Spring Cave, Indiana, after Palmer (1984): an active branching vadose stream cave. The broken lines show abandoned high-level passages. A diversion maze lies beneath a large collapse doline.

joints. Such motion with solar tidal periods has been recorded in caves in Hungary and the United States (Davis 1966).

When tubes or half-tubes exceed a critical diameter of 5–15 mm diameter, turbulent flow is likely to take over. Consequent enlargement may not necessarily change morphological style of growth. If velocities remain small through lack of much hydraulic head, irregular, inter-connecting cavities form what is called *spongework*, for example in Piano Cave, Walli, NSW. Alternatively, *networks* or *mazes* of joint- and bedding-plane-controlled passage may develop, e.g. Cameron Cave, Missouri; these may be two- or three-dimensional (figure 51(a)).

Caves

Another product of slow movement in the water-filled state is the *rock pendant*, a solutionally smoothed bedrock projection from ceiling or inclined wall. They can be of large dimensions, such as in Ryan Imperial Cave, Chillagoe, Qld. Sets of small rock pendants often end in flat surfaces at a common level. These are usually due to the removal by breakdown of the lower rock at a bedding plane or joint. Alternatively, they can be due to aggradation reaching to the roof and impressing solution in the roof. This latter is one kind of *paragenetic* cave development (Renault 1967–8). Ochtinska Cave, Slovakia, in metamorphosed limestone, and Wellington Caves, NSW, are examples of caves that seem never to have experienced action other than of this kind, though their volume is not to be despised.

The slow flow characteristic of this domain is a few metres a day, the diffuse flow of W. B. White (1969). The domain has been called the deep phreatic zone but it need neither lie deep nor be of much thickness, e.g. in Jewel, Easter and other caves near Augusta, WA. Glennie (1958) argued that the term 'phreatic' should be restricted to such conditions as this because of its closer resemblance to Darcy flow through sands and gravels than other karst hydrodynamic domains; his plea has gone unheeded. Lest its role, which is important in some karst forms, be neglected, the term *nothephreatic* was devised to distinguish it (Jennings 1977).

Dynamic Phreatic Action

Slow flow permits numerous interweaving routes to function at the same time, but if there is sufficient head to drive water through at normal river speeds, one will grow at the expense of the others (Ewers 1966). It is a self-promoting effect. As a tube gets larger, the frictional loss of energy at the rock surfaces becomes smaller in relation to the total frictional drag and velocity increases. As velocity increases, mass transfer of solute from the surface is enhanced, enlarging the passage further. In the roof of the Grand Arch, Jenolan, NSW, a large-solution half-tube wanders through a wide area of roof pendants; its development must have reduced movements between the neighbouring pendants greatly.

In this way pressure tubes or conduits come to play a greater and greater part in the water movement and so in cave development (see plate 29 and figure 52(a)–(d)). These need follow not the most direct route to the outflow but the most efficient, which depends more on the size of the preferred opening at the beginning (Palmer 1984). Therefore their paths may be roundabout both in plan and profile because of the available pressure head. They may be circular or elliptical in cross-section, according to whether a joint or bedding-plane exerts a strong influence or not, but with solutional attack on all surfaces. Both in plan and profile,

144

Plate 29 A pressure tube in Mares Forest Creek Cave, Wombeyan, NSW, carrying current markings.

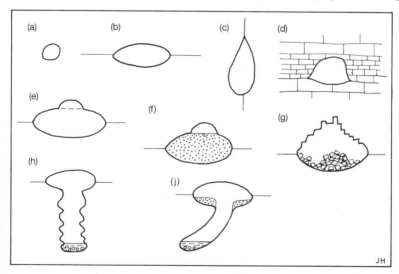

Figure 52 Cave passage cross-sections, after Renault (1958), Bögli (1956) and Ollier and Tratman (1969). Phreatic passages: (a) circular in massive rock; (b) elliptical in horizontal bedding; (c) elliptical in vertical joint; (d) in a group of more soluble beds; (e) with ceiling half-tube due to bubbles along roofline; (f) aggraded to form ceiling half-tube paragenetically; (g) modified by breakdown. Vadose canyon: (h) incised in the floor of the phreatic passage, with channel incuts; (j) with inward meandering during incision into the aggraded floor of the phreatic passage.

145

they are liable to structural control; Ford (1965b) describes how, in steeply dipping beds, Mendip caves such as Swildons Hole have former pressure conduits repeatedly alternating between longer, gently inclined tubes running downdip, and shorter, steep chimneys in joints in which the water regains height.

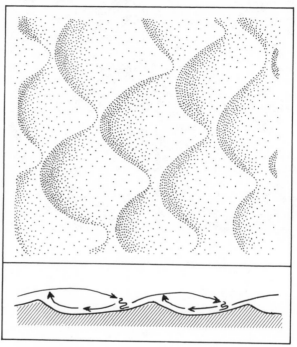

Figure 53 Current markings or scallops developed from initial irregularities by eddy solution; flow after Curl (1974).

Pressure tubes tend to have smoothed surfaces all over, but they may also be covered in *current markings* of the *scallop* type (Goodchild and Ford 1971) (figure 53). Small eddies develop at original roughnesses in the surface; here, solution is greatest and hollows develop. They are asymmetrical, with a semi-circular, steep upstream slope and a gentle rise downstream narrowing to a point between the backs of the next downstream pair of hollows. The slower the flow, the larger the eddies and the hollows also, which range from a few centimetres to more than a metre in length. It is possible to estimate the velocity repsonsible for scallops of a given size, given the diameter of the passage (Curl 1974). Empirical studies indicate that scallop size is related to flood discharge rather than mean discharge (Pisarowicz and Maslyn 1981; Lauritzen *et al.* 1983). The possibility of determining both the direction of former flow and its speed in abandoned stream passages is most useful in elucidating cave evolution. As regards the nature of the former flow, scallops on roof and upper walls imply dynamic phreatic flow, but if only on the lower walls and floor they may be the product of vadose flow.

Corrasion contributes to the formation of pressure conduits, and even coarse gravels are deposited at extremely steep uphill angles on the downstream, rising sides of U-tubes or loops.

Epiphreatic caves

At the top of the phreas there are passages subject alternately to vadose flow at lower discharges and dynamic phreatic flow at higher discharges. This zone, together with the top part of the permanently saturated zone,

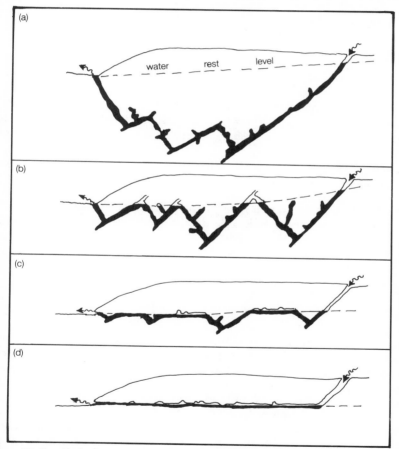

Figure 54 Four kinds of dynamic phreatic cave profile according to Ford and Ewers (1978): (a) bathyphreatic cave; (b) multiple-loop dynamic phreatic cave; (c) mixed-loop and epiphreatic cave; (d) epiphreatic cave.

has been regarded as particularly effective for cave formation (Sweeting 1950; Davies 1960; Moore 1960a; Palmer 1984). Velocities are likely to be greater because routes are more direct and involve least undulation to the outflow points (Ger. *Vorfluter*). Undersaturation is more likely here also, and there are more opportunities for the renewal of corrosive power in the ways discussed in chapter 3. More or less horizontal caves at or just below the level of the springs are the product of action here, e.g. the cave of the River Ourthe in Belgium (Ek 1961). Flat solution roofs are typical, e.g. the Punchbowl, Signature and Dogleg Caves system at Wee Jasper, NSW (figure 49).

Even where the flow is strong, some solutional features occur that interrupt the smooth pipe forms. A half-tube may occupy the highest part of the roof, following the trend of the passage, though it may superimpose its own smaller meanders (figure 52(e)). Bögli (1978) attributes this feature to the entrainment of air bubbles by the current, which may be compressed as they descend, increasing partial pressure of CO_2 and so causing solution to form this foam channel (Ger. *Wirbelkanal*). However, Renault (1967–8) ascribes a paragenetic origin to this kind of feature (figure 52(f)). Also common are hemispherroidal pockets in wall and ceiling (where they are called 'bellholes') and similar smooth recesses elongated along joints. Bögli (1964a) attributes the latter to mixing corrosion, where seepage water enters the main underground flow.

Many terms have been applied to this zone: 'water table stream cave' (Swinnerton 1932) has the disadvantage that nothing approaching a water table may be present; objection can be made to 'shallow phreatic' (W. B. White 1960), in that it may indeed refer to a zone of small vertical amplitude, but at a considerable depth beneath the surface. The 'epiphreatic of Glennie (1958) has the most correct etymology and least misleading overtone (figure 54(d)). Caves in this zone are important in that they may preserve a detailed record of valley-deepening, of importance for regional denudation chronology (Palmer 1984).

Bathyphreatic caves

Davis (1930) stressed the possibility of caves developing to great depths because groundwater has the capacity to descend deeply under pressure head and rise to the surface again. He was relying on Darcy law hydrology based on primary permeability, whereas most karst depends on secondary permeability and pipe flow obeying different laws.

Nevertheless, in following years fresh evidence to support him came from drilling for dam foundations in limestone in the Tennessee Valley (Moneymaker 1941). Cavities as much as 100 m below the valley were encountered. It is true in general that drilling indicates a decline in the size of cavities in limestone downwards until everything is closed up, and that water yield from them also decreases in the same sense. Yet cave divers have boldly traced large caves extending a long way down. The Fontaine de Vaucluse in southern France rises up a smooth pressure tube of some 15 m diameter from a water depth of more than 100 m. In the Sierra de El Abra in eastern Mexico, such a system, now elevated and dry, loops downwards more than 300 m (Fish 1977).

For such development Ford and Ewers (1978), who name it *bathy-phreatic* (figure 54(a)), maintain that a great depth of pure and strong limestone subject to high effective precipitation is not sufficient. It is also necessary that planes of bedrock weakness be widely spaced, though they may be extensive. The El Abra Caves are in massive reef limestones. Steeply dipping beds also favour this kind of hydrology, especially in tight synclines, provided the tectonism has not increased joint frequency too much.

Multiple-loop phreatic caves

Ford and Ewers (1978) recognize two intermediate states between the epiphreatic and bathyphreatic. With greater frequency of planes of weakness than suits the latter condition, a sequence of downward loops develop below water rest levels, as in the Hölloch, Switzerland (Bögli 1978), which has several substantial loops as much as 170 m in amplitude (see figure 54(b)).

Mixed-loop and epiphreatic caves

Swildons Hole, Mendip Hills (Ford 1965b) provides the type case for this condition (figure 54(c)). Horizontal passages – bypass tubes – link the lower parts of loops, and their top parts may be cut through by vadose trenches.

Vadose Flow

Assuming a uniform water supply, the enlargement of phreatic caves entails a lowering of water rest levels so that a vadose zone is created. Flow in this unsaturated zone will be due not only to the gathering of percolation water underground. As closed depressions develop at the surface of karst, so will autogenic streamsinks form part of the hydrologic system. Often these two components from within the karst will be supplemented by allogenic contributions from surrounding and inlying impervious rocks. The streamsinks of blind valleys and the ponors of those poljes that are partly walled or floored by such non-karst rocks will contribute to the vadose flow in caves.

The vertical component in this part of karst hydrology attracts much attention though in fact it is rarely dominant. Shafts down which streams pour to the depths constitute classic elements of karst scenery. Such a one is Gaping Gill Hole in Craven, where Fell Beck, one of England's highest waterfalls, in flood falls 110 m. In base flow, the stream sinks upstream and enters the shaft below the surface only. The beck flows from overlying shales and sandstones not far upstream, and as the margin weathers back, the stream may sink farther back altogether into another shaft, and Gaping Gill Hole will be abandoned.

Plunge pools and swirlholes have already been discussed as characteristics of free surface streams underground, and these are also associated with steep downhill gradients. In that discussion they were linked also to mechanical erosion, but it is important to remember that solution is enhanced in them too. Corbel (1963) thought he could demonstrate that corrosion was many times greater than corrasion in two river reaches consisting of these features.

River canyons are cut in the floors of former pressure tubes and these may exhibit sequences of curved horizontal incuts in their walls which represent successive channel levels in the cutting down of the gorge (see figure 52(h) and plate 30). The steeper the stream gradient, the narrower will be the canyon, except where falls break into spray which broadens the passage for the size of the stream (Palmer 1984). Vadose trenches are liable to develop meanders, with asymmetrical cross-section in which a slip-off slope opposes an undercut one. Meander niches (Bretz 1942) may be cut in the walls of larger passages on the outer side of bends, and meander spurs may be undercut and left suspended (Jennings 1964). Alternatively, meanders may be cut off and oxbow passages produced. Cave meanders can contract inwards as they cut down in a manner that has no parallel on the surface (figure 52(j)) (Ollier and Tratman 1969). Vadose flow operates only under gravity, sometimes developing an exponentially concave longitudinal profile as do surface streams (see figure 49(a)).

A distinction is to be made between invasion vadose caves (Malott 1937) and drawdown vadose caves (Ford and Ewers 1978). In the former, vadose flow develops along small routes formed by vadose seepage and early nothephreatic solution, vadose characteristics predominate, and mainly vertically developed caves are the most likely to evolve this way. Drawdown vadose caves are those where free surface streams inherit and modify phreatic passages which have developed to some size, as for instance canyons cutting across the tops of phreatic loops to convert the multiple-loop state to the mixed state described above.

A vadose cave necessarily assumes a tributary branchwork plan, resembling that of normal surface streams (figure 51(b)). However, this branchwork pattern may comprise only part of an inherited phreatic network. In addition, a stream is confined underground with no

Plate 30 A vadose canyon in Ugwapugwa passage in Atea Kananda, PNG. Successive lowerings of the bed have resulted in matching channel incuts in the inclined bedding. Photo by Julia M. James.

floodplain over which to dissipate flood discharges; at these times it reoccupies higher level passages as the flood overflows, and so a three-dimensional braiding pattern persists.

F

In vadose caves, breakdown, subsidence and weathering come to the forefront, though the role of breakdown in phreatic caves has not been considered very much as yet (figure 52(g)). Breakdown produces domes and rock piles and may even break through to the surface, producing first small daylight holes and ultimately collapse dolines, windows and gulfs, breaking the system into separate remnant caves. Smaller-scale spalling can fashion rounded passages, which superficially resemble pressure tubes, from formerly more angular shapes (Powell 1977). This happens at shallow depths where there is no question of rock plasticity from lithostatic load.

Cave deposits take on a greater variety in the vadose zone, adding to the fluvial sediment and rockfall components to be found in the water-filled passages such additions as speleothems and entrance facies deposits (see chapter 8). These accumulations affect the further course of cave evacuation (Renault 1967–8).

Diversity from Context and Event

The preceding analysis conceals the prevalent complexity of caves, which results from the efflux of time and the interaction of external factors such as climatic change and static but geographically variable controls such as geological structure, both considered below. It is not a matter of a single, necessary sequence of evolution from one hydrodynamic state to another; the history of each system has to be worked out. Palmer (1972) illustrated this principle abundantly in his study of Onesquethaw Cave, New York, and argued the general standpoint forcibly later (1984).

It is true that some stages of development must precede others and can make certain consequences inevitable. Thus, Ford and Ewers (1978) argue that the very development of caves, altering stress patterns, increases fissure frequency in the rock mass, and this in itself will result in progressive development, for instance from the multiple-loop condition to the mixed-loop and epiphreatic one.

Local factors may, however, cause what can be regarded as departures from and reversals of normal evolution. Thus, inputs of allogenic gravels may block flow along substantial vadose passages and bring about phreatic mazes around the obstacle, as Palmer (1975) shows happened in Big Brush Creek Cave, Utah. Similar consequences may stem from big rockfalls as in Skull Cave, New York. The only partially lithified Pleistocene dune limestones of western Australia are especially liable to collapse, and the same kind of effect was early recognized by Bastian (1964). Thus, variation in style from vadose to phreatic can occur along the one level of a cave in other than the expectable downstream succession, e.g. in the Castleton Caves, Peak District, England (Ford

1977). In the caves fed by Wombeyan Creek, NSW, base flow runs through Fig Tree and Junction Caves at a higher level than flood flow does through Creek Cave and its downstream gorge; it is postulated that collapse is responsible for this anomalous arrangement, flood waters usually lifting themselves into higher levels (Jennings *et al.* 1982).

Ponding to cause floodwater mazes in a cave system can have a number of causes. Palmer (1975) cites backflooding from a permanent and through-flowing allogenic river, whereas Williams (1982a) attributes those at the start of the Xanadu Cave system near Punakaiki, NZ, to episodic overflow of an 'open' polje down Bullock Creek.

Large chambers in caves illustrate the diversity of factors that can give rise to basically the same endpoint. The junction of several passages is where they may be expected to form, with wider roof spans increasing the likelihood of roof and wall breakdown. Other large chambers, however, lie off main passages, and these are sometimes due to specially favourable structural factors such as faults or local lithological weakness. In Ballroom Cave, Limestone Ridge, Rockhampton, Qld, weathered andesite of a dolerite sill has been removed preferentially to form the large chamber giving rise to its name. The Grotte de la Cigalère in the French Pyrenees has large chambers where the cave lies at the contact of the limestone with surrounding schists.

The huge halls of Mullamullang Cave in the Nullarbor Plain are attributed by Hunt (1970) to collapse, merging several levels of nothephreatic labyrinth. More common are rock piles beneath flat solution roofs in lofty chambers, which testify to the collapse of the former mass of rock between just two former cave levels, e.g. the Opera House in Fig Tree Cave and the Cathedral in Wollondilly Cave, Wombeyan, NSW. In Punchbowl Cave, Wee Jasper, NSW, where there are four main epiphreatic levels, the main chambers are found where the former cave stream stayed in the same course through three or four of these stages of development (figure 49(b)). In horizontal limestones, retreat of a waterfall down a shaft linking two passages accounts for some large halls of vadose origin.

It is not suprising, therefore, that diverse cave morphologies are to be found even close together within the same karst, e.g. in the Sierra Nevada (Halliday 1957, 1960), the Mendip Hills (Ford 1965b) and Wee Jasper, NSW (Jennings 1967).

Cave Morphometry

Being underground makes repetitive measurements for morphometry more arduous than on the surface. It is not surprising, therefore, that most of what has been done derives from dimensions, dominantly planimetric ones, that can be extracted from ordinary cave surveys.

The commonest exercise has been to correlate the directional frequency pattern of straight passage segments with structural controls such as the strike of beds and joints. There is usually a strong direct relationship, though Glennie (1948, 1950) found that, in one part of Ogof Ffynnon Ddu, Wales, the joint-controlled passages departed significantly from strike and dip directions, and this he attributed to earth movements subsequent to the formation of that part of the cave. Coase and Judson (1977) stress the need for accuracy in the mapping used for this purpose, and they employ underground geological measurements to relate to cave passages rather than surface measures, often used in previous studies. For Dan yr Ogof, Wales, they point out that the simple arrangement of one joint along the length of a passage is not the prevailing condition in which more complex relationships with joints are found.

Few have enquired into the morphometric relations between cross-sections and the dip of planes of weakness, though Maucci (1960) did this for a large set of caves near Trieste in Istria. With nearly horizontal limestones, it is not surprising that elongation in the vertical and the horizontal directions was true of nearly all cross-sections. The vertically developed shape is the result of seepage under the pull of gravity, whereas the horizontally flattened passages are the product of streamflow. A similar exercise in karst such as the Mendip Hills, with a dip around 45°, would be more revealing; here, various authors have claimed an importance for triangular cross-sections controlled by the dip.

Using data available in normal surveys, Curl (1966, *inter alia*) applied queuing theory to predict the relationship between length of cave and number of entrances and related the results to observed relationships and theories of cave origin. His work involved operational definitions, e.g. as to what constituted a unit cave, which occasioned some doubt as to the value of the calculations (Ollier 1963), and this direction of analysis has not been followed up.

Smaller cave features require specific measurement for mathematical analysis of their morphology; Ongley (1968) analysed passage directions in Serpentine Cave, Jenolan, NSW, and from their randomness argued that current action had destroyed any joint influence there might have been. Logging left-bending and right-bending survey legs indicated a tendency to meandering with mean wavelength of 4.6 m, mean wavelength/passage width ratio of 5.5, and sinuosity of 1.4, though true meanders were not present. Deike and White (1969) came to the conclusion that true bedrock channel meandering was present in a few caves in both vadose canyons and pressure tubes. Their wavelengths had power function relationship with channel width comparable to those determined for surface streams. Although they demonstrated some surface meander characteristics in cave meanders such as downstream migration over time, Smart and Brown (1981) also pointed to the differences to be related to such factors as the dominance of solution in caves.

An empirical exploration of the relationship between scallop size and flow velocities discussed above depends on a measurement of their lengths, both in field and laboratory, but determination of former direction of flow from relict sets of them has chiefly relied on simple inspection. Lauritzen (1981) advocates putting this on a firmer basis by measurement of their asymmetry from profiles obtained with a field drafting device. The carpenter's profile gauge used for surface flute and ripple morphometry is a simpler method, but scallops are frequently too large for this instrument to be generally effective with them.

Processes Underground

Speeds of water movement derived from water-tracing transit times are almost always calculated from straightline distances between points of injection and detection and so underestimate actual velocities. Nevertheless, the average of 8 cm s^{-1} that Gèze (1965) gives for French caves is in close agreement with the sense of a large number of Mendip tests (Drew 1975). As a rule, flow through caves is clearly slower than on the surface. From cave to cave, however, the range is from very slow rates such as 0.3 cm s^{-1} recently recorded in the large lakes of the Nullarbor Plain caves, formerly thought to be virtually stationary, to terminal velocities in cave waterfalls as fast as occurs on the surface. From baseflow to floods, individual cave streams also register a great range; Gèze quotes 0.15 to 140 cm s^{-1} in the Sourciettes Cave in France. Since solution of limestone depends so much on the kinetics of the process, this implies large variations of corrosion in space and time.

Process observations from shallow caves were discussed above in connection with the hydrology of dolines. Such information belongs also to the mosaic of cave water behaviour as studied, for example, in Poole's Cavern, Peak District (Pitty 1966), and various Craven caves (Halliwell et al. 1974, Pitty 1974, Richardson 1974). The different drip rates and inlet discharges, different water chemistries and different responses to antecedent temperatures and precipitations indicative of transit times from the surface testify to the discrete and highly variable nature of vadose seepage as Gunn established at Waitomo, NZ. In peninsular Malaysia, Crowther (1983) found regional differences in vadose seepage into caves in Perak karst towers and in plateau karst along the Thailand border. In the former, percolation is mainly slow and delayed in passage through vertical joints, which, even where widened by solution, close up before reaching caves. In the latter, there is greater and quicker seepage along horizontal bedding planes, which integrate flow and hasten response to storms.

Caves

Many studies have shown that the bulk of underground solution takes place through seepage water in joints and fissures in the top few metres near the surface (the Mendips (Smith and Mead 1962); Slovenia (Gams 1966); Clare (Williams 1968); Peak District (Pitty 1968a); Cooleman Plain (Jennings, 1972)), and that caves themselves contribute proportionately little to the total loss of limestone. This small proportion is nevertheless important because the whole hydrology hinges round the functioning of the caves.

Different patterns of water chemistry in caves have been demonstrated between Clare (Smith *et al.* 1969) and the Mendips (Smith and Mead, 1962). With caves like Poulnagallum, Clare, most of the cave water comes from higher shale country with low carbonate contents of 15–50 mg l^{-1} at engulfment (figure 55(a)). Drips, trickles and tributary inlets entirely of percolating water feed in concentrations of 170 mg l^{-1} on the average. As a result, the risings fluctuate violently in solute concentration with discharge, though remaining at all times below saturation. Halliwell *et al.* (1974) have shown that basically the same pattern applies in Craven.

In Mendip, a much lower proportion of the cave supplies is fed in by allogenic streams because of the geology (figure 55(b)). In addition, their hardness varies with weather conditions more than in Clare, with values between 20 and 150 mg l^{-1}. In G.B. Cave and other caves there is a consistent increase along the main stream from drips and trickles, solution of the main passage contributing little (figure 56) (Stenner 1970; Drew 1970). The rate of increase in $CaCO_3$ content declines exponentially with increase in the volume of the cave stream, which is consistent with that interpretation. Drip and trickle hardness varies less than that of streamsink water, and it exhibits an increase in relation to depth from the

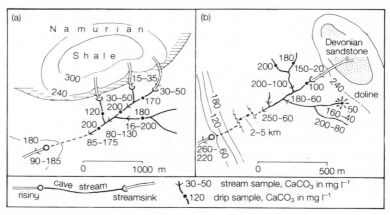

Figure 55 Limestone solution regimes along caves; (a) with important allogenic input at Clare, England, after Smith *et al.* (1969); (b) with dominantly autogenic input at Mendip, England, after Smith (1975).

156

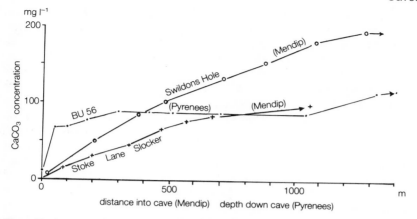

Figure 56 Changes in calcium carbonate concentration with distance from the cave entrance in Mendip caves, England, after Drew (1970), and with depth in Pyrenean cave, after Maire (1982).

surface to be related to increasing CO_2 in the cave atmosphere derived from decaying organic matter (Atkinson 1977). Cave tributary stream waters of autogenic origin are intermediate in nature between main passage flow and drip sites. Saturation at a consistent concentration is reached at the lower end of the system.

A large spring in cockpit karst in Belize has an unusual regime in which hardness increases with discharge. Miller (1983) explains this in terms of cave bottlenecks limiting inputs during floods from a major allogenic river traversing the karst to a flank into the main conduit feeding the spring. On the other hand, harder water entering the system is not restricted in its increase in volume, though it retains its hardness as it increases. As a result of this increase in hard autogenic water relative to the flow that it captures from the less hard allogenic river as total discharge increases, the spring chemistry behaves in this abnormal way.

Observations in caves in the Castleton area of the Peak District (Christopher *et al.* 1977) show increases of hardness along streamways that can be related only partially to oxidation of organic matter. The Peak District is hydrochemically a more complex area than the other karsts mentioned in this discussion, because of igneous rocks in the carbonate sequence, present thermal activity, minerals and mining, and greater modern anthropogenic pollution. This has encouraged fuller chemical analyses of waters here, but Christopher (1975) advocates the general use of this approach. He finds that the potassium–sodium ratio decreases during passage underground through differential ion exchange with clay minerals. When this ratio is studied in conjunction with the saturation index for calcite in springs, inferences about the nature of the cave system behind can be made, especially as regards the relative lengths of free surface stream and phreatic flow in it.

Figure 56 shows the take-up of hardness down the deep BU 56 cave in the Spanish Pyrenees, which has an autogenic circulation. The bare alpine surface supplies water of low hardness, but there is a rapid increase in joints and shafts near the surface. Thereafter there is a slow increase to saturation at −300 m. A further increase below −1100 m is attributed to a mixing with tributary water of higher carbonate content (Maire 1982).

Much more effort has been made to measure solution in caves than mechanical attack on the rocks, though calcite is a soft mineral and quartz sand is usually present in caves, even if large clasts to act as tools are sometimes absent from them. The most notable attempt to get more facts on this subject in recent years is that of Newson (1971). He exposed tablets of limestone caged in nylon thread in different mesh sizes in Mendip cave streams. Much greater weight loss was experienced with the two larger meshes, permitting abrasion (by silt and sand, and fine gravel respectively) as well as solution. Jennings (1981a) has performed the same exercise over a number of years at River Cave, Cooleman Plain, and determined that at this one site the tablets lost nearly as much by abrasion as by solution.

A more generalizing method is to measure solid load as well as solute load emerging from a cave, and Newson did this for springs at Cheddar and Burrington in the Mendip. He found that corrosion was between five and ten times as important as corrasion; only in floods was more solid load carried than dissolved. Nevertheless, the importance of floods must not be underestimated; speleologists familiar with G. B. Cave in the Mendip were amazed by the drastic changes wrought in it during an exceptional storm in 1968.

8   Cave Deposits

Cave deposits often occupy much of the space eroded out of bedrock; they affect processes enlarging that space, supplement erosional records of cave history, provide means of absolute chronology and even give evidence of regional environmental change. In the last decade increased study of them has enhanced their importance in karst and cave science (cf. Bull 1983).

These deposits possess tremendous variety, both lithologically and genetically; their inheritance of characteristics acquired outside the cave environment and their liability to especially complex stratigraphy make for difficulties in their study, including their classification. Kyrle (1923) proposed a division between materials formed in place in the caves and those transported to their place of deposition. This does not correspond exactly with the split by Kukla and Lozek (1958) into allocthonous (exogenetic) and autocthonous (endogenetic) deposits, respectively derived from without and within the cave; for instance, cave streams may deposit sediments from both sources. Others have relied chiefly for classification on the process immediately responsible for their deposition within the cave, even though the sediments may retain characteristics belonging to earlier agents, e.g. fluvially redeposited glacial till (Wolfe 1972a). In this chapter an empirical division will be employed to present a selective outline.

Speleothems

Many minerals are deposited in caves as chemical precipitates; these take on many forms, for which the generic term *speleothem* has now largely replaced earlier ambiguous names (White 1976; Hill 1976) (plate 31). Calcite is by far the most important mineral and it is chiefly precipitated through diffusion of CO_2 from water into the cave atmosphere. Rates of precipitation are widely variable; Ford and Drake (1982) give a range of $0.1–10.0$ cm ka^{-1} but this is conservative. In Postojna Cave, Slovenia, the growth depends more on the amount and hardness of the water than on variations in P_{CO_2} of the cave air (Gams 1968).

Cave Deposits

Plate 31 Stalactites, stalagmites and a fringed canopy, 'the Judge's Wig', in Strong Cave, south-western Australia, a cave formed in Pleistocene aeolian calcarenite. Photo by D. C. Lowry.

Calcite formed from drips before they fall from ceilings and hanging walls creates downward-growing *stalactites* (figure 57(a)). With straw stalactites, the drip precipitates a circular ring which builds a hollow tube about 5 mm in diameter (Curl 1972). A common rate of growth for them is 0.2 mm a^{-1} (Moore 1962). Their length ranges up to more than 6 m in various caves in western Australia and France, e.g. Cabrol (1978), but they are fragile and broken fragments are common on floors. They usually block internally before any great length is achieved and then films of water flow down the outside, depositing radial crystals around the central tube. This leads to a conical form with sheath laid on sheath to give a tree-ring type of structure. Very large stalactites can be built in this way, one in the Aven Armand, Lozère, France, being 30 m long. Ultimately they fall down under their own weight. They commonly develop in lines along joints or bedding planes through which the water percolates. Small shifts in dripping points may give rise to complex forms.

Drops falling to the floor build *stalagmites* upwards as a result of splash and (figure 57(d)). A minimum diameter for a stalagmite is about 3 cm (Curl 1973). Uniformity in drip rates, hardness and cave atmosphere result in constant-deposition and uniform-diameter stalagmites; a conical form results from a decreasing rate of deposition; whereas a tiered-cake shape implies varying rates. Growth layers form caps on top of one another over the summit of stalagmites, thinning away down the sides. The height of drop fall, shifting drip points and growth of

160

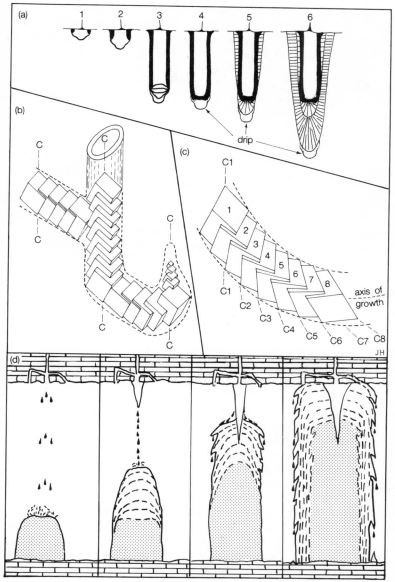

Figure 57 (a) The development of a straw stalactite, showing blockage of capillary and growth of conical form; (b) the crystalline structure of an angular helictite, after Prinz (1908); (c) the crystalline structure of a curving helictite, after Prinz (1908); (d) the growth of a column from stalactite and stalagmite, after Gams (1981b).

stalactites are other factors modifying the shape of stalagmites, which can grow into very bulky and tall features.

Stalactites and stalagmites can meet in growth to become *columns* figure 57 (d)), when further growth depends on films down the sides. Trickles down walls create *curtains* and *shawls*, whereas wide films of water form *flowstones* as they do more commonly on floors. *Rimstone dams* grow on floors, slopes and in streams to impound pools of various sizes and depths. A fine series occupies over a kilometre of stream in Croesus Cave, Tasmania. Aeration over a growing rim promotes loss of CO_2 and so increases calcite precipitation; discharge and velocity are greater through lower parts, which are built up to level off with the rest. Underwater deposition in cave pools assumes external crystalline shape in accord with the internal lattice, e.g. *dog-tooth spar*. *Floe calcite* forms as a layer of thin plates held up by surface tension on pools till they break through and accumulate on the bottom.

In contrast with previous forms, which are controlled in their growth by gravity, eccentric speleothems grow in ways that show that this force is subordinate to others, notably crystal growth forces, but locally also wind currents and light-directed algal growth. *Shields* consist of two parallel plates growing out from cave walls at any angle; water is forced out from joints or bedding planes under hydrostatic pressure to form them. *Helictites* comprise smooth-surfaced, elongate growths disregarding gravity. Again, they are thought to be the result of hydrostatic pressure causing slow extrusion of water from capillaries. Angular helictites (figure 57(b)) possess abrupt changes in orientation of their crystal lattice. Curving, even spiral, forms result from gradual changes in crystal axis orientation, perhaps because of impurities – foreign ions – distorting the lattice and causing growth in the form of successive wedges (figure 57(c)).

Many other kinds of speleothem occur, with many other minerals involved (Hill 1976). Colour also departs from the translucency and whiteness of pure calcite. Impurities within the crystal lattice, along crystal interfaces and over growth surfaces are responsible for the wide spectrum of colours found. Iron can give reds and oranges, manganese black, copper green and so on; but organic impurities are now thought to be responsible for much colour, from yellow through browns to blacks. Also, smoke dusts are blown in which coat speleothem surfaces.

Speleothems can form in active river caves where, however, they are liable to both damage and coatings of mud. In stream-abandoned caves, on the other hand, they can predominate to the point of completely blocking passages. Crystallization on almost all surfaces in formerly water-filled caves, e.g. Jewel Cave, South Dakota, is generally thought to be either hydrothermal in origin or due to special hydrochemical conditions. Corbel (1952, 1958, 1959) is the protagonist of climatic control of speleothem formation, maintaining that speleothems are rare as temperatures approach freezing point, that stalactites outnumber stalagmites in cool temperate climates, and that stalagmites and bulky forms are particularly characteristic of tropical caves. The first proposition at least has found wide support.

Cave Ice

In climates with prolonged winter freezing, whether because of latitude or altitude, ice forms in caves in several ways. Snow will drift into open shafts or downward-inclined cave entrances, as at Owen Ice Cave, Southern Alps, NZ. If the snow blocks them, or if they are dead ends, warm air is stopped from melting it totally in summer and parts of the drift turns into ice of semi-permanent nature. Meltwater from the snow also turns into sheets of ice on the floor.

Larger and more varied ice bodies form in the lower parts of climatically dynamic caves where cold air enters, e.g. Grotte Valerie, Nahanni, North West Territories, Canada. Seepage water is frozen into icicles, stalagmites and columns of ice (plate 32); pools become ice rinks – more than 6 m thick in Coulthard Cave in the Canadian Rockies – and smooth icefalls develop. Also, hoar frost sublimed from the cave air assumes a variety of styles on ceilings and walls; there are hexagonal plates 50 cm across in Mountain Ice Cave in the Canadian Rockies. Condensation water can gather together and freeze.

Tourist caves with ice, such as Eisriesenwelt, Tennengebirge, and Rieseneishöhle, Dachstein, in Austria, allow regular observations which show that large masses can form and then degenerate over comparatively few years in accord with climatic variability (Kyrle 1923).

Vincent (1974) considers both local and regional factors in the occurrence of caves with ice in them, best called *glacières* (Balch 1900).

Clastic Sediments

Clastic cave sediments vary in size, shape, structure and lithology probably more than in any other environment. This is because cave sediments can derive from both internal block breakdown of the limestone rock resulting in a whole range of unsorted debris, and also from external sources to be deposited by gravitational, fluvial, aeolian or lacustrine processes within the cave. Caves not only act as dustbins, collecting vast amounts of surface derived material, but they also exhibit unusual sedimentation mechanisms rarely (or even never) seen in non-cave environments (Bull 1981). Increasingly, clastic cave sediments are being studied by geologists and archaeologists, utilizing the recent advances made in our understanding of cave sedimentology and enabling detailed histories of the cave environment to be reconstructed from hitherto 'sterile sediment layers' (Green 1984).

Plate 32 Ice columns in Castleguard Cave, Canada. Photo by Tony Waltham.

Breakdown, weathering and mass movement deposits

Breakdown of roofs and walls results in piles of unbedded, angular blocks (plates 2, 3 and 36), conical in shape below a roof dome, fan-shaped against walls and extending like rivers into neighbouring confining passages. Inside such piles, further fracturing of blocks can be seen to accompany the settling down. What other movements may be affecting these piles apart from further addition from above has not been studied.

Finer aggregates result from the weathering of cave surfaces, especially as a result of salt crystallization in dry passages. Textural sorting is poor and clasts are frequently bimodal in size frequency because inherited textures are superimposed on breakdown textures.

Cave breccias (gash-, bone-breccias) have long occasioned interest (Pengelly 1864). These are very mixed deposits with large bedrock fragments in clay matrix; bones and speleothems, both forming in place and transported, also contribute. Mass movement, of a sliding or flowing nature, is responsible for bringing together bedrock clasts, insoluble residues, soils, secondary precipitates and animal remains. Sometimes clasts are rounded by subsoil solution so that in strict terms the result is conglomerate, and Lozek and Skrivanek (1965) attach this style to fissures that have formed downwards, whereas angular debris point to upward growth of the containing cavity. Sometimes the subsided mass seems disproportionately large in relation to possibilities of entry at the surface for the materials originating there, e.g. Dip Cave, Wee Jasper, NSW (Jennings 1963). In that cave there are also bodies of breccia which suggest much cave enlargement since the emplacement of what are usually fissure fills. Care must be taken to distinguish cave-breccias as described above from fault-breccias, stylo-breccias and other pene-contemporaneous breccias.

Stream and pond deposits

Waterlaid clastic sediments in caves range from coarse bedload boulder beds to fine, suspended load clays; good sorting and rounding are common. Size frequency is often skewed to the fines because of clays inherited from the karst bedrock. However, many detailed studies have stressed the great importance of material of external origin (e.g. Reams 1968; Wolfe 1972b; Gospodarić 1974), which ensures variety of rock and mineral composition of coarser fractions. Quartzose sands and silts may be from either the host rock or surrounding impervious rocks. Calcite sand is rare but not so dolomite sand, e.g. Grotte de Moulis, French Pyrenees. Cementation is common and can be rapid because of carbonate-rich waters.

Extreme flattening of gravels, considered the result of passage through inverted siphons under pressure (Siffre and Siffre 1961), is more probably an effect of thin bedding of the bedrock at their sites (Bull 1978).

Most fluvial sedimentary features and structures are found in caves, including armoured channels, braided floodplains, point bars, cross-bedding, cut-and-fill, etc. Depositional cycles of bedload to suspended load are characteristic (Wolfe 1972b) and graded beds are especially

165

common, the effects of big floods given the geometry of cave systems. They occur not only in caves affected by Pleistocene glacial meltwaters but even in arid Nullarbor Plain caves (Frank 1971).

Within this class of cave sediments, the greatest controversy has been occasioned by fine-grained sediments. Red or ochreous clays are found widely in karst caves especially in phreatic sections; kaolinite is their most common clay mineral. Sometimes they are massive, but they also occur in fine laminations when there is likely to be a silt component. The colouring is thought to be caused by ferric oxide. Originally regarded as insoluble residues from the limestone, they were later considered by Bretz (1942) to be derived from surface soils and to have entered the caves during an intermediate phase between a slow phreatic development beneath a subdued erosion surface and a succeeding phase of valley incision and vadose modification of the caves. Bretz based his ideas on the Ozark Caves in Missouri, but regarded them as of general applicability. However, Reams showed the fine sediments were brought in by streams after the Ozark valleys had been cut down and the caves occupied by free surface streams. The interpretation of 'cave loams' in Austrian and Swiss caves, dark-coloured sandy loams to heavy clays, similarly changed from one of residual origin from the limestone to recognition that most of them were transported into the cave (Bögli 1961b).

Reams found that the Ozark silty clays were commonly laminated with a special tendency to accrete parallel to the bedrock surface whatever angle that had, even vertical. These steep depositional dips have been

Plate 33 Fine-grained clastic sedimentation to the roof. Ogof Ffynnon Ddu, South Wales. Photo by Peter Bull.

recognized in many caves but they have been studied most thoroughly by Bull (1981) in Agen Allwedd and other Welsh caves. Other distinctive characteristics are that the laminations retain the same thickness and grain size along considerable lengths of the passage, and that they accumulate right to the roof in places (plate 33). Bull argues that weather events inject pulses of sediment-rich water down fissures by a translatory flow (shunting) mechanism into standing water in the caves. Glacial meltwaters pass through caves and deposit varves in standing water. Pleistocene varves need careful distinction from laminated silty clays laid down in caves with no intervention of cold climate effects.

There are other unusual aspects about the stratigraphy of cave sediments. Although the sediments in a particular passage will usually show normal superposition of younger upon older, separate bodies of sediment spaced vertically within a passage or over sequences of passages and caves will normally be in the reverse order, having been successively emplaced, each one lower than the last. Pengelly (1864) was well aware of problems associated with *false floors* of flowstone; complex stratigraphy results when flowstone forms on clastic fills which are partially removed later (figure 58(a)). Also, subsidence through bedrock solution below commonly disturbs bedding and may create what are virtually tunnels in older sediment which are filled with younger sediment, a confusing structure more common with mass movement sediments than with fluvial (figure 58(b)).

Small patches of sediment high up in cave walls have too readily been taken to be remnants of thick or complete cave fills. Often they are no more than slip-off slope deposits or channel incut fills, which were never much bigger than they are now and register only former levels in the

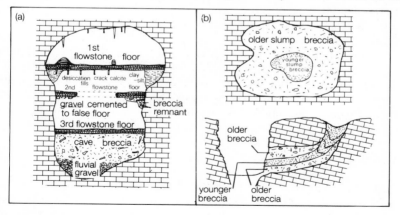

Figure 58 Complex cave sediment stratigraphy: (a) a flowstone floor laid on clastic fill which is progressively removed from beneath, after Pengelly (1864) and Deep Cave, Walli, NSW; (b) younger deposits surrounded by older ones through slumping of core, after P. Osborne (personal communication).

course of vadose stream lowering and cave incision. Moreover, a flood can deposit films of fine sediment on ledges at many levels at the same time. This happens over a height range of 13 m today by floods of the Green River backing up the Flint Ridge–Mammoth Caves passages (Collier and Flint 1974).

Biogenic Deposits

Plant growth in caves is so meagre that deposits from it are negligible though bacteria affect calcite precipitation (Caumartin and Renault 1958). Drift timber is washed into caves in floods and is sometimes incorporated in stream sediments. The black colour of Alpine cave loams is thought to be of humic origin.

Likewise with animals; those that live completely in caves make too small a biomass to give rise to significant deposits, whereas those that feed outside leave behind substantial deposits in some caves. Large masses of excreta derive from colonies of larger animals using caves for rest and breeding. Bat and bird guano in conical piles beneath roosts are the chief expression of this, leading to a corrosion of bedrock and the formation of special minerals at the contact.

Animal skeletons also accumulate. These may be from animals sheltering in caves; for example, at Drachenhöhle, Mixnitz, Austria, enormous quantities of cave bear bones accumulated, more from long continued occupation over 40 000 years than by large numbers at any one time, though the overall total amounts to 30 000–50 000 individuals (Abel and Kyrle 1931). Open shafts act as animal traps and bones accumulate at their bottoms. The hunting and scavenging of cave-living animals also lead to bone accumulations, including owl pellets and human food refuse.

These organic materials mineralize in time, forming phosphates, nitrates, etc., which are also liable to transport and incorporation in clastic sediments. Many of these minerals have been mined for economic purposes – fertilizer, gunpowder, aphrodisiacs – causing much disturbance as well as the removal of sediments.

Entrance Facies

Some external agents can be effective far into caves. Sinking streams are especially significant in this respect, though the temperature and humidity effects of air circulation also penetrate deeply into many caves. Other agents are restricted in their effects to cave entrances and nearby parts. Because of this, there is a great spectrum of deposits and more complex stratigraphies at these points, and also the most numerous archaeological

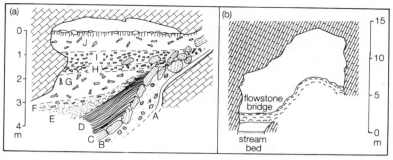

Figure 59 (a) Entrance facies, Elderbush Cave, Peak, England, after Bramwell (1977): A, white clay; B, yellow sandy clay with concretions; C, fractured flowstone; D, laminated green clay; E, aeolian sand; F, sand with last Interglacial vertebrates; G, red clay with bones of cold and warm faunas; H, talus with Late Palaeolithic occupation and cold fauna; I, late Last Glacial frost talus; J, brown stony clay, with humic surface and Bronze Age to Roman remains; (b) section in Tunnel Cave, Borenore Cave, NSW, where a stream ceased to flow through the passage and flowstone formed across the whole floor before resumed flow removed the support, after Frank (1973).

associations (figure 59(a)). Together with greater accessibility, these facts account for the much greater sedimentological investigation here (Schmid 1958). Kukla and Lozek (1958) distinguish this *entrance facies* from the interior facies of the rest of cave deposits.

Here surface materials fall, roll, slide, creep and flow into caves, and become interbedded or mingled with autochthonous materials. This is especially true in periglacial climates, present and past, because there the regolith is exceedingly mobile and frost wedging provides much angular rock. At first it was in temperate parts of Europe that caves were recognized to contain material of these kinds entering in Pleistocene cold periods, but later it has been found widely; for example, talus entered Cyrenaican caves (Hey 1963) and more mixed material by debris flow entered Tasmanian caves (Murray *et al.* 1980), in both cases during the last Glacial Maximum.

Pleistocene glaciers have forced glacial till into the forward parts of caves, e.g. Aillwee Cave, Clare (Drew and Cohen 1978), and down shafts, e.g. Waterfall's Folly, Craven (Warwick 1971). But much sediment regarded as till in caves is probably reworked and sludged farther in. Cold climate is not necessary for mass movements to penetrate caves: three major mudflows have advanced much farther into Selminum Tel, Hindenburg Range, PNG, than is in keeping with entrance facies (Gillieson 1984).

With the baring of much surface in cold climate, wind deflation and transport take on real importance, and caves near the glacial outwash plains of Europe and North America received much loess, which actually was blown into entrance chambers but then was commonly reworked by water and moved on to become part of the interior facies. In hot, arid climates aeolian sand is liable to enter and even fill caves and shafts, e.g.

in the Daoura Hamada, Algeria (Conrad *et al.* 1967). Drotskys Cave in the eastern Kalahari, Botswana, has suffered several invasions of dune sand (Cooke 1975), and red quartz dune sand is found in some Nullarbor Plain caves (Spate *et al.* 1983a).

Wild animal occupation of caves leads to the inclusion of much bone and excrement in entrance facies. Humans have similarly left a physical record of their presence, with tools and hearth ashes as well; fire distinctively modifies sand grain surfaces, and is detectable by scanning electron microscopy (Gillieson and Mountain 1983). Human occupation results in much disturbance of the sediments complicating already complex stratigraphy of entrance facies, in which strong depositional dips are common. In sandstone caves, human occupation has been shown to accelerate roof fall and weathering by physical contact and by fires (Hughes 1978); a similar effect appears to have gone on in a shallow limestone cave at Fromms Landing, SA (Twidale 1964).

Studying a scattered set of archaeological caves in impure dolomitic limestone in South Africa, Brain (1958) found that the amount of soil material contributed to the entrance facies depended on the size of the contemporary entrance, and that there were changes in shape of residual quartz grains derived from bedrock, those from the surface being rounder than those directly from the bedrock in the cave, except in arid climate.

In the normal course of events, natural breakdown products are intercalated with allocthonous sediments of various kinds or incorporated in them. Periglacial periods accentuate this because frost wedging may then reach tens of metres into the cave. In addition, calcite floors are liable to form over entrance areas when conditions allow and authigenic cave minerals, mainly calcite, fill voids in earlier sediments. In central Europe, foam sinter, a distinctive loose tufa, formed on walls in certain periods and fell down to form layers in the entrance facies sequence (Lozek 1965).

This is by no means a complete inventory of even the broad types of components in entrance facies, still less of the sedimentary structure, but it suffices to indicate the interest they possess.

Dating

The dating of cave deposits is a matter of import not solely to the study of the sediments themselves. Whereas the age of the host rock is commonly grossly antecedent to the time of formation of caves in it, cave deposits are associated much more closely in age with speleogenesis, even though the dating of many a deposit will say no more than that the passage in which they lie was excavated before then. Other deposits may provide a maximum age for parts of a passage clearly created after they were laid down in it (cf. figure 52(j)). More than that, if the oldest deposits in passages or caves in a vertical sequence also make a time sequence, getting younger downwards, it is possible to infer the dates between which given passages were formed. Finally, dating the course of cavern development in an area by such ways has significance for the geomorphological history of that region (see chapter 11).

Formerly the dating of cave deposits was dependent largely on the stratigraphic assignment of included fossils, especially of vertebrate bones and teeth, even though these are not very good stratigraphic markers in the Quaternary. Perhaps the most famous of all are the Middle Pleistocene beds, which yielded Peking Man in an unroofed cave at Zhoukoudian near Peking; Chinese Quaternary chronology has until recently depended very largely on a mammalian sequence derived from cave deposits. Small mammal bones and snail shells place cave deposits at Kozi Grzbiet, Poland, into the Lower Pleistocene Cromerian (Glazek *et al.* 1977). Breccias with mammal bones of Mid-Eocene to Upper Oligocene age are found remnant in caves in Quercy, France, which were re-excavated and partly refilled in the Upper Pleistocene when a fresh suite of mammal bones was introduced (Gèze 1949). Mammalian teeth of Lower Jurassic age were reworked into marine caves in the Mendip in Middle Jurassic times (Halstead and Nicoll 1971). Chances of dating terrestrial caves by animal bones are meagre at earlier times than this.

Floral remains have a longer range in dating caves, though unfortunately the interior facies of terrestrial caves is frequently poor in pollen and spores, the best means of terrestrial biostratigraphic correlation. Entrance facies are more useful, as witness the dating of postglacial to last Interglacial deposits in the Hyena Den on Mendip (Tratman *et al.* 1971). The deep introduction of marine silts and clays at a certain phase in the history of Kairimu Cave, NZ, allowed the placing of that stage in the Late Pliocene or Early Pleistocene by means of its microflora (Barrett 1963). A completely filled cave exposed in a quarry section at Eugenana, Tasmania, has been recognized as Devonian in age from the spores in the sediments, which are certainly of interior facies (Burns 1964).

The Devonian is the earliest period with extensive land vegetation, so the possibility of dating earlier caves by fossils is slight, and for times before that dating by cave deposits must depend on lithological correlation. On such bases perhaps the oldest cave deposits known are those of Lower Proterozoic age from the Transvaal (Martini 1981b).

Over not much more than a decade, the study of cave deposits has been drastically improved by the introduction of radiometric and geophysical dating techniques. Radiocarbon was the first of these and has been used most, chiefly by its application to charcoal and organic carbon sources in entrance facies sequences, especially those of an archaeological nature. Then carbon-14 became of more general use in cave geomorphology when its use with speleothems was devised (e.g. Hendy 1970). This

171

introduces a large error term of $+3\,500$ to $-5\,000$ years because of dead carbon atoms from the limestone going into the newly formed calcite. In many contexts, however, this is less of a disadvantage than the fact that its effective range of 40 000 years commonly covers only a small part of the history of most caves. More of the development of Abercrombie Caves, NSW, has been dated by carbon-14 results going back to 34 000 BP than of any other Australian cave as yet, but even so less than half of their volume was excavated since then and the route of the present underground cutoff of a former surface meander had already been established before then (Frank and Jennings 1978).

More important for the chronology of cave evolution is proving to be the uranium radioactive decay series, employing the ^{230}Th/^{234}U ratio on the calcite of speleothems, in effect stalagmites and flowstone floors, because its range is 350 000–400 000 years. Several conditions must be satisfied: there must be sufficient uranium for satisfactory measurement of ^{234}U; there must be a very low content of insolubles, which may contain detrital thorium, and the ^{230}Th/^{232}Th ratio must be high as a measure of low detrital thorium content; there must have been no recrystallization of the calcite since precipitation and no re-solution; finally, the tests of increasing age from top to bottom of the stalagmite and of agreement with an independent dating method such as carbon-14 should be applied. In Metro Cave, Westport, NZ, ^{230}Th/^{234}U dates from different passage levels show an increasing age upwards through the system between 20 000 and 120 000 BP, but satisfactory samples from the uppermost level were not obtainable (Williams 1982b). The limitation of even this method is well illustrated from the Flint Ridge–Mammoth Caves, Kentucky, where a speleothem from low down in the system was beyond the range of the method (Hess and Harmon 1981).

A method of dating right through the Quaternary is clearly needed, and the one to be successfully employed so far is that of palaeo-magnetism. Fine-grained clastic sediments in quiet water, such as is frequently to be found in caves, settle in accord with the contemporary earth magnetic field, though the dip is some 30° shallower because of a final motion of particles on the irregular accumulation surface. Clay to sandy loam textured sediments of a cave in the Holy Cross Mountains, central Poland, were dated by this method, showing that much of the cave belonged to the Lower Pleistocene. Schmidt (1982) successfully applied this method to the Flint Ridge-Mammoth Caves, with the Brunhes–Matuyama reversal of 730 000 BP occurring less than halfway up their sequence of levels. Events are not so clearly registered higher up, and there are alternative interpretations, allowing the top to be either about 1 million or something more than 2 million years old. There are geomorphological arguments for preferring the latter. The Dogleg–Punchbowl–Signature Caves at Wee Jasper, NSW, have yielded a parallel story, though the silt and clay came into this small system from a streamsink end, in contrast with the huge Kentucky system, where it was the backflooding of springs from the Green River that deposited the necessary sediments with detrital remanent magnetization (Schmidt et al. 1984).

It is chemical remanent magnetization that speleothems acquire and that may be determinable despite modern field overprint (Latham et al. 1979); it has been used to supplement uranium–thorium dates from caves in the Canadian Rockies (Ford et al. 1981).

Other methods with potential for determining ages of calcite over a period of the order of 10^6 years are the related methods of thermo-luminescence (TL) and electron spin resonance (ESR). In both, defects in the crystal lattice act as traps. In TL they trap free electrons from natural radiation, and thermoluminescence is a measure of the natural radiation trapped since precipitation of the calcite. With ESR the traps are measured by their absorption of microwaves in a magnetic field. For both, it is also necessary to measure the annual dose rate of natural radiation in the cave. This latter method has been used to construct a detailed time scale for the Holocene from a stalagmite from Lynds Cave, Tasmania, calibrated against radiocarbon dates (Goede 1983); the advantage is that ESR, like palaeomagnetism, is a much simpler procedure than either radiometric dating by radiocarbon or the uranium–thorium series.

Palaeoenvironmental History

Caves have long contributed to the reconstruction of regional environmental history; a classic example was the finding of an assemblage of animal bones, including rhinoceros and hippopotamus, indicative of warmer climate than at present, when the entrance facies of Victoria Cave, Craven, was largely dug out late last century. But dating uranium–thorium has given precision to this by allocating that warm fauna to the warmest part of the Last Interglacial, around 120 000 BP (Gascoyne, Currant and Lord 1981). Similar progress has been made with faunistic and sedimentologic evidence of former colder climate, but it will be more convenient to consider this in chapter 10 below, except for one aspect.

This is the question of the presence or absence of speleothems. If the climate becomes severely cold, percolation water freezes and consequently dripstone and flowstone cease to form. Thus the frequency distribution of dated speleothems over time may reveal the dates of the cold periods when percolation water dried up. The time distribution of speleothems in northern North America, Britain and Tasmania (Goede and Harmon 1983) shows a clustering into distinct groups which is interpreted as a glacial–interglacial sequence (figure 60).

Cave Deposits

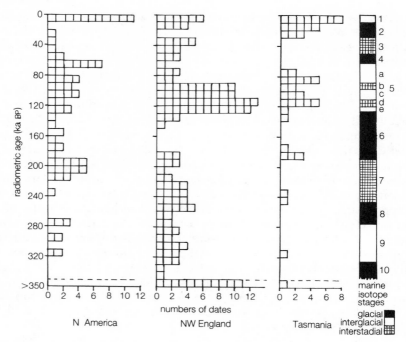

Figure 60 Histograms of dates from speleothems, after Goede and Harmon (1983).

It is also appropriate to outline here the valuable source of thermal history provided by the determination from speleothems of the stable oxygen isotope ratio, $^{18}O/^{16}O$. There is fractionation of the isotopes on crystallization of the calcite, which increases with temperature, and this can be used to gain a record of temperature in the cave (and so approximately of the mean annual air temperature outside) by the sampling from top to bottom of a stalagmite or flowstone floor. This depends on the precipitation having taken place slowly and consistently by degassing of CO_2 and not by evaporation. This can be tested by seeing whether the isotope ratio is the same through a given growth layer and whether the oxygen ratio does not change sympathetically with the stable carbon ratio, $^{13}C/^{12}C$, since evaporation causes such correlation. Even if these conditions are satisfied, there remain difficulties about interpreting the $^{18}O/^{16}O$ record obtained because of factors other than the crystallization one, since all changes of state cause fractionation. The building up of glaciers and ice sheets in cold periods leaves the ocean waters heavier than in interglacial times, and this is the ultimate source of the dripping water in the caves. This factor reinforces the previous one, but there are contrary effects from the temperatures at evaporation of oceanic water and the condensation of rainwater, with lighter water relating to glacial times, to distance from the Equator, to winter as opposed to summer

174

precipitation, and to the paths of weather systems. Fortunately, to help unravel the effects of this complex of factors, the presence of fluid inclusions in speleothems can give us the isotopic ratios of the water at the time of crystallization. This is done by the medium of their deuterium/hydrogen ratio, which correlates with the stable oxygen isotope ratio.

In this way temperature records for the Holocene in New Zealand (Hendy and Wilson 1968) and Germany (Franke and Geyh 1976) and for the Last Interglacial in North America (Harmon *et al.* 1978) were obtained. It was also found that in certain karsts, chiefly maritime, speleothem growth continued through the glacial times, so that temperature records could be got for those times also, e.g. from Vancouver Island, Canada (Gascoyne *et al.* 1981). Consequently the temperature record of the last 200 000 years in North America was established (Harmon *et al.* 1978), with high temperatures at 190–165, 120–100, 60 and 10 ka, and low temperatures at 165, 115, 95–65 and 55–21 ka (figure 61).

Determination of the stable carbon isotope ratio, $^{13}C/^{12}C$, is usually carried out as well as the stable oxygen ratio for calibration purposes,

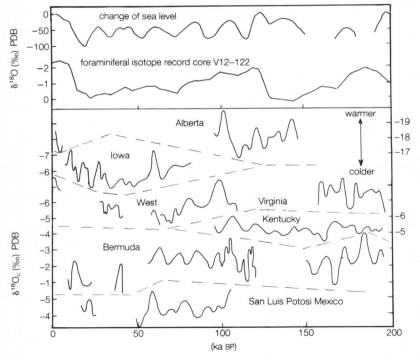

Figure 61 Oxygen palaeotemperature curves from North American speleothems over the last 200 000 years, after Harmon *et al.* (1978).

175

but, since it is affected by changes in vegetation, it also may yield a palaeoenvironmental record when it is understood better.

Caves also throw light on wetter/drier climatic oscillations, as has been indicated in mention of the introduction of aeolian sand into caves where there is now no dune movement. This is perhaps unmistakable in its meaning.

This is not always the case when wet periods are argued from the prevalence of calcite deposits at particular times. In general terms, no doubt, calcite deposition in caves implies a supply of water and vegetative growth sufficient to enrich soil water with carbon dioxide for limestone solution. In the Nullarbor Plain it is now clear that there was at least one period when calcite speleothem formation was much more substantial than now and a wetter period can be inferred from it, especially as in many caves halite and gypsum speleothem production is characteristic of the present time with its dry climate.

However, in a humid climate, heavy calcite growth may be interbedded with clastic fluvial and mass movement deposits, including soil from outside. Then the implication may be the opposite, that the wetter times were those when slope and stream processes overwhelmed the effects of seepage water from the cave roof (Frank 1975a,b). There is an instance in a cave at Borenore, NSW, where, in a dry period at 30 000–25 000 BP, a cave stream dried up completely and flowstone was laid across the whole width of the only passage through the cave (figure 59(b)). Even subaqueous calcite forms may be indicative of drier times because pools are not being filled with clastic debris then.

Particularly with evidence relating to water in caves, it is essential to consider the extent to which a given sequence of deposits can be the result of site factors, i.e. to the cave itself.

Finally, there is the matter of sea level changes; in coastal regions deposits in karst caves can fill out the picture obtained from more usual sources of evidence. This is more conveniently considered, however, in a broader context in chapter 11.

Karst immunity confers longevity most of all on caves (Ford 1980), and this combines with the stability that cave environments provide for the deposits within them; the potential that caves possess, therefore, for contributing to landscape history is probably not yet fully appreciated.

9   The Influence of Geological Structure

It is geological structure that determines not only the very existence of karst – in the broader geomorphological sense of the lithological nature of rocks as well as their stratigraphic and tectonic arrangement – but also most of the variety in karst manifestations. This is why there has been frequent reference to geological structure in earlier chapters, and why there is now a need to consider the subject in some detail.

Tectonic forms and structural forms, in the sense of forms due to differential erosion, find excellent expression in karst; as a result, karst appears disproportionately in landform atlases and geomorphological textbooks to illustrate them. This tendency can be linked to the idea of karst immunity; the surface of karst is not readily transformed because so much water goes underground. With streams farther apart, more interfluve survives unattacked for longer periods, and minimization of slope processes dependent on water as a lubricant slows down valley widening.

Nevertheless, various studies of limestone removal have shown that the bulk of it is taking place at or near the surface so that relief is being destroyed. Aubert (1969) pointed out that in the Jura Mountains, at the present rate of surface lowering of about 50 mm ka^{-1}, 500 m of limestone will have been removed if it has been continuous since the Pontian orogeny created the relief. On these grounds, Aubert doubted the survival of any of a Tertiary erosion surface that had previously been postulated. The same argument applies to survival of structural and tectonic forms. P. W. Williams (personal communication) has suggested that in some cases the paradox can be resolved through uniform reduction of surfaces allowing preservation of form.

Regional Effects of Structure

The classic distinction that Cvijić (1893) made between the Yugoslavian holokarst and merokarst is structurally based in the sense given above. The broad coastal belt of the Dinaric karst, which has great thickness of pure limestone reaching deep below sea level as well as high above it, is holokarst, as outlined in chapter 1. Here the full gamut of mid-latitude karst landforms and drainage, including poljes of erosional origin, is present; karst processes are dominant and boundary effects, either downwards or laterally, are virtually absent, though inliers of impervious rocks or less pervious ones such as dolomite have promoted polje formation.

In the inland belt of the Yugoslav karst the karst rocks are thinner and are interrupted more by impervious rocks, which greatly influence this merokarst. The karst is less complete, poljes are almost absent and normal river valleys are frequent. This was later designated *fluviokarst* by Roglić (1960), and Cvijić (1918, 1925) himself transferred his own term to other types of karst with lithologies even less favourable to karst development, especially through impurities leading to the accumulation of impervious residual covers. Integrated valley systems prevail, while caves are poorly developed and so are dolines, occurring more frequently in the covers rather than modulating the karst rock surface. Subsoil solutional sculpture is more important than that of bare bedrock through the comparative rarity of the latter. The Jurassic limestones of lowland England give rise to this kind of merokarst, e.g. in the Cotswolds. So does the Cretaceous chalk of England and France, though in this case it is due not to impurities, which are minimal, but to its mechanical weakness, antagonistic to cave development, with all that means for the nature of the drainage system.

Dolomite dissolves more slowly than limestone of equal purity and

Plate 34 Klippen karst in the Low Tatra, Slovakia. Tectonically isolated small masses of limestone form separate mountains with a limited range of karst features because of the restricted area.

yields much dolomite sand in the process. These characteristics are not conducive to the development of either vigorous karst surface relief or conduit flow and caves. Other factors being equal, dolines are shallower and fewer in dolomite than in limestone. However, diffuse flow reaches deeply down sand-filled joint fissures and feeds saturated springs.

In their typologies of Czechoslovakia's karst forms, Mazur and Jakal (1976) and Stelcl (1976) rely to a large extent on structural divisions. These comprise monoclinal ridges, horsts and fold/fault structures, klippen and tectonic basins, all of which impose constraints on karst development of one kind and another, even if only because of the small size of unit that the structure defines (see plate 34). In both the Czech and Slovak republics, which broadly belong, respectively, to the ancient Hercynian and young Alpine orogenic belts of Europe, the most complete karst development is to be found in massifs where a truncating erosion surface has been subject to later uplift. Also, high mountain karst above the treeline has to be segregated in Slovakia. So although most divisions rely on structural factors, this dependence is not complete; factors of denudation chronology and bioclimate also play their parts.

In the section in chapter 6 on doline karst in the American Midwest, there was some illustration of the role played by varying lithology in a succession of dominantly carbonate rocks. A greater variety of karst response can be found in the humid tropics, as Monroe (1968) sets out for northern Puerto Rico, where different associations of karst forms correspond with the strike belts of five northerly dipping calcareous formations. Cockpit karst is found on pure, massive limestone, whereas *mogote karst* – a karst of steep-sided, residual hills scattered over a plain – requires similar limestones, which, however, formerly had a younger cover of marine sands and sandy clays. The latter now veneer the plain between the towers as a result of solution subsidence. Less pure and closely bedded limestones give rise to *zanjones* country; zanjones are shallow trenches elongated along joints in the bedrock. Interbedding of mechanically strong and weak limestones gives rise to deep doline karst in which are found the greatest cave developments and impressive natural bridges. Monroe recognizes one additional factor bringing about this variety, namely greater uplift in the south than the north.

The structural geomorphology of the limestone rangers of north-west Australia has acquired even greater interest than before because of contrary views emerging about their structure. The generally accepted interpretation is that they are Devonian biogenic reefs only modestly disturbed tectonically (Playford and Lowry 1966). Mesozoic burial, planation, Tertiary uplift and rejuvenation have led to the removal of weaker impervious basin and inter-reef facies, so that the former barrier and patch reefs stand out as low limestone plateaus and ridges from shale plains. Pediments have cut back into the reefs to margin the ranges with cliffs and scarps parallel to the strike of the fore-reef beds (Jennings and

Sweeting 1963) (see figure 4 above). The narrow band of biolithites of the reef proper is solutionally lowered to form a shallow trench below the surface of fore-reef and back-reef facies. Where either of these facies (though mainly the lagoonal) is impure, rounded relief with a normal valley system prevails, with only minor solution sculpture, some caves and springs. At the most it is a merokarst. Where pure, both facies give rise to rugged holokarst (see plate 26), evolving from giant grikeland – intricate karst corridor and fissure cave terrain, through an angular, box-valley stage to a pedimented towerkarst. Differences between the two facies here, arising from the strong depositional dip of the fore-reef and the mainly horizontal bedding of the back-reef, are obvious but not important; the mega-breccias of the fore-reef are etched out into castellated blocks on the depositional dipslope.

Logan and Semeniuk (1976) take a conflicting view, that the whole structure began from carbonate shelf banks, which are still to be seen little altered in the supposed back-reef facies. What is regarded as fore-reef is to them a vast mass of former bank now dynamically metamorphosed by great tectonic stress from the south-west into stylo-bedded, stylo-laminated and stylo-brecciated limestones. The dip is not depositional but is the attitude of the pressure solution planes resulting from the pressure field, and the supposed bands of undisturbed reef growth are instead the most intense zones of pressure solution and tectonic disturbance.

The interest in this for the karst geomorphologist is that the new view, if it were to find acceptance, would incur little or no revision of geomorphic interpretation, which depends on rock attitude and lithology, and not on how these were acquired. With calcium carbonate, diagenesis and metamorphism can result in products that differ little in their geomorphic properties.

Structural Effects on Landform Types

Structural influence expresses itself also at lesser scales then the whole karst assemblage, as Wilford and Wall (1965) aptly illustrated with limestone towers in Sarawak (figure 62). Where the rocks are steeply dipping, the top and bottom of the limestone succession may define the towers on two flanks (figure 62(a)). Where there is a sharp change in facies, the cliff margin may lie close to it when the beds are not far from the horizontal (figure 62(b)). Some of the Sarawak towers develop in pure, massive, recrystallized biolithites while the plain to the flank is in less pure, well bedded calcarenites and calcirudites, a much less pronounced facies change but morphogenetic enough (figure 62(c)). Faults define some tower flanks (figure 62(d)), and the limestone may be cut up by corridors following felsite dykes (figure 62(e)). Nevertheless,

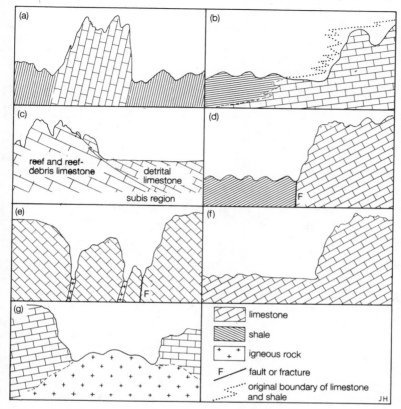

Figure 62 Types of limestone tower margin in Sarawak, after Wilford and Wall (1965).

the chances of a tower being defined structurally all round, other than in the way of detail by joints (plate 35), are not great. It does seem to be true of some of the towers in the karst of north-east Queensland at Chillagoe and farther north between the Mitchell and the Palmer Rivers. This has been explained by their coinciding with bioherms in vertical bedding or with fault slices (Ford T. D. 1978). More frequently, the margins will be the product of lateral solutional undercutting from alluvially veneered limestone plains (figure 62(f)), as in the Kinta Valley, Perak, or of sapping at the basal contact with underlying igneous rocks (figure 62(g)), as with Bukit Takun, Selangor, to give complementary examples from peninsular Malaysia.

Sweeting (1973, 1978, *inter alia*) has devoted much effort to demonstrating how differences in limestone lithology modify landforms. The succession in the Carboniferous limestone in Craven was examined closely for proportions of micrite and sparite and for intergranular porosity. Thick bedding and low porosity is associated with a high

181

Plate 35   A joint-controlled karst corridor in tower karst in Kinta valley, Perak, Malaysia.

sparite content, micrites with even lower porosity, but biomicrites have a higher porosity. Thick bedding and less frequent jointing relate to a high sparite content and vice versa. Solubility and propensity to weathering are greatest with the biomicrites. As a result, the sparites make high cliffs or 'scars' along the valley sides, and, where streams cross them, they do so in narrow gorges. Also, glacially scoured limestone pavements are best

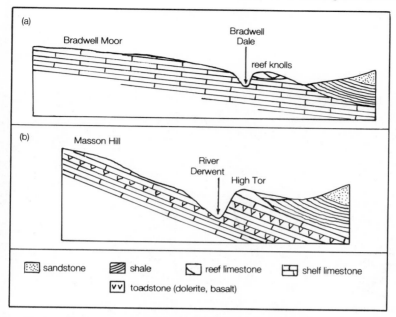

Figure 63 Anomalous gorges on the eastern flank of the Peak District: bioherms stopped the uniclinal downdip shift of streams, after Ford and Burek (1976).

developed over the sparitic beds; these are more resistant to erosion and have been less dissected by postglacial solution. Vertically walled open shafts also develop better in this style of limestone. The biomicrites do not form scars so readily and their pavements are more densely jointed and suffer more frost action. Screes form more readily from them than from the sparites. Valleys in them are wider and shallower; collapse dolines occur more frequently with the biomicrites and micrites.

Bioherms not only give rise to reef knolls (see chapter 1) but also have affected drainage patterns in karst (Ford and Burek 1976). On the eastern flank of the Peak District there are gorges, such as those of the Derwent at Matlock and the dry gorge of Bradwell Dale, across the noses of plunging anticlines. Streams superimposed from overlying shale cover were obstructed in their uniclinal shift eastwards downdip by the presence of mounds of reef limestone (figure 63).

On a small scale, but arising from differential erosion, are the inverted relief features formed from solution pipes. Cementation around solution pipes formed in weak materials fosters the survival of hollow residual projections. Such cementation was mentioned in connection with lithification of calcareous sands in chapter 5; subsequent aeolian erosion removes still unconsolidated sand around the indurated pipe walls and

G

the soil inside to leave hollow pillars such as the Tombstones near Jurien Bay, WA (Jennings 1968). The tubular chalk stacks at Sheringham, Norfolk, England, have been similarly etched out, but there by wave attack (Burnaby 1950) in a striking instance of form convergence (Jennings 1978a).

Plate 36 A rectangular passage and slab blockpile in horizontal Ordovician limestone in Exit Cave, Tasmania. Photo by R. Curtis.

The Influence of Geological Structure

Structural Effects Underground

Geological factors are particularly important in localizing cave beginnings (Ford 1971); but also, as they enlarge, caves are developed preferentially within particular beds in a geological formation. Rauch and White (1970) analysed this thoroughly for the Nittany Valley in Pennsylvania. Nearly all caves were found in the Champlainian limestone and very few in dolomite formations. Within that formation, most of the total volume lay within six of its thirteen members and beds, comprising only a quarter of its thickness. Purity of limestone and small grain size were favourable factors, while clay and dolomite content were unfavourable. In the Swago Creek area of West Virginia, W. B. White (1963) found that cave development was favoured just above argillaceous members in the limestone sequence, while Waltham (1977) pointed to many Craven caves at the base of the Carboniferous limestone just above basal shales or slates of greater age below. The Mississippian formations of the American Midwest are the host for innumerable caves, many of them huge systems, including the greatest of all, the Flint Ridge–Mammoth Caves. However, there are facies changes through this immense basin of deposition, and with them caves are found to shift from one favourable horizon to another (Palmer and Palmer 1975).

With horizontal carbonate rocks, cave plans often show much joint control, whereas in cross and long section bedding tends to delineate roof and floor with the walls often in joint planes, e.g. in many caves in Craven and Clare (plate 36).

When dips are great, strike directions become important in the plan. Along the strike, level passages occur in particular beds, and cross-sections tend to be triangular with a sloping bedding-plane roof. Down

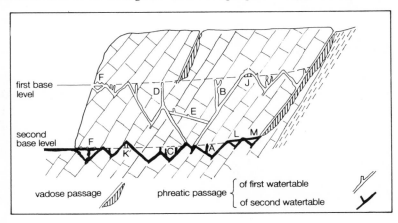

first base level

second base level

vadose passage   phreatic passage { of first watertable
                                     of second watertable

Figure 64 The influence of steep dip on Mendip, England, cave development, after Ford (1965b).

the dip, different profiles result. With considerable relief, steeply inclined passages in the dip alternate with gravity-controlled, vertical descents as in the Gouffre Berger, French Alps. With modest relief, as in Mendip Caves (Ford 1965b) (figure 64), up-and-down profiles develop in dynamic phreatic flow, with dip tubes in the bedding and lifting chimneys in joints.

When beds dip more or less vertically, the cave plan is likely to be dominated by the strike of the beds because of lithology varying horizontally quickly, and the walls of the passages often lie in bedding planes, e.g. Mairs Cave, Flinders Ranges, SA (figure 65).

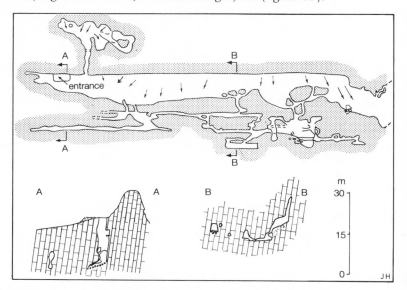

Figure 65 The influence of vertical bedding on cave morphology, Mairs Cave, SA, after Cave Exploration Group South Australia survey.

Diverse views on the relative importance of joints and bedding planes have been presented. Many papers discussing individual caves have shown much correlation between cave passage and joint directions, and some have deliberately tried to weigh the relative importance of joints and beds. In complex structure, the Grotte de Remouchamps, Belgium, has its passages controlled much more by joints than by beds, according to Ek (1970) in a paper accompanied by an excellent coloured map of the underground geology. Powell (1977) takes a similar view of the greater importance of joints in nearly horizontally bedded Indiana karst; he mentions how a dolomite bed has been preferred for cave formation to adjacent limestones because of a greater degree of jointing, whereas limestone is usually the main host for caves because of its readier solution.

However, in a broad survey of Slovenian caves, Gams (1963) comes to the contrary conclusion that, overall in a variety of structures, bedding is the more important factor influencing cave plans. Bögli (1969) argues that in the initiation of caves bedding-planes will be the more important because of their continuity, but that this association may become less apparent through secondary enlargement because of breakdown along joints. Very long caves, such as the Hölloch, Switzerland and the great Kentucky caves (G. H. Deike 1967), do not owe much to joints for their passage directions.

The issue may be confused by the fact that the most important joint set may follow the strike (R. G. Deike 1969). The joint pattern may be reflecting other factors still, as Charity and Christopher (1977) argue for Ogof Ffynnon Ddu, Wales, where they maintain that open joints along anticlines favour development there rather than along synclines where the joints are tight. In apparently nearly planar bedding, shallow folds, which need very precise surveying to be recognized, can exercise a powerful influence, as Palmer (1981) shows for the Flint Ridge–Mammoth Caves system, as for instance in the way Cleaveland and Marion Avenues follow round the structural contours of the nose of a syncline in a quasi-horizontal epiphreatic tube. At the other extreme, Kavalieris and Martini (1976) use the contradiction between joint control of western Transvaal dolomite caves and their disregard of folding to argue that the jointing is a much later event in the tectonic history of the region.

Similar diversity appears to be present in the role of faults in cave formation. In the Peak District, many caves are developed in close association with faults and the mineral veins are often emplaced along the faulted zones (Ford and Worley 1977). In Craven, Rift Pot, Long Kin East Pot, Hull Pot and Meregill all lie along faults (Myers 1948). The Great North Road appropriately designates a great linear passage some 800 m long in Dan yr Ogof, Wales, with prominent slickensided surfaces. Faults strongly influence this cave because they coincide with dip direction. However, faults are not always favourable; in neighbouring Ogof Ffynnon Ddu, two main systems are separated by a zone of few passages which coincides with a fault zone (Glennie 1950). Mineralization may seal faultplanes, or fault-brecciation may be too weak to support caves. Palmer (1972) attributed part of the alignment of Onesquethaw Cave, New York, to a fault, which, however, Gregg (1974) maintains is a small movement along a joint actually occasioned by the development of the cave. In the Matienzo caves of northern Spain, faults are sometimes favourable and at other times unfavourable to cave passage formation (Mills and Waltham 1981).

Faults often place alongside rocks of high and low permeability and so act as hydrological barriers, as is well illustrated in south-central Texas in the case of the karstic Edwards limestone (Maclay and Small 1983).

Longitudinal drainage along a narrow strike belt of limestone is likely to prevent much departure of underground drainage from the former surface drainage line, as is illustrated by the systems between the Zaton and Bulba Caves in the Mehedinti Plateau, Romania (Goran 1978).

Cave Hydrogeologic Systems

The differences in view about the way the geological structure influences cave development arise in part from intrinsic differences in the structural attributes from one region to another but also from the intervention of other factors, such as the general relief and drainage patterns, which may in their turn be responses to larger structural units. In this regard, W. B. White (1969) and Ford (1971) have generalized from many detailed studies of their own and of others. Thus, where the relief is such that drainage trends down the dip in steeply dipping limestones, the caves have to pass up through the succession to the outlets. But the dip is often steeper than the hydraulic gradient, and the response is a sequence of phreatic loops made up of long dip tubes and short joint-chimneys. As the development of caves is likely to increase the effective joint frequency, there may be a sequence of development from a few large loops in earlier trunk routes to many loops and finally to an epiphreatic stage with few and shallow U-tubes as successive routes through the karst from at lower levels (see figure 54).

However, the main drainage in karst of steep dip is more likely to be along the strike. In these circumstances, the trunk caves tend to run along the strike. Initially and with widely spaced jointing, this results in an up-and-down course, irregular in plan, with short dip tubes linking rising sections acutely oblique to the strike as in the Hölloch in Switzerland. The greater the joint frequency, the more nearly those trunks will become horizontal strike passages corresponding roughly with water rest levels of the time they form, though of course they will be abandoned later. Ford (1971) cites Postojna Cave, Slovenia, as an example of this style of system.

In nearly horizontal rocks, dipping at 5 deg and less, though water intake will be predominantly through joints, the greater continuity of bedding planes ensures that passages in them provide trunk routes to the outflows. Deep looping is unlikely to develop, and even a small lowering of springs can drain lengthy sections of shallow looping so that epiphreatic and vadose caves early come to dominate the systems in flat-lying rocks (figure 66(b) and (c)).

Almost paradoxically, the same is true of rocks in tight, small-scale folds, which are liable to much fissuring by close joints accompanying intense flexuring; here epiphreatic caves are those most favoured by the structure (Davies 1960).

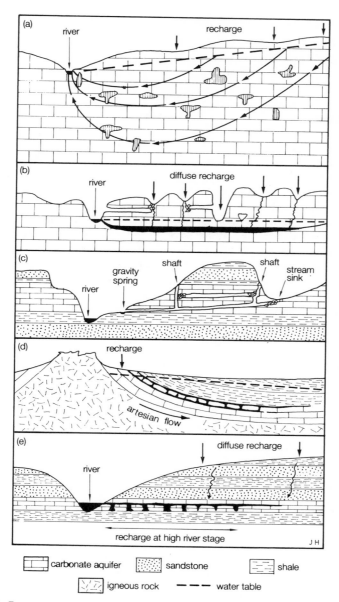

Figure 66 Types of hydrogeologic system in low to moderate karst relief according to W.B. White (1969): (a) *diffuse flow* reaching slowly but deeply beneath subdued surface relief; interconnected, structurally guided but scattered cavities beneath the water table; (b) and (c) *free flow* to valleys cut in horizontal beds, without (b) and with (c) a cap of impervious rocks. Intakes are from many dolines (b), or along margins of caprock (c). For karst rock below valleys, waterfilled caves feed rising springs (b); perched on impervious basement, free surface streams feed gravity springs (c). Abandoned caves at higher levels result from earlier halts to incision. (d) and (e) *confined flow*. In an artesian situation (d) water moves slowly to considerable depth in the uppermost karst beds, creating an inclined joint maze; in sandwich conditions (e) there is small diffuse discharge through the cap into thin karst beds, and backflooding from river develops a horizontal network.

In artesian situations, where carbonate rocks dip under an impervious cap, water is forced deep under hydrostatic pressure but movement is slow. The result is a maze of joint passages but restricted to a few beds, a three-dimensional network under complete structural control (Deike 1960; Howard 1964) (figure 66(d)).

If thin, nearly horizontal limestone is sandwiched between impervious rocks, nothephreatic networks in two dimensions develop as encountered in mining in the Yoredale Beds in the Yorkshire Dales (Ryder 1975) (cf. figure 66(e)). Much of the presently surveyed length of 57 km of Mamo Kananda in the Muller Range, PNG, resides in separate levels of network in several pure limestone beds sandwiched between impure limestone as well as siltstone (J. M. James, personal communication).

This survey does not take stock of all the broad frameworks within which caves are initiated and evolve, but it is sufficient to underline the diversity that sustains a continuing intellectual quest to match the physical challenge they present to the speleologist.

10 The Influence of Climate

At the present time there is no greater dividing issue among geomorphologists than climatic geomorphology. It has long been recognized that, since much of the modelling of the earth's surface is done by exogenetic agencies motored by the sun's energy, there are going to be differences in landforms in response to variations in climate over the earth. Around the middle of this century this approach to geomorphology received great attention, particularly by those who approached the discipline from the side of geography, and morphogenetic systems were conceived as arising in all major climatic types with substantial characteristic responses in the landscape. But in the last decade or so there has been a reaction against this standpoint.

Among the arguments that have been levelled against climatic geomorphology has been recognition of the frequency and magnitude of Cainozoic climatic changes, the realization that similar forms may result from different processes (the equifinality issue), the recognition that climate is only one of the many influences on landforms and the rate of operation of process, and a dissatisfaction with gross-scale generalizations and regionalizations. Many detailed local-scale quantitative studies of process and form have failed to reveal some of the patterns that have been proposed by the early climatic geomorphologists.

The study of karst has run a parallel course. Early this century the dominant mode of thought was to range all karst phenomena into a single evolutionary sequence (e.g. Sawicki 1909; Grund 1914). Even karst forms from tropical humid Jamaica and Java, observed to have striking attributes of their own (Daneš 1908, 1910), were given their places in such schemes, and landform terms from the Dinaric karst were employed world-wide, almost with the effect of mental blinkers, as Lehmann (1960) deplored.

Yet early in the development of ideas about karst, climate was being called upon to explain differences perceived between karsts such as the greater proportion of covered karst in central Europe compared with that in the Dinaric region; Grund (1910) invoked differences in frost incidence and rainfall intensity. Altitudinal zonation of karst features in the Austrian Alps was thought by O. Lehmann (1927) to be climatically controlled. This coincided in time with the publication of the proceedings of a German conference on the morphology of the climatic zones which can be regarded as the beginning of the modern blooming of climatic morphology. It was nevertheless H. Lehmann's fresh view of the central Javanese karst as a style of karst evolving along distinctive lines because of its tropical humid climate (see plate 40) that set a fashion which culminated in the 1953 meeting of the International Geographical Union's Karst Commission, when no fewer than eight climato-morphogenic regimes for karst were propounded (Lehmann et al. 1954).

Since that time, there has been growing criticism of what is regarded by some as facile attribution of climatic causes to karst styles on inadequate evidence. Thus, Panoš and Stelcl (1968) argued that many aspects of Cuban karst previously attributed to processes special to humid tropical conditions by Lehmann et al. (1956) were to be explained more simply as direct expressions of geological structure. Karst border poljes were found to be floored by impervious rocks, not the limestone of earlier writing. Complementarily, Brook and Ford (1976, 1978) think that tower karst, regarded as a characteristic tropical humid karst style, is present in subarctic climate in the north Nahanni karst, North West Territories, Canada, and has formed recently; instead, they prefer a structural control for the distribution of tower karst. Williams (1978) finds parts of the Waitomo karst in warm temperate New Zealand to approximate closely to conekarst, again considered typical of the humid tropics. Whereas Jennings and Bik (1962) thought their reconnaissance of Papua New Guinea karsts showed an altitudinal zonation of a variety of karst types, on the basis of much fuller study Löffler (1977) largely demolished their framework in favour of structural explanations. Structure is now thought to play a larger part in the tower karsts of north-east Queensland (Jennings 1982b) than was allowed previously (Jennings 1969).

Rates of Karst Denudation

The climatic approach to karst participated in the quantitative study of modern processes pursued vigorously from the 1950s. In particular, estimates of karst denudation by the generally dominant process of solution became central to it, to a large degree because of the active example of J. Corbel and because Corbel took up a stance contrary to the prevalent view that solution went on most rapidly in the humid tropics.

The formula that Corbel (1959) employed was:

$$\text{Limestone denudation rate} \cdot (\text{in } m^3 \ km^{-2} \ a^{-1}) = 2.5 \ \frac{E.t.n}{1000}$$

where E = runoff (in decimetres), t = $CaCO_3$ concentration (in millgrams per litre), and $1/n$ = fraction of catchment in limestone and limestone alluvium.

However, runoff records in karst are commonly unavailable, so Corbel and others often substituted annual surplus of the water balance (precipitation – evaporation). But estimates of actual evaporation from such varied surfaces as are involved are bound to be unreliable. Therefore some workers have recorded the discharge themselves. Other weaknesses of Corbel's formula were early corrected; the assumed bulk density of 2.5 was replaced by actual measured rock densities from the specific karst, and magnesium carbonate plus calcium carbonate concentration took place of the earlier simplification of calcium carbonate equivalent. Corbel often employed far too few samples to arrive at his mean concentration, which was then applied to the annual runoff. Later workers have sampled through the year and regressed hardness against discharge on the sampling occasions. A weakness arises from using a single year's sampling; long-studied rivers such as the Green River in Kentucky have yielded different exponents for the power function for each year. The regressions are employed to calculate daily loads. Other sources of error are carbonate inputs from other than the karst rocks – in the rain from dusts blown into the catchments, in allogenic streams from the weathering of non-karst rocks, and from subjacent karst in some cases (Jennings 1972). A further problem arises from the difficulty in determining the underground catchment, which often does not coincide with the topographic one. These considerations imply that the meaning and reliability of published karst denudation rates are highly variable.

Figure 67 is modified from Atkinson and Smith (1976) by the addition

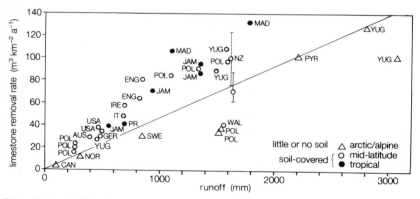

Figure 67 A plot of limestone removal rate against runoff, amplified from Atkinson and Smith (1976): AUS, Australia; CAN, Canada; ENG, England; GER, West Germany; IRE, Ireland; IT, Italy; JAM, Jamaica; MAD, Madagascar; NZ, New Zealand; NOR, Norway; POL, Poland; PR, Puerto Rico; PYR, Pyrenees; SWE, Sweden; USA, United States; WAL, Wales; YUG, Yugoslavia.

193

of further results, mainly of the more reliable kind based on discharge records and numerous water analyses. This compilation demonstrates significant climatic control of karst denudation in two ways. Much the more substantial effect is the increasing rate of limestone removal in solution with increasing runoff. The lesser effect lies in the reduction in solution load in passing from soil and vegetation-covered terrain to dominantly bare rock country, whether because it is high in mountains or in arctic cold climate. Longer contact with soil-covered rock and higher P_{CO_2} levels in the soil account for this. The climatic effect that many would expect but does not appear in the plot is a greater rate of solution in the tropics than in the mid-latitude karsts, runoff being equal: they are actually mingled together along the plot from low to high values. Though not included here, Corbel (1959) has given much higher rates still for high-latitude mountain karst such as 500 mm ka^{-1} with 4000 mm runoff in Svartisen, Norway, based upon comparatively few water samples; but these are to be matched by equally large estimates of 430 mm ka^{-1} with 6400 mm runoff from New Britain (Maire 1981). Ford and Drake (1982) recommend that comparisons for this purpose should be made only with measures from springs with waters saturated for calcite.

Thus, although the water availability factor emerges clearly from the denudational data, temperature, independently of its indirect and inverse effect through evaporation, appears only in a muted and truncated way. W. B. White (1984) calculates saturation equilibrium denudation rates on the basis of his latest analysis of the kinetics of the $H_2O-CO_2CaCO_3$ system and finds they agree with the dominating linear relationship between denudation and runoff (or $P-E$). In addition, the rate varies with the cube root of P_{CO_2}, thus making it range over a factor of 5; this supports the dichotomy between soil-covered and bare karsts proposed by Smith and Atkinson (1976). However, the theoretical denudation rate increases by only 30 per cent as temperature rises from 5 to 25 °C, so the effect of this factor can easily be lost in the scatter of empirical determinations. Individual karst studies reveal sharp variation in spatial distribution of solution within given climatic situations (Gams 1966; D. I. Smith 1975). Undoubtedly, the search for the operation of the climatic factor led to claims of greater interpretative certainty than was justified in the face of complex interactions with other factors such as structure. Therefore only the more clearcut variants in karst deriving from climate will be discussed below.

The Arid Extreme

Poverty in water, in vegetation and so in soil carbon dioxide lead to a theoretical expectation of poorly developed karst in dry climates,

Plate 37 Arid karst of Nullarbor Plain, almost featureless but with occasional collapse dolines which are modified only slowly.

especially hot ones, where great evaporation renders low precipitation even less effective. The Nullarbor Plain, a vast expanse of horizontal Eocene and Miocene limestones, much of it treeless through aridity, is an unbroken low plateau (Lowry and Jennings 1974) (see plate 37). There has been only a little lowering since it emerged from the sea in Miocene times, and only a little diversification by the creation of large but

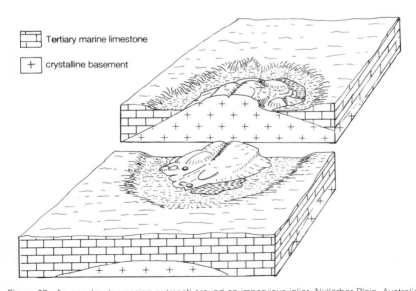

Tertiary marine limestone

crystalline basement

Figure 68 An annular depression or 'moat' around an impervious inlier, Nullarbor Plain, Australia.

195

extremely shallow circular depressions and of ridge-and-corridor relief of 3–5 m amplitude. A few collapse dolines break the monotony with a sharpness they retain for long periods. Annular depressions or 'moats' around impervious inliers are distinctive forms but of restricted occurrence (figure 68). Solutional microforms are poorly developed and also are restricted in distribution; on the other hand, there is widespread induration of the surface with calcrete. (For a review of calcrete see Goudie 1983a.) There has also been deflation of the soil in the past.

Less than a score of deep and large caves are known, some of which reach down to elongated lakes, up to several kilometres long, in a flat water table with brackish water moving slowly coastward (plate 38). Shallower caves are more numerous, but on a unit area basis underground development is as retarded as surface modelling. Slow phreatic solution may have enhanced importance here. In contrast, cave breakdown seems widespread and pronounced; halite crystallization shatters bedrock into finer detritus, which can occur in large quantities. Here is an exception to the usual inertness of caves lacking streams. Calcite speleothems are rarely forming now, though in south-central parts caves are rich in inactive forms and broken calcite from them; halite and gypsum speleothems occur in unusual quantity and variety.

Williams (1978) points out that much of the Nullarbor limestone is mechanically weak and porous and in part accounts for its character. Nevertheless, the calcrete at the surface could have supported quite sharp relief development if there had been water enough to dissect it. Jennings (1983b) therefore regards this karst as typical of subtropically hot, dry climate, though its individuality depends more on impoverishment in forms found more widely than in distinctive forms. Tafoni loom large in

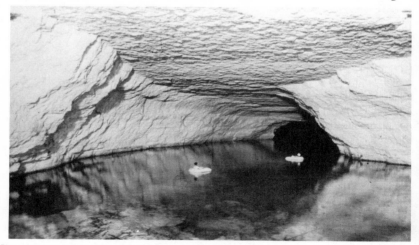

Plate 38 Weebubbie Cave, Nullarbor Plain. A few deep caves contain large lakes with slowly moving, brackish water. Photo by E. G. Anderson.

the Hadhramaut, Arabia (Wissmann 1957), in the Negev, (Nir 1964) and in the north-western Saharan hamadas (B. J. Smith 1978), and halite crystallization is marked in some of these. *Rillensteine*, micro-rilled

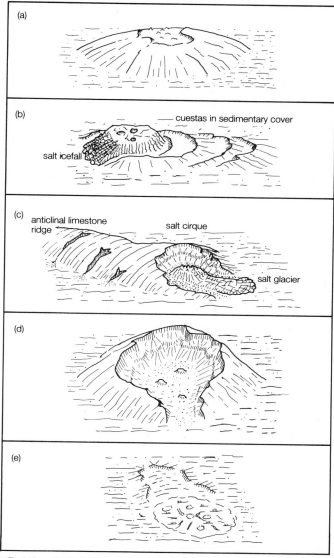

Figure 69 Evolution of halite karst in an arid climate: the surface expression of salt domes in Laristan Desert, Iran, based on maps and sections in Harrison (1930): (a) salt dome with nearly complete sedimentary sheath; (b) exposed salt dome with a flat top (e.g. Kuh-i-Shur); (c) denuded salt dome in salt cirque with salt glacier flowing out on to a plain (e.g. Kuh-i-Siah); (d) salt cirque (e.g. Tang-i-Zangur); (e) truncated salt dome with dolines, crevasses and salt swamps (e.g. Kuh-i-Finu).

boulders, are attributed to fog and dew in desert karst, and travertine dams such as the Band-I-Amir Lakes, Afghanistan, may owe growth to evaporation as well as CO_2 degassing in this climate.

In the arid lands of North Africa and the Middle East, limestone surfaces are often dotted with shallow depressions, called *dayas* (Mitchell and Willimott 1974). These and other limited forms in Bahrain have been described by Doornkamp *et al.* (1980, section 8.5), but on many of the island's limestone and dolomite surfaces wind abrasion features (*yardangs*) are of greater importance than solutional forms.

Dry lands, which disfavour carbonate karst, allow the survival at the surface of evaporite karst (Jennings 1982b), whereas in humid climates such karst is dominantly restricted to the subjacent condition because of much greater solubility. Gypsum karst is perhaps best developed in semi-arid lands such as the Gypsum Plain in Texas and New Mexico, though it is not restricted to this climate. Halite karst is characteristic of deserts, e.g. Djelfa, Algeria (Gautier 1914–15); the endogenetic factor of diapiric rise is nevertheless necessary for its fullest expression by offsetting rapid exogenetic destruction (figure 69).

The Cold Extreme

The freezing of water renders it inactive in terms of solution, so that with geophysically polar glaciers and in permafrost country glacial and periglacial processes largely take over and may substitute their kinds of landforms for karst ones if they have sufficient time. In other contexts, glaciers may have preservative and stimulative effects as well as these destructive and inhibitive ones (Ford 1983a).

In the permafrost zone, surface lowering by solution proceeds slowly because of small amounts of liquid water, even in summer, and because of low vegetative productivity of CO_2, e.g. Somerset Island, North West Territories, Canada (D. I. Smith 1969). Frost wedging destroys or damages solutional microforms and shillow – angular limestone debris – clutters outcrops, as Corbel (1957) describes from Spitzbergen. The surface is lowered parallel to itself, tending to structural forms, though solution will be locally more active beneath snow patches. Shallow caves – frost pockets – develop in cliffs through frost wedging (Schroeder 1979).

Beneath the permafrost, high-solute contents may be found in ground-water; for example, in Alaska (Corbel 1959) and in central Siberia large springs, marking local breaks or 'taliks' in the permafrost, indicate that there persists circulation at depth (Popov *et al.* 1972). Ford (1984) thinks such circulation is not entirely inherited from a former warmer climate but rather that large bodies of water can create and maintain routeways through the permafrost and so form caves. The partially permafrosted north Nahanni karst in north-west Canada is rugged, with numerous dolines, solution corridors and active poljes, and it is evident that this has evolved in times at least as rigorous as today. Farther north in the Mackenzie lowland, reaching into the continuous permafrost zone, fields of dolines in glacial drift are due to evaporite solution below. Here the karst may be inherited from warmer times as well as being specially favoured lithologically. In the Canadian archipelago, in continuous permafrost, karst relief on limestone is generally absent or weakly developed in the top metre or two that are subject to summer defreezing, though it has to be recognized that horizontal bedding and slight regional relief are unfavourable also. In some areas there are fields of solution corridors with maximum dimensions of 1 km long, 30 m wide and 12 m deep (and with unplumbed depths of fill); Ford suggest that these were formed by subglacial meltwater, the great Laurentide icesheet insulating the karst and conserving geothermal heat in these areas. More studies of the far northern karsts of North America and the USSR are called for to discriminate between the effects of inheritance and those pertaining to frigid morphogenetic systems.

In the less rigorous cold climates of maritime polar and lower-latitude high-mountain climates, where glaciers are at pressure melting point and ground freezing is only seasonal, infiltration into bedrock is feasible and snow and ice melt provide seasonal water abundances. Here there can be good development of karst in some respects. Close-set fields of small-solution dolines and open shafts occur both beyond the limits of

Plate 39   Dolines and shafts in bare alpine karst in Palaeozoic marble on Mt Arthur, Southern Alps, NZ. They tend to be blocked by shillow, the product of frost wedging.

vegetation, e.g. on the Astraka Plateau, Greece (Waltham 1978), and in alpine meadows, tundra, boreal and alpine forest (plate 39). On outcrops, solutional microforms can be formed despite competition of frost action. Some kinds, such as solution heelsteps, have been linked genetically with snowmelt, though they are not found exclusively in these circumstances.

Cave development is often substantial, and in the high-mountain varieties of these climates very deep systems are characteristic, as in the European Alps and the Pyrenees. That it is not just a question of inheritance from different palaeoclimates is readily illustrated from the Castleguard karst in the Canadian Rockies (Ford 1983b). Castleguard Cave is a long and largely inactive cave that passes beneath the Mt Castleguard glaciers to reach well under the large Columbia Icefield, where one branch heads in a blockage of glacier ice (figure 70). Injection

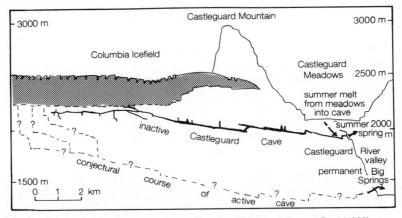

Figure 70 Castleguard Cave in the Canadian Rockies, after Schroeder and Ford (1983).

of till into the cave has been followed by leaching of it and transport of residual fines to form varves farther forward in the cave (Schroeder and Ford 1983). That cave emerges high up the side of a glacial valley, but some 250 m below is its modern active equivalent feeding large springs at the bottom of the same valley. These springs derive most of their water from the glaciers. Subglacial action of meltwater, both chemical and mechanical, is a factor to be reckoned with where the climate is not of the most rigorous kind (Nicod 1976b; Pierre and Pierre 1980).

Corbel (1957, 1964) claimed that karst developed in these conditions in part because of high CO_2 saturation equilibria in the characteristically cold waters and also because of an inferred high CO_2 content of the air trapped in voids in snow and ice. However, observations such as those of Ek (1964) on the meltwaters in the French mountains showed higher pH and lower carbonate concentrations than Corbel claimed and no special aggressiveness of these waters. Nevertheless, high precipitation and low evapotranspiration are undeniable in areas such as Svartisen in northern

Norway and Vercors in the French Alps, for which Corbel calculated high limestone denudation rates. Even in the inland taiga–tundra karst of the River Tanana in Alaska, Corbel (1959) arrived at a substantial rate of solution from reliable discharge and chemistry data. But this depends on a short summer season of great flows when carbonate concentrations are lowest. Sheer volume of water in fast, turbulent flow dominates solution.

The 'Botanic Hothouse' Extreme

It is in tropical humid climates, with or without a dry season, that the greatest variety of karst and the most striking expressions of it have been found. This has been regarded by most as a pointer to extremely active karst processes, though there are also strongly maintained views to the contrary.

A great many names have been introduced to identify different types of karst here; unfortunately, not just synonymy but a real confusion has developed through later users' not employing particular terms with their connotation. No attempt will be made here to retail all of the names, and the matter will be approached through the morphometry that certain investigators have pursued in part to clarify this terminological morass.

The system of Williams (1972a, b) was discussed in chapter 6 in connection with cockpits and is not applicable to all kinds of tropical karst. It implies a threefold division into:

1 *doline karst*, where dolines perforate a geomorphic surface of some kind, either erosional or structural, but leave enough of it for the dolines in large measure not to interfere with one another;
2 *polygonal karst*, where any prior surface has been consumed in the development of closed depressions so that all surfaces are part of them. Here, residual hills along the roughly polygonal divides defining the depressions are the dominating landscape features, though the reduction features – the depressions – are in fact the seat of process activity changing the geomorphology;
3 *plains karst*, where planate surfaces occupy most of the area, though residual hills, commonly of tower type, may prevail visually, and closed depressions play a subordinate role.

Only polygonal karst is the subject of Williams's morphometry, which orders the polygonal catchments on the basis of the re-entrant systems in their flanks. The O order must be doline in type with concave inward contours all round, whereas the other orders, with one of more re-entrants, represent cockpits of varying degrees of elaboration. In Papua New Guinea, Williams distinguished statistically three subsets within the overall category of polygonal karst: *cone karst, pinnacle karst* (plate 40) and *aligned karst*. In the last category, the residual hills exhibit a strong

Plate 40 Pinnacles, Gunoug Api, Mulu, Sarawak. Photo by Mick Day.

tendency to form parallel lines and the depressions are in chains like the 'glades' of Jamaica. The other kinds lack this preferred grain in their relief and are distinguished from one another by the shapes of the residual hills (plate 41).

Balazs (1973), in contrast, centres his analysis on the residual hills,

Plate 41 Cockpit/cone karst, Puerto Rico. Photo by Mick Day.

hinging it on the ratio (*d/a*) of the diameter (*d*) of the base of each hill to its altitude (*a*) above that base. Coupled with this index are the ranges in heights of the hills and in their areal frequency. On this basis he recognizes (without statistical analysis) four major types.

1 *Yangzhou*, with *d/a* less than 1.5, is based on the karst around Yangzhou, Guangxi, China, which dominantly falls into the *tower karst* (Ger. *Turmkarst*) category with steep-sided residuals rising like islands from a plain. The towers are 100–300 m high and typically run to 5–10 per square kilometre.
2 *Organos*, with *d/a* of 1.5–3, is named after the Sierra de los Organos, Cuba, where there are towers with this shape, locally called *mogotes*, 50–200 m high and with 10–20 per square kilometre.
3 *Sewu*, with *d/a* of 3–8, recalls the Gunung Sewu, the 'Thousand Hills' of south-central Java, with its hemispheroidal and sinusoidal hills and star-shaped depressions. Lehmann (1936) originally designated this conekarst (Ger. *Kegelkarst*), but it also corresponds largely with the cockpit country of Jamaica and Puerto Rico (figure 71).

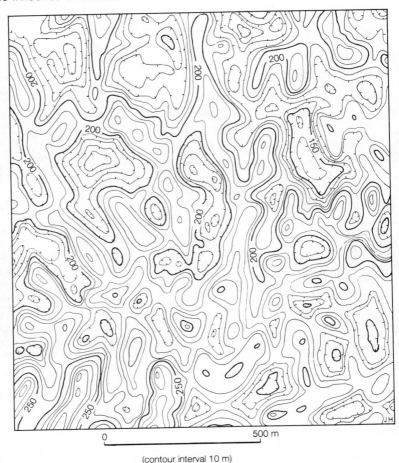

(contour interval 10 m)

Figure 71 Cockpit karst in northern Puerto Rico, from US Geological Survey map.

There is a relative relief of 30–120 m and a density of 15–30 per square kilometre. Conekarst is something of a misnomer, because the cone form is not the most characteristic form of the type area (Flathe and Pfeffer 1965), though this shape of residual karst hill is found in some areas, in parts of southern China, for example. In perhaps the most detailed application of what is basically Balazs' approach, Day (1978) ascribes an area of limestone residuals in northern Puerto Rico to the Sewu type.

4 *Tual*, with *d/a* greater than 8, is typified by weak relief on Kai-Ketjil Island, Indonesia, which is not far removed from a doline karst, with a local relief of 10–50 m and up to 50 hills per square kilometre.

Each of these is considered by Balazs to be divisible into two subtypes on the basis of the intervening relief, in the one case with the hills linked together to enclose depressions, in the other with them isolated over plains. This aspect of the relief is central to the way the Chinese regard the immense karst that straddles the tropic in the south of their country and extends into the four neighbouring countries to the south. They divide this karst into: (a) *fengcong*, where clustered residual hills are joined basally and closed depressions are general; (b) *fenglin*, generally with lesser relief and with valleys dividing up the hills also; and (c) *ku feng*, where the hills are scattered over plains and may become quite low. There may have been evolution from (a) to (c) in some circumstances but this is not thought to be always the case; and, although all are thought to be dependent on a hot, humid climate, the variations, especially the diverse forms of the residuals, are considered to be brought about by structural factors in the broad geomorphological sense (Yuan 1981; Zhang 1980).

In densely populated karst areas of these kinds, the amount of bare rock exposed can be striking, with only the bottoms of the closed depressions and the alluvial plains presenting continuous covered karst. Where the natural rainforest is retained, as for example in some New Guinean and Central American karst forms, it is amazing how covered in vegetation they are. Even vertical faces of rock can be concealed by plant growth, with roots of higher plants penetrating the slightest weakness and widespread covers of lower plants, mosses, liverworts, etc. (Crowther 1982b). Forest litter accumulates in all kinds of hollows and recesses and even roofs over deep fissures and shafts (figure 72). Only on

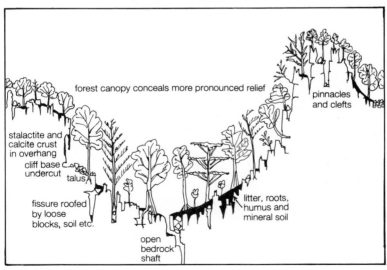

forest canopy conceals more pronounced relief

pinnacles and clefts

stalactite and calcite crust in overhang

cliff base undercut talus

fissure roofed by loose blocks, soil etc.

litter, roots, humus and mineral soil

open bedrock shaft

Figure 72 Schematic section through a cockpit.

overhangs, which can be dry, is bedrock to be seen over large expanses, and here there is great likelihood of speleothem growth in the open.

How much of the typically craggy slopes is covered by minerogenic soils is extremely variable (Pfeffer 1969), though this is accentuated by the intervention of slash-and-burn gardening and more familiar forms of agriculture. In New Guinea, the amount of ashfall from both nearby and distant volcanoes is undoubtedly an important factor in the amount of soil on karsts there, and it is possible that a byproduct is the occurrence of pedogenic chert coatings of the soil–bedrock interface.

In Jamaica the bauxite that is found substantially in depressions up to large-polje size in some of the karst has given rise to controversy as to its origin. The volumes are such as to be reasonably attributable to residual accumulations provided the concentration from the whole karst into its lower parts is allowed for and the modern rate of limestone removal in solution is employed (D. I. Smith 1971); Sinclair (1967) had earlier argued from trace elements in the bauxite that the constituents fit better with a residual hypothesis than theories of allocthonous origin such as fluvial transport from volcanic inliers within the karst.

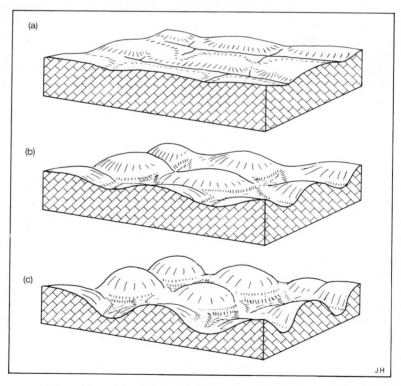

Figure 73 Evolution of cockpit karst of the Gunung Sewu type, according to Lehmann (1936).

Modern ideas on humid tropical karst evolution can be said to start with the interpretation by Lehmann (1936) of the cockpit karst of the Gunung Sewu, Java (figure 73). A prior planation surface is thought to have been gently domed tectonically which rejuvenated surface drainage. This produced ridges and valleys aligned down the flanks of the domes. Then, with the development of vertical infiltration and underground drainage, the valleys were broken up into chains of star-shaped closed depressions of surface-solutional origin. Aub's (1969) work on Jamaican cockpits basically supported the latter part of this evolution, though he pointed out that cliffs commonly interrupted the steep flanks of the residual hills so that dichotomy between towers and hemispheroidal hills is blurred in reality. His short-term measure of more throughfall in the depressions than on the hills is potentially so significant that it is a pity, though not surprising, that it has not been tested exhaustively. Williams's New Guinea morphometry of solution depressions also stressed the role of centripetal fluvial action in them as a result of high-intensity rainstorms, and is supportive. Nevertheless, it is unlikely that the earlier stages in Lehmann's scheme apply to all cockpit karsts. Thus, on the lower Kikori River, PNG, where karst is developed in Miocene limestone in broad, shallow folds of Plio-Pleistocene age, it seems unlikely there was any planation and development of valleys of normal kind before the karst modelling.

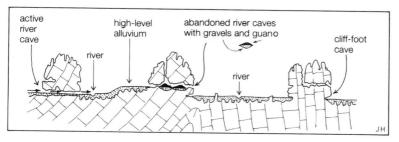

Figure 74 Schematic section through tower karst as in Kinta valley, Malaysia.

Although some have regarded tower karst (figure 74) as a later stage of development of cockpit karst (e.g. Gerstenhauer 1960; Pfeffer 1969), most authors have thought it independent in evolution, differing from structural causes. Among the favourable factors have been cited low primary porosity (Verstappen 1960a), great compaction and widely spaced planes of weakness (Renault 1959), great depth of karst (Sunartadirdja and Lehmann 1969), subjacent development beneath superficial deposits (Monroe 1969), with the opposite conditions leading to cockpit karst.

Vertical and overhanging lower slopes of the residual hills; areal predominance of swampy, alluvial plains and surface drainage around the towers; flat-floored depressions basically of polje type within the towers; deep karst corridors separating some towers niggardly; accompanying karst margin plains; horizontal tunnel caves through towers so that polje levels may be governed by the outflow (Ger. *Vorfluter*); abandoned, higher-level caves marked by big guano deposits, with derived phosphates, and bulky stalagmites – all are characteristics common in the tower karsts of the Kinta valley, Perak (Crowther 1982b), of Sarawak (Wilford 1964, Wilford and Wall 1965), of the Sierra de los Organos, Cuba (Lehmann *et al.* 1956), of southern China and its neighbours (Wissmann, 1954; Gellert 1962; Silar 1965; Yuan 1981; Zhang 1980).

Most attention has been directed at mechanisms leading to oversteepening of the flanks of the residuals. For a long time lateral solution undercutting by river floods and swampwaters was relied upon, of which the chief evidence was in the form of *foot caves* – low-roofed, narrow caves elongated along tower margins, with occasional passages leading inwards more deeply (figure 75; plate 42). Swamp slots and solution notches are smaller features which may accompany them or occur independently (see chapter 5). Jennings (1976) mapped the distribution of foot caves round Bukit Batu, Selangor, Malaysia, and came to the conclusion that their frequency of occurrence was compatible with this mechanism being the prime factor in development of towers. However, this was contingent on foot caves being essentially developed in subsoil locations, so that actively forming ones would not be widely visible today.

Others have thought that the role of foot caves has been overemphasized. Miotke (1973) stressed the role of subsidence along the margins of the sand-covered plains between the towers of Puerto Rican plains. This was regarded as arising from water being fed to the plains'

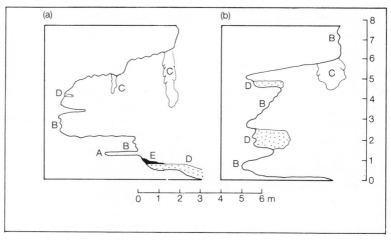

Figure 75 Foot caves, Kinta valley, Malaya, after Walker (1956): (a) in Gunong Temperong; (b) in Gunong Rapat. A, swamp slot; B, solution notches; C, stalactite; D, alluvium; E, bat guano.

Plate 42 A foot cave in Gunung Rapat, Kinta Valley, Perak, Malaysia, about 7 m high. Successive incurves are suggestive of progressive lowering of the soil level and exposure of smoothed solution notches.

margins, only to be lost in 'sumideros' there and creating caves beneath. This undermines the flanks of the towers where collapse occurs. Depressions round the sides of towers are found in the Kinta Valley also, and McDonald (1975) thinks that the slow engulfment of lakes in such peripheral depressions in Belize tower karst is more important than foot cave formation. In the Maros karst, Sulawesi, Indonesia, foot caves are important, but McDonald (1976) regards them as having been formed predominantly by mechanical fluvial action. For him, lateral solution has been grossly exaggerated in its role in tower formation. The same standpoint is taken by P. Smart (1981) with reference to the Gunung Mulu karst in eastern Sarawak. Two of the more isolated towers in this area were examined closely by McDonald and Ley (pers. comm.), and they argue strongly for the formation of these foot caves by lateral erosion of allogenic rivers.

Asymmetry in the residual hills in northern Puerto Rico has attracted attention since Thorp (1934) attributed it to greater rainfall and solution on windward eastern sides, giving gentler slopes there. Monroe (1966), alternatively, proposed thicker superficial *induration* – formation of calcrete – on the eastern sides because more frequent wetting and drying there caused more solution and reprecipitation in the profile. The thinner caprock on the western side was more easily breached to steepen those flanks. More detailed later work has undermined both of these interpretations by finding that the asymmetry does not have a simple east–west pattern (Day 1978) and that the case-hardening is remarkably uniform in thickness and is not patterned on the asymmetry (Ireland 1979). Day finds that the steep sides correlate with the streamsinks (sumideros) and that local undermining of hill flanks is responsible. Some north–south asymmetry is explicable by various effects of a gently northward dip of the rocks.

In northern Puerto Rico Monroe (1969) has explored the role of a former cover of superficial deposits, the marine blanket sands. Not only is this cover regarded as the cause of tower karst on bedrock formations that are in cockpit karst where the cover did not reach, but also it is thought to cause ramparts – linear ridges of limestone – along the edges of marine terraces and also across the karst along river valleys (figure 76(a),(b)). Greater solution beneath the blanket sands away from the steep slopes and surface induration of the exposed rock of the latter are thought to combine to produce these elevated margins by differential erosion. Circular ramparts also are described from Okinawa, where collapse dolines in emerged reefs provide steep slopes round which annular ridges develop, with covers reducing the surface of the rest of the

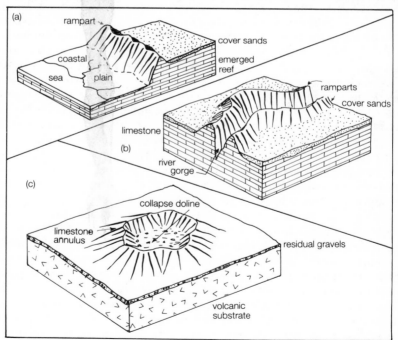

Figure 76 Ramparts: (a) along the margin of a marine terrace; (b) along a river valley; (c) around a collapse doline. Based on Monroe (1969) and Flint et al. (1953).

terrace around (figure 76(c)) (Flint *et al.* 1953). There has been an objection from Ireland (1979) that in the Puerto Rican area calcrete can be traced from the tower slopes beneath the blanket sands of the plains between and therefore the towers antedate the emplacement of the sands. The various kinds of ramparts remain intriguing problems which should attract further attention.

Tropical limestone towers are not always set in alluvial plains. In Malaysia many stand with customary abruptness on steep granite slopes; in New Guinea (Jennings and Bik 1962) and elsewhere they often rise from supporting conical or pyramidal limestone hills. It is easier to understand how the sharp angle around the foot of towers is initiated and maintained in the first circumstances than in the second, since the limestone–granite contact is the line of both entry and emergence of water. This resembles in some respects the tower karst on the margins of some 'interior valleys' in Jamaica, which are floored by impervious basement (Sweeting 1958). The second circumstance, where a cliff rises from generally a 30–40° bedrock Richter slope along a nickline which commonly rises and falls in level and certainly transgresses structure, does not yet appear to have been seriously studied.

Though climate is moderated underground, mean air and water temperatures do range significantly from cave to cave. Nevertheless, large geomorphic differences between mid-latitude and tropical caves have not been thought to occur, though minor differences such as pronounced guano corrosion of bedrock and the good development of phototropic bedrock 'sticks' (Bull and Laverty 1982) are present. Ford (1971) suggested that epiphreatic caves are more common relatively in tropical karsts but explained this in terms of young limestone with greater than usual primary permeability. Yet the same applies to Malaysian caves, where the limestones are old and highly compacted, depending on joints for permeability. Earth history makes it unlikely in the extreme that such structural factors are tied to latitude.

If speleogenetic mechanisms are the same in kind everywhere, their rates of operation might still be different and quantitatively the response could vary. However, depth in caves depends in the first instance on available relief and depth of suitable limestone, and thus the deepest known caves are in the mid-latitude Alps and Pyrenees. The longest cave by far is the Flint Ridge–Mammoth Caves system in mid-latitude; here, nearly horizontal limestones allow of great extension with a thickness permitting much replication vertically, but protective capping of sandstone to permit survival of higher levels is critical (Palmer 1981). This leaves volume, and it is in this respect that very large chambers in tropical caves have come to the fore, if only latterly because of understandably late efforts in exploration, e.g. Alam Cavern, Gua Tempurong, Perak (Crowther 1978). As yet this point can be made only tentatively (Jennings 1981b). The wide and deep collapse dolines of New Britain,

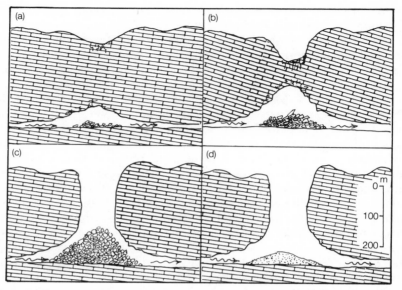

Figure 77 The evolution of a doline-aven at Nare, New Britain, PNG, after Maire (1981). A cockpit and a breakdown dome have developed one above the other (a) and (b), leading to collapse (c) and (d).

named 'dolines-avens' by their French explorers (Maire 1981) (figure 77) and reaching widths over 300 m and depths of over 350 m, are surface expressions of large voids below. It is elsewhere in the tropics that matching features are to be found – and, one can hardly fail to mention at this juncture, in other rocks, such as quartzite, as well as in limestone.

Undoubtedly, there has been enormous removal of limestone to create most of the distinctive tropical karst styles, and with particular regional instances this has happened quickly. A bioclimatic explanation has long been firmly held (Lehmann 1936; Birot 1954). Chemical reactions and mass transfer in solutes proceed more rapidly with higher temperature; high rainfall and high intensity of rainfall should make for rapid solution and removal; rapid plant growth and decay and intense microbial activity with high soil P_{CO_2} should make tropical water very aggressive.

Long-term measures of carbonate content from karst springs, e.g. from seasonally humid parts of Madagascar (Rossi 1976), have shown that high values can be sustained through the year, with highest values obtaining in the wet season when soil carbon dioxide values are at their greatest. It is more common to measure high CO_2 levels in tropical soils than in mid-latitude ones (cf. Pitman 1978), but, within a given karst, measures are so variable that the limited data available can scarcely be said to prove the 'botanic hothouse' viewpoint (Miotke 1974). However, it seems likely that methods of measuring soil carbon dioxide are inappropriate for these problems; saturated subcutaneous flows in karst in Perlis, western Malaysia, have calcite concentrations far greater than measured P_{CO_2} in the soils there (Crowther 1982a).

This bioclimatic interpretation has been opposed from more than one quarter. Corbel (1959) relied theoretically on low-saturation equilibria for CO_2 and carbonates with high temperature and empirically on low-carbonate determinations in tropical karst waters; in addition, absolute precipitation is proportionately reduced more to its effective level by greater evapotranspiration here. As has been discussed earlier in this chapter, rates of limestone removal so far obtained do not separate tropical from mid-latitude types of karst. Protagonists of high rates in tropical karst point out that such determinations are of net loss and that transfer within a karst area may be greater in the tropics because of readier redeposition in the form of speleothems and surface tufa and travertine.

Corbel (1958) also employed historical arguments to explain the fact of great karst elaboration in the tropics. He postulated greater age for tropical karst types, but tectonic activity suffers no climatic limits and both old and young karsts phenomena are found in all latitudes. Much of the classical tropical karst of the Caribbean and southeast Asia belongs to Alpine orogenic belts. Likewise, Corbel's argument that Pleistocene glacial and periglacial periods interrupted mid-latitude karst development is counterbalanced by our present knowledge that the same cold periods were drier periods in much of the tropics, where rates of solution would have been cut down by reduced water availability, though evapotranspiration would also have been lower because of lowered temperature and smaller biomass. This factor must have operated, for example, in the north-east Queensland karst, since palynological evidence from nearby Atherton Tableland shows that, between 10 000 and 80 000 BP, less hygrophytic vegetation (implying lower precipitation) prevailed than before or since.

Certainly, the massive quantity of palaeo-environmental research that has taken place in the tropics since Corbel wrote has demonstrated that the climates of low latitudes have been anything but stable in the Pleistocene. There have been both major altitudinal (Flenley 1979) and latitudinal changes (Goudie 1983b) in climate and vegetation, and ancient ergs, indicative of marked aridity, have been identified by remote sensing and field study in many savanna and rain-forest environments. Conversely, it has also been demonstrated that at certain times fluvial and lacustrine activity have been rather greater than today. Most landforms have not evolved under long-continued climatic stability, even in the cores of the great rainforest belts of the equatorial regions.

Further reference is now necessary to some of the morphological evidence cited earlier this chapter in order to countervail the argument that many tropical karst types depend on that bioclimatic environment. The Nahanni karst at the taiga–tundra boundary in north-west Canada is cut up by karst corridors, precipitous cenotes and cliff-walled poljes, and a few towers. Jennings (1981b) argues nevertheless that this karst differs substantially from the limestone ranges in north-west Australia, to which Brook and Ford (1978) likened it. Fields of towers are lacking and occasional towers are present in many karst contexts, e.g. as plateau outliers (Fr. *buttes-témoins*); also, pediments typical of the Australian tropical karst are absent in the Nahanni. Moreover, there may have been more time available for its formation than these authors allow, given the possibility that some ice masses fail to erode their substrate. On the other hand, polygonal karst with bold relief in moderate temperature regimes, as at high altitude in New Guinea and as at mid-latitudes in Waitomo, NZ, does give much support to Williams (1978) in his case that high water availability and dense rainforest are sufficient conditions for it and that high temperatures are not essential. At very least, it must be admitted that there is not such a gulf between tropical and mid-latitude karst as has been assumed in the past.

Overall rates of denudation will not resolve these issues, and Ford and Drake (1982) point to the distribution of solution within karsts as the key. W. B. White (1984) has tackled this broadly on a mathematical basis. Given the characteristic high intensity of tropical rains, there is greater liability for stripping of soils from the more susceptible parts and thereby to induce greater variations in the P_{CO_2} of water attacking the rock. Rainfall intensity and fast water movement also prolong aggressiveness. The undersaturated solution kinetics of these circumstances imply pronounced differential solution and so lead to the drastic geometry of much tropical karst. More empirical studies directed at the internal operations of karst systems are required to test such calculations.

11   Coast and Karst

It is typical of karst that its processes result in a special prominence in continental landscapes of vertical and horizontal forms. Bedrock coasts tend to the same pattern because of the edgeplane action of the sea; these intrinsic coastal traits are exaggerated in free karst forms.

Cliffs

Marine cliffs tend to be more continuous in karst because of underground drainage eliminating valleys, and to be more nearly vertical because of the reduced availability of water for slope processes. The Cretaceous chalk cliffs of England and France accentuate these tendencies because the formation is mostly of weak limestone and the seas have high wave energy. Dry valleys undulate the crest of these cliffs but otherwise do not affect them; these truncated valleys are called 'valleuses' in Normandy and 'crans' in the Boulonnais. Adjustment of valley longprofiles to cliff recession is impossible without significant streamflow.

The mechanically weak and soluble chalk is unfavourable to stack development, though stacks are present at Flamborough Head in Yorkshire; the Needles in the Isle of Wight owe their existence to an exceptionally hard zone of the chalk and to its nearly vertical attitude there.

Continuity in the Bunda and Baxter Cliffs of the dry Nullarbor Plain in horizontal Tertiary limestones with a stronger member above weaker ones is extreme, and provoked attempts at explanation even from the first seaborne explorer, Flinders (plate 43). Stacks are rare, perhaps even absent, over hundreds of kilometres of cliff, though the Twins at the Head of the Bight is a stack in Pleistocene dune limestone. Nearly vertical to overhanging profiles are exceedingly common, but so are rockfall rubble piles. Excavation of shallow marine caves leads to these collapses; notches and platforms are not frequent. Mechanical action of waves is powerful here, but nothing is known about the role of solution. Solution will at least assist wave attack by removal of debris as solutes, adding to loss by transport of solid particles. As yet, no karst caves debouching in

H

Plate 43 Part of the Bunda Cliffs of the Nullarbor Plain, showing great continuity of marine cliffs in horizontal, pure Eocene and Miocene limestones in a dry climate.

the cliffs are known; they are sure to be rare because of the sparsity of caves inland. The cliffs were much reduced in angle by subaerial weathering during last Glacial low sea levels; these degraded cliffs survive behind emerged and prograded coastal plains. Along the present shoreline they have been almost entirely removed, failing to persist even partially in a slope-over-wall profile, owing to the conjuction of a weak geological structure and the strong attack of the Southern Ocean over the last 6000 years, when sea level was at its present level, or within a metre or two of it.

Mechanically strong carbonate rocks and more complex structures naturally give rise to cliffed coast of a different aspect. Though the folded and faulted Carboniferous limestone coast of south Pembrokeshire, Wales (Leach 1933), matches those already discussed in precipitousness and continuity (within a smaller regional compass), it differs in its irregularity in plan, and its diversification by many caves, arches, blowholes, geos and even stacks. Limestone can give rise to these smaller coastal landforms because solution cavities of terrestrial origin in the rock mass under wave attack provide ready-made opportunity for the effects of air compression and decompression (implosion), and facilitate deep entry of abrasion tools to open up planes of weakness still further. The partial pressure of CO_2 in air trapped in cavities by waves is

216

undoubtedly increased by compression, but whether there is significant opportunity for this to enhance solution of the rock may be questioned. Sea caves may capture part of karst caves, as on Cabrera Island in the Balearics (Montoriol-Pous 1971). In middle Holocene times, the sea invaded Pollsalagh, Poulcraveen and Doolan Cave in Clare, Ireland – all karst caves.

Shore Platforms

Cliffs may plunge below sea level and steep slopes may also submerge without interruption, yet generally shore platforms front them. In karst, shore platforms are more likely to be exposed to view since supplies of sand and shingle that might cover them may be in restricted supply. Bird (1984) identifies three basic types: (a) intertidal, where mechanical wave erosion is dominant and produces a sloping platform reaching below low tide; (b) high tide, where water layer weathering through wetting and drying and associated chemical actions fashions a subhorizontal surface close to high tide mark; and (c) low tide, where erosion of biological origin and by solution results in a subhorizontal surface around low tide mark.

The dominance of varieties of low tide platform is to be expected in karst, but high wave energy and a supply of tools from the karst itself or of allocthonous origin which may have drifted either alongshore or onshore ensure that sloping platforms are to be found, e.g. along the Cretaceous chalk coasts already discussed through the provision of durable tools in the form of flints from the chalk. However, even here, on the lower platform seaward of flint shingle ridges storing water, solution combines with abrasion to cut parallel sets of grooves running down to low-water mark and below (Guilcher 1953).

Horizontal platforms may be backed by concave abrasion ramps where other processes play important roles, as in aeolian calcarenites at the Head of the Bight, Nullarbor Plain, and at Warrnambool, Victoria; there is always sufficient percentage of quartz grains in these rocks to provide the necessary abrasives.

Low tide platforms are associated with low wave energy, warm waters and carbonate-rich rocks are frequently accompanied by notches in the cliff behind. Notches, pans and pits are taken by many to be morphological evidence of solution despite the saturation of sea water with calcium carbonate. The explanation is thought to be biochemical. At night water on the platforms is lower in pH and higher in CO_2 than during the day because of emission of CO_2 by algae and invertebrates, leading to solution of calcium carbonate. The reverse is true during the day through plant and animal respiration, and finely divided calcium carbonate is precipitated, which is swept away by water movement, though some may adhere to ridges that dry out. The time of tidal stages during the day will influence these processes. Deepening of pools by solution appears to have a lower limit near to the low water level. Guilcher (1958) considers that wetting and drying has a mechanically disintegrative effect on many limestones and this contributes to the formation of littoral platforms in karst.

However, others think that the lateral cutting of notches and lowering of the platform are due more to the indubitable destruction of carbonate-rich rocks by plants such as blue-green algae and a wide range of animals that graze, browse, rasp, burrow and bore into the rock, producing pipes, perforations, galleries, tunnels, cavities, burrows and boreholes (McLean 1974; Trudgill 1976a). Different tolerances for exposure above water level commonly enforce a strict zonation of the different organisms and so of consequent forms.

Also influencing shore platforms, even though these are dominantly erosional forms, is biological protection and construction, especially of

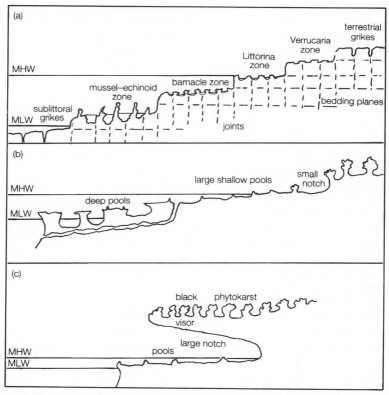

Figure 78 The zonation of forms in limestone shore platforms, after Lundberg (1977b), Guilcher (1953) and Wentworth (1939): (a) Burren, Clare, Ireland; (b) Atlantic Coast, Morocco; (c) Oahu, Hawaii.

calcareous algal crusts and rims. A higher rim on the outer edge of broad platforms is attributed to wave splash promoting algal growth there even at low tide.

The interaction of wave action, tides, solution and biological processes results in great and distinctive variety of shore platforms in carbonate rocks, with wave energy, tidal range and temperature in prime control (Guilcher 1953). A few examples must suffice.

Figure 78(a) illustrates a typical profile from Clare, Ireland, which can be used as an indication of coastal karst in cool temperate, high wave energy and macrotidal conditions (Lundberg 1977b). In the terrestrial zone solution is strictly governed by joints, and joint enlargement is also the rule in the sublittoral zone of permanent immersion. The littoral zone between those two is not regulated closely by these planes of weakness but by the ecology of the organisms involved. Uppermost is the *Verrucaria* zone of sharp-edged shallow pans affected by wave spray, rain and lichen growth. Next comes the *Littorina* zone, with deeper, more rounded and crowded pans attributed to limpet erosion. In the barnacle zone the pans have undercut walls; the ridges are covered with barnacles which tend to smooth them. The hollows are larger, deeper and more connected in the mussel-echinoid zone. The echinoids drill hemispherical holes over the bottoms of the hollows and mussels live on intervening ridges; bioerosion appears most rapid in this zone.

Ley (1979) gives a very different picture from the Bristol Channel, also macrotidal and of high wave energy. Applying a general measure of shape to the detail of the shore platforms here, he finds microrelief greatest just below mid-tide. This is correlated with greatest frequency of occupation by the swash zone, where solution, quarrying and abrasion are most active and dynamic equilibrium prevails. Above, the features are gradually being developed as the platform eats into the land; below, they are gradually destroyed through lateral erosion becoming dominant. Ley's discussion is entirely in terms of physical processes, surprisingly.

Guilcher (1953) gives the Atlantic coast of Morocco as an example of warm temperate, mesotidal but still energetic conditions (figure 78(b)). The terrestrial zone is marked by larger and sharper pitting than in Ireland; it is known to form within a few decades from historical data. Next come small, flat-floored pools with overhanging edges. Reaching down from the mean high water mark are terraced, shallow but large pools with flat bottoms separated by long, continuous ridges of bedrock covered by barnacles which protect them. Significantly, behind the pool terraces there is in places a notch or nip. On the outer margin of the platform there are much deeper holes, reaching below mean low water mark with pipes leading back to blowholes.

On many tropical karst coasts, dominantly in 'coral' reefs and microtidal areas, such a notch, of solutional and bioerosional origin, is much larger and is commonly the dominant feature separating a planed or

Plate 44 Low tide notch on Aldabra c. 2 metres high. Photo by Steve Trudgill.

terraced bench below from the spray-pitted zone above (Wentworth 1939 (figure 78(c), plate 44). The latter may overlap the former because of a projecting visor which may be 2 m wide (plate 44). Hills (1971) thinks that visors in aeolian calcarenites in southern Australia are partly the result of induration through carbonate precipitation from the seawater in voids. Where the bench is terraced, the ridges holding up the shallow pools may be entirely algal in construction or else low bedrock ridges protected by algal crusts. Stacks can assume a mushroom form through this impressive development of notch and visor. Deep notch and benches are found in highly consolidated Palaeozoic limestones in the Langkawi Islands, Malaysia (Hodgkin 1970). The pitted zone above the visor is rougher, more ragged and more honeycombed in tropical than in mid- and high-latitude equivalents; it is hideous to traverse. It is often dark grey to black in colour and this points to the cause, namely algal boring. This is *black phytokarst,* which Folk *et al.* (1973) appropriately describe from Hell in the Cayman Islands in the Caribbean (chapter 4).

Rates of surface lowering measured by the micro-erosion meter on karst shore platforms are comparatively few. But they do suggest that, whereas there is a difference in mid-latitude karsts between terrestrial bare rock and subsoil sites on the one hand and marine platform sites on the other (with the latter having the faster rates), this is not true at Aldabra Atoll in the tropics (Trudgill 1976a,b) where they have the same sort of range. On the other hand, Trudgill (1977) found platform losses much greater at Aldabra (1.01 mm a^{-1}), compared with losses at such sites in Clare, Ireland (0.20 mm a^{-1}). Nevertheless, he attributed most of the difference to the Aldabra reef limestone being much less consolidated than the Carboniferous limestone of Clare; the high losses (0.96 mm a^{-1}) that Kirk (1977) determined on weak Tertiary limestone at Kaikoura, New Zealand, support this stance.

The formation of *beachrock* – beach sands indurated by calcium carbonate precipitation at the water table in warm climates – is not a direct concern of this book, but the patterns of rounded hollows, which develop on exposure of beachrock from beneath sands, may be mentioned here appropriately, because solution and bioerosion as well as abrasion contribute to their excavation. Zonation of these features, however, is dependent mainly on length of exposure, consequent case-hardening and joint development (Hopley and Mackay 1978).

Karst in Coastal Dune Limestones

Karst may develop when calcareous dune sands of biogenic origin consolidate into aeolian calcarenites. Once these sands are fixed by vegetation, diagenesis of the originally dominantly aragonitic and high-magnesium calcitic mineral grains is crucial to lithification, yet it is a complex matter (see Gardner (1983) for summary). There is leaching by percolating soil water either incongruently, removing Mg^{2+} selectively, or congruently, disolving whole grains and then precipitating low-magnesium calcite cement as a result of evaporation or degassing of CO_2 or supersaturation with respect to calcite when pore water is in equilibrium with aragonite. In addition, there is wet calcitization of aragonite *in situ*, producing new low-magnesium calcitic spar. The roles of these different mechanisms in different hydrological zones are not yet fully assessed. Field observation makes it clear that first there is a case-hardening effect in the zone of aeration, as it were freezing dune form, with only localized induration below along roots and bedding-planes. But lithification also takes place in the saturated zone lower down. Eventually the whole mass may be calcreted and any loose sand remaining at the surface deflated to expose rock. Successive invasions of sand reveal the progress of these changes.

Most of the invasions occurred during Quaternary high sea level stands. The multiple sequence of dune ridges in the lower south-east of South Australia is the product of combined glacio-eustatic sea level oscillations and tectonic uplift over a period of more than 700 000 years (Cook *et al.* 1977). In the coastal fringe of the south-west of West Australia the ages of a lesser number of invasions are not known, though one calcarenite is less than 100 000 years old.

It is here that the most elaborate karst is found, with underground drainage, well decorated large caves and collapse dolines. To a certain

221

Coast and Karst

extent this karst is syngenetic (Jennings 1968) in that its development accompanied consolidation of the sands; some caves occur in only partially consolidated sands even now. This leads to some distinctive features: calcite deposition is a constituent part of solution pipe creation; some gorges are depositional in origin; collapse plays a precocious part in cave formation; differential lithification and the form of the underlying crystalline basement affect it also. Apart from young collapse dolines, it can be difficult to distinguish between closed depressions of karst origin and primary dune hollows. Confusion of this nature is compounded in the lower south-east of South Australia, where the Pleistocene dune ridges were emplaced on Oligocene–Miocene marine limestone.

Emerged Biogenic Reefs and Marine Terraces

Marine limestones are the host rock for most karst forms but the emergence of Quaternary 'coral' reefs has done more than provide the karst rock in conferring their primary depositional relief on young karst formed of them, preserved by karst immunity. Verstappen (1960b) describes various styles of such relief, which vary according to the steepness of the basement, vigour of reef growth and course of uplift (figure 79), and he also discusses the course of their denudation. Rapid emergence of fringing reefs on the north Huon coast of Papua New Guinea has left a staircase of marine constructional terraces in this way in a tropical humid climate, ranging to about 450 000 BP in time and up 500 m in height (Chappell 1974). Narrow, close-set sequences relate to times of rapid negative movement when tectonic uplift and falling eustatic sea level operated together; broad terraces with lagoon facies as well as reef rim mark stillstands, when rising land and rising sea level

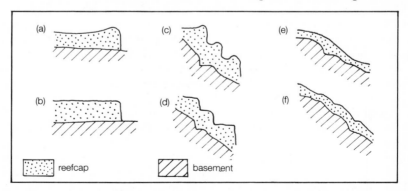

Figure 79 Types of emerged reef relief according to Verstappen (1960a). A plateau reefcap on a broad platform: (a) with good reef growth, (b) with poor growth. Terraced reefcap on steep basement with intermittent uplift: (c) with good reef growth, (d) with poor growth. Undulating reefcap with thin reef: (e) with no reef edges, (f) with occasional reef edges owing to rapid growth.

were matched. The main modification of their original form so far has been the development of parallel valleys crossing the terraces; their cross-sectional form changes with the age of the reef (Dunkerley 1980).

Most of Barbados consists of a flight of emerged reef terraces with a basically similar history to that of the Huon peninsula mentioned above. The terraces carry many solution dolines, but the features that have attracted most attention are the systems of dry valleys, which run mainly radially across the terraces at right angles to the former shorelines, though a few run along former lagoons. Fermor (1972) argues, from increasing density of these valleys with age of terrace, that they have not gone dry as a result of progressive development of underground drainage. Instead, he attributes the desiccation to reduced rainfall intensity, disfavouring surface runoff; dry valley density is closely related to present rainfall intensity.

Emerged atolls such as Rennell Island in the Solomons have an annular outer ridge which was the former reef and a swampy interior plain which was the former lagoon. On Niue Island, in the southern Pacific Ocean, the former passage to the lagoon is now a dry valley through the peripheral ridge (figure 80) (Schofield 1959). With a considerable rainfall, the island has a thick freshwater body beneath it, deepest beneath the former atoll rim (Jacobson and Hill 1980). Kitava in Papua New Guinea is basically similar to Rennell, but, as with the other Trobriand Islands, tilting has made the former lagoon into a surface which rises from sea level on the west towards remnants of the former reef proper which are now ridges on eastern and northern sides (Ollier 1975). A variety of caves, of both vadose and phreatic nature, is the chief karst aspect, though there are also collapse dolines and cenotes in association with them. They have been formed by freshwater, which

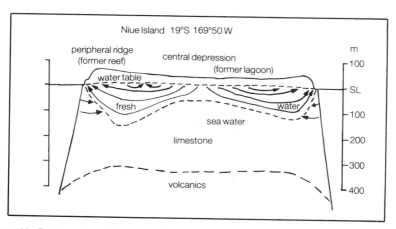

Figure 80 Emerged atoll of Niue Island, Pacific Ocean, after Jacobson and Hill (1980); its high rim affects the form of the freshwater lens.

223

forms a lens throughout every island except the smallest, Vakuta, where there is a fringe of brackish water. In the latter, caves may have formed through solution by this mixed water. Ollier thinks that none of the caves in these islands is a primary form inherited from the reefs prior to uplift. All water movement appears to be slow and an absence of scallops is attributed to this.

There *are* primary caves in active coral reefs, as Vasseur (1974) describes from reefs at Tuléar, Madagascar; they extend backwards from the grooves of spur-and-groove relief on the outer face of the reef. Iliffe (1981) describes similar primary reef caves on the seaward face of Bermuda's fringing reefs. Nevertheless, emerged caves of this type have yet to be recognized.

Marine terraces may be cut in older limestones and then emerge tectonically. Caves developed in the karst may have definable genetic relationships with the marine benches (Williams 1982b). At Paturau in South Island, the upper part of Wet Neck Cave is graded to a major marine terrace there and large marine shingle was washed into it along with the worn fragments of marine molluscs; this implies that part at least of the cave is older than the terrace and it contains a stalagmite dated 450 000 BP, effectively beyond uranium–thorium range. Cascade Cave runs below the terrace and has a speleothem dated at 275 000 ± 70 000 BP. These determinations date the terrace to at least the Interglacial before the last, and some idea of the rate of tectonic uplift here can be obtained.

Submerged Karst Coasts

Karst phenomena in the sea have been recognized since classical Greek times in the form of submarine springs (chapter 4), identifiable by and useful for the rising freshwater, though in calm conditions they can also be seen even from a distance as circular boils (cf. Milanović 1979).

On some coasts, karst landforms can be followed from the land into the sea with scarcely any modification. This is plainly the case with tower karst of Haiphong Bay in Vietnam (figure 81) and in the Langkawi Islands of both Malaysia and Thailand, where towers of varied dimensions make up an archipelago of islands and islets in a shallow sea (to −20 m in the former locality). The sea in some cases has flooded depressions enclosed within large towers through cave passages, places that have at lest the reputation of being former hideouts of pirates. Marine erosion could not have created such patterns of islands, and submergence of terrestrial relief is implied.

Semicircular coves in karst coasts may simply be the result of the interplay of marine erosion and geological structure, as is the case with Lulworth Cove in the chalk in Dorset, England. But others are certainly

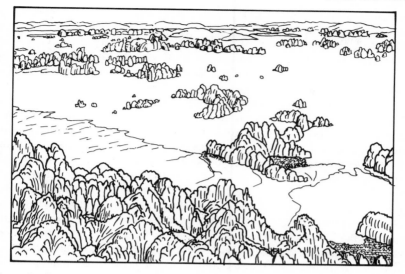

Figure 81 Drowned tower karst, Haiphong Bay, Vietnam, after Wissmann (1954). A distant archipelago of impervious rocks protects the towers from marine erosion; the shallow sea is fringed with tidal flats and mangroves.

modified karst features. Paskoff and Sanlaville (1978) distinguish two kinds of karst cove in Malta. The first, exemplified by Dweyra Bay on Gozo (figure 82), is the result of marine erosion breaching the side of a collapse doline; Qawra, an immediately neighbouring feature, is a similar but unbreached circular cliffed depression simply flooded by the sea through a cave. Their second type, such as the Blue Grotto on the main island, is due to the sea eroding its way into a large cave system and causing subsequent roof collapse. Some of the submarine springs of the Adriatic coast of Yugoslavia lie so close to the cliffs as to create small

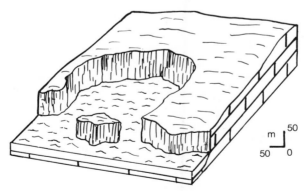

Figure 82 Dweyra Bay and Fungus Rock, Gozo, Malta, after Paskoff and Sanlaville (1978): a semi-circular cove created through sea invasion of a doline.

225

semicircular coves of a third type, caused by solution by the rising water – for example east of Omis, Croatia.

Related to these coves are gorge-like, coastal inlets such as the *calanques* of Provence, though the one leading to the Great Smoo Cave at Durness, Scotland, may be cited also to indicate that the form is widespread. They are more often continued inland in dry valleys, and this makes it clear that, not only are there different types, but there is a broader fundamental question about the extent to which karst features can develop below the sea without any change in the relative level of land and sea. Chardonnet (1948) explains the Provencal calanques as being due to the formation of caves to levels below the sea by freshwater solution and the destruction of the seaward side to allow the sea to enter without any change in its level. This might apply to cases like the Scottish example given above, but where the inlets are simply the continuations of valleys and match them in character, origin by submergence seems inescapable. At Malta, Paskoff and Sanlaville (1978) distinguish: (a) steep-walled calanques proper, e.g. Wied iz-Zurrieq; (b) wide and gentle-sided, 'glove-finger' calanques, common in the north-eastern sides of the islands, e.g. Salina Bay; (c) digitate calanques as at La Valetta, where a branching valley system has been drowned. These authors also categorize other calanques as having a cave roof collapse component, but they still envisage them as drowned dry valleys with caves beneath which collapse after marine invasion, e.g. the channel between Comino and Cominetto.

Related features on the east coast of Yucatan have been explained by a completely different mechanism by Back *et al.* (1984). Because of its greater density, seawater wedges inland beneath the terrestrial ground-water (the Ghyben–Herzberg effect). The outflow of freshwater never-theless usually reaches somewhat below sea level but entrains a return flow of seawater, with a mixing zone between (figure 83). In recent years it has been recognized that this mixing zone may be a locus of pronounced solution (cf. Panoš (1976) on Cuban karst coasts). In

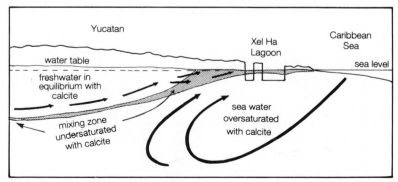

Figure 83 The discharge of brackish water from the mixing zone of terrestrial groundwater and a Ghyben–Herzberg wedge of oceanic water into a Yucatan coastal lagoon (after Back *et al.* 1984).

Yucatan the mix of freshwater, even if it is saturated with respect to calcite with 10–60 per cent of supersaturated seawater, is significantly undersaturated. 'Coves' (narrow, short coastal inlets here), fine-scale spongework in caves, collapsed caves near the coast and crescentic bays are all attributed to solution where this aggressive water reaches the coast. Rudnicki (1980) had earlier attributed cave formation along the coast of Apulia in southern Italy to this mixing, though here the resulting capacity to dissolve is thought to be confined to a mix up to 10 per cent seawater. There are Pliocene and Pleistocene emerged clifflines inland where the same hydrochemical situation will have prevailed at certain past times.

Marine charts, even from the days of line sounding, have led to the recognition of completely drowned features, e.g. two travertine dams with bases at −14 m near Skradin in the submerged lower part of the River Krka, Croatia. Roglić (1967) considers that these must have formed in the early Holocene; it was too cold for their biogenic deposition before that, and in any case the river was in an erosive phase and sea level would have returned to its normal level by 5000–6000 BP. However, there was also a phase of formation of karst depressions interrupting the river profile before the dams formed.

Larger karst depressions are surveyed beneath the sea in Sibenik Harbour and the Bay of Kotor, and the 23 km by 9 km Novigrad Bay is regarded as a polje invaded by the sea. Permanent freshwater lakes not far above sea level, such as Vransko, south-east of Zadar, and Vratna in the island of Cres (Gavazzi 1904), also appear to occupy the floors of poljes, which were deepened when sea level was lower relatively and became permanent lakes when rising sea level elevated surrounding water rest levels above their floors.

Sonic sounding permits the contouring and profiling at great depth of karst features such as the large closed depressions south of Florida at −300 to −500 m on a fault block above a fault scarp (G. F. Jordan 1954). They are between 40 and 160 m in depth and between 900 and 2200 m across. From the context, tectonic lowering explains their location. Nevertheless Pleistocene low sea levels may also have contributed, since phreatic circulation at great depth is thought to have been responsible for the deep, water-filled dolines of the Florida peninsula itself; R. H. Jordan (1950) reports artesian circulation in cavities of diameters in metres at −1000 m and some circulation to −1800 m beneath Florida. Springs at these levels are therefore expectable, but whether they could create depressions of this magnitude at the depths at which they are found is another question. Deep circulation close to the coast is known elsewhere, e.g. at −500 m in southern Debrogea, Roumania, by the Black Sea (Bleahu 1972).

Modern diving methods – free, diving chamber and submarine – have permitted direct observation of underwater karst features. Siffre (1961) reports grikes filled with terrestrial quartz gravels and red loams at −200 m off Toulon, Provence. This is below the limit generally given for Pleistocene glacio-eustatic low sea levels of the world ocean, but, of course, the Mediterranean fell even further because of the Gibraltar sill shutting it off and the aridity of much of its catchment starving it of water. Here, deep karst phenomena do not necessarily call for tectonic explanations.

Caves beneath the sea cannot yet be traced to such great depths for technical reasons, but in the western Mediterranean karst caves have been surveyed at depths as great as −50 m (Flemming 1983). Most submarine cave diving has been done in modern biogenic reefs, which will be discussed below separately because there are several aspects to be considered.

Karst Effects in Modern Reefs

Although the rival themes of tectonic subsidence and glacio-eustatic oscillations of sea level have long been central to controversy about the origins of barrier reefs and atolls, it is only latterly that the role of karst in reef development has come to be recognized as significant. During the Pleistocene, reefs have been subject to subaerial karst processes in each glacial low sea level stage, when the theoretical inference that they must have been largely exposed cannot be gainsaid. Drilling in reefs has exposed old surfaces of weathering and soil formation below present sea level and these have been extrapolated by seismic sounding.

However, the plainest evidence has come from diving, mainly in *blue holes*. These are deep holes in reefs, readily recognizable by the much darker blue colour of the water as seen at the surface. Some of these circular depressions are found to have cliffed walls, with rockfall ridges at their feet and caves leading off from the walls, and in these caves speleothems of indubitable subaerial formation have been found (figure 84(a)). These blue holes are drowned collapse dolines. Some of the best caves are found where the holes in their roofs, which reveal their presence, are quite small. So far they have been investigated chiefly in the Bahamas and off Belize. Detailed bathymetrical surveys, e.g. around Bikini and Truk, show that they are to be found widely. Dimensions given by Doran (1955) are so variable in depth/width ratio that it must be argued either that the collapse dolines differ widely in age and have suffered variable degradation of their sides to reduce that ratio drastically, or that some of them are of solution doline origin. Two blue holes in the Australian Great Barrier Reef (Backshall *et al.* 1979) appear to fall into the former category of collapse dolines which have suffered a great deal of modification, at least by burial with later marine sediment (figure 84(b)). Whereas many of the West Indian blue holes are so fresh in form that on that count they could be thought of as products of low sea level exposure of the last glacial stage, these Australian examples are referable to an earlier glacial stage for their terrestrial development.

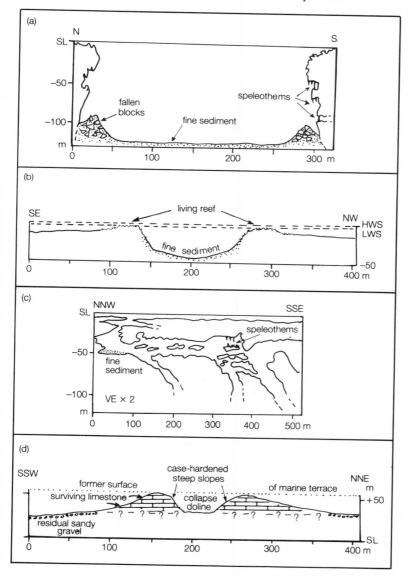

Figure 84 (a) A young blue hole, Lighthouse Reef, Belize, after Dill (1977); (b) an old, sedimented blue hole, Cockatoo Reef, Queensland, after Backshall *et al.* (1979); (c) a submerged cave with a dated speleothem leading from a blue hole, Andros Island, Bahamas, after Dill (1977); (d) collapse dolines rampart, Kawasaki, Okinawa, Japan, after Flint *et al.* (1953).

Dating evidence needs to be sought where possible, and the most striking result obtained so far has been from a cave off Andros Island in the Bahamas, entered through a small blue hole, in which stalagmites collected at a depth of −45 m have been dated by the uranium decay series as between 160 000 and 150 000 years old (figure 84(c)). This shows both that the cave must have formed prior to that time in the penultimate glacial stage or in an earlier one still, and that at that time sea level was below −42 m, allowing for 3 m of tectonic movement (Gascoyne et al. 1979).

There is good evidence that the shape of a reef formed in a previous interglacial time of high sea level but modified in the course of a subsequent glacial low sea level influences the course of fresh growth in the following interglacial, including the present one which we call the Holocene. Some reef scientists such as Purdy (1974) have related the patterns of present reefs to karst characteristics acquired by the earlier reef structure. Thus, it has been suggested that patch reefs may have grown upon the scattered towers of a tower karst into which the older reef mass was cut; that atolls derive, from the development of solution, rims round the margins of reefs when exposed; and that, similarly, ramparts developing along the sides of reef passes, which become valleys when exposed, are preferred for recolonization the next time they are submerged, so accentuating their character. Hopley (1982) reviews this antecedent karst hypothesis of reef configuration soberly and finds it applicable to the Great Barrier Reef only to a modest degree.

Sea Level Oscillations

Emergence and submergence have been segregated artificially above for simplicity's sake; in fact, oscillations of sea level are the rule, even though in particular regions a tectonic shift may be overriding. It is advisable now to consider the effects of such oscillations.

Bermuda is built of four carbonate formations comprising both marine and dune limestones, separated by three palaeosols. Corals and stalagmites have provided good opportunities for dating many of these events by uranium–thorium (Harmon et al. 1978); soil and cave development appear to take place chiefly in glacial low sea level times and emplacement of dunes in interglacials and interstadials. Caves are not found in the youngest formation and are most elaborate in the oldest, formed by a fresh groundwater body (Bretz 1960), with further sea level lowering allowing air to enter and speleothems to form. A contrary view has been defended recently by Palmer et al. (1977b), who considered that most of the cave excavation was performed at high sea level times near the coast in the zone of mixing above the Ghyben–Herzberg seawater intrusion; this was followed by roof collapse to create air-filled caves. The island has an intricate coast with many bays and sounds, which Bretz takes to be the product of much cave collapse, but Swinnerton (1929) thinks that only a few, such as Castle Bay, are of karst origin, most being due to flooding of primary dune hollows. Sea level oscillations between +16 m and −11 m over the last 200 000 years have been dated, though of course the deeper cold-period downswings of sea level escape measurement even here (figure 85).

Sea level does not act for karst as the ultimate base level in quite the same way as it does for fluvial relief on impervious rocks (Siffre 1961; Roglić 1965). Whether phreatic circulation can, on its own, develop outflows deep below sea level is still debatable, even though it can loop below it inland. What is certain is that outflows that have become submarine, either by tectonic subsidence or development during a former low sea level, can continue to function afterwards in submarine condition.

Oscillations of sea level can cause corresponding upwards and downwards movements of water tables and water rest levels inland in

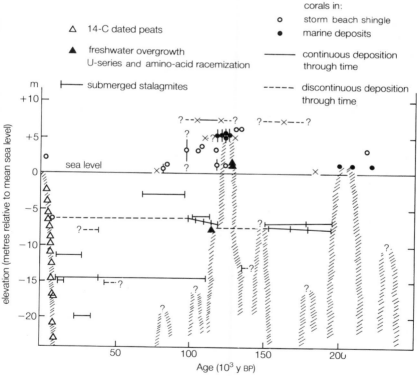

Figure 85   Sea level changes determined from speleothems in submerged caves and other sources in Bermuda, after Harmon et al. (1978) and Harmon et al. (1983).

231

free karst. The operation of this factor at short range from the shore is well illustrated in coastal karst caves in Mallorca, where carbonate pool deposits alternate with stalagmites deposited in the cave atmosphere (Gines *et al.* 1981). This is the result of sea level movements altering the groundwater level in these caves. $^{230}Th/^{234}U$ dating of some of these materials shows that the stalagmites were precipitated during glacial low sea levels and the subaqueous forms belong to high sea levels and range up to +35 m, the highest ones belonging to the Mindel–Riss Interglacial. In the warm Riss–Würm Interglacial there was much aragonite precipitation.

Long-range action of basically the same type is to be found in the Nullarbor Plain because groundwater gradients are so gentle. The long lakes in some of the deep caves have been shown by diving to reach below sea level, e.g. to −47 m in Koonalda Cave, which is 14 km from the coastal cliffs (Lewis 1979). More recent diving has found stalagmites and soil material 7 m below water level in Cocklebiddy Cave and also scallops up to 20 m above present water level (Grodzicki, 1985). Grodzicki interprets the evidence by oscillations of water level between +20 and −10 m. Although there is little dated evidence from the Nullarbor Plain for climatic change it is likely from reconstructions elsewhere in Australia that low sea level times were also climatically dry. It is possible, therefore, that both causes are involved in these water table oscillations in the Nullarbor Plain caves, which certainly helped in their formation by lowering the level at which solution chiefly operated.

12 The Historical Geomorphology of Karst

The history of karst landforms and drainage has perforce entered earlier pages, but it is appropriate to end this book on this theme, which is essentially synthetic of the particular aspects of previous chapters, all the more because the record of landscape evolution is often better preserved in karst than elsewhere (Palmer 1984). Nowadays the tendency is to view historical geomorphology as a sequence of episodes, each with its own rationale, whereas the classical approach was in terms of 'cycles', in which a particular course of landform evolution progressed either to completion or at least significantly along the way to it. The rapidity of change in exogenetic processes in the Quaternary and the persistence of tectonic movements through that period at rates comparable with those processes lies behind that switch in viewpoint. It is estimated that climate such as is experienced now prevailed over only some 10 per cent of the last 700 000 years. But the tempo of geomorphic change varies much between different parts of the world – in some being very slow – so that it is unhelpful to let the older conceptual framework fade into oblivion.

The Karst Cycle

Soon after W. M. Davis's 'cycle of erosion' made impact in Europe, theoretical conceptions of a karst cycle of erosion appeared from that of E. Richter in 1907 onwards. Of these, the most universally based was that of Grund (1914) (figure 86). With the creation of a landsurface, dolines develop at points favouring solution. In youth these are irregularly scattered, as in much European karst (figure 86(a)). Youth ends when dolines, increasing in size and numbers, destroy all vestiges of the initial surface and are separated by ridges only (b). Then the more favoured dolines expand at the expense of their neighbours, eliminating intervening divides. Uvalas develop in this way (c). Flat floors then appear in the depressions and cone-shaped hills result from ridge lowering. This is maturity, and is based on Grund's conception of

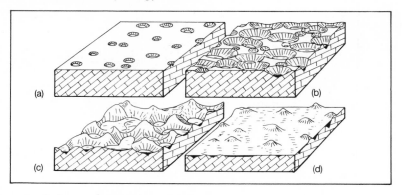

Figure 86 The karst cycle according to Grund (1914).

Jamaican and Javanese cockpit karst, though in fact it corresponds more with some kinds of montane karst in New Guinea (Jennings and Bik 1962). The whole surface is progressively lowered until depression floors reach the water table, when gentle streams run across them. At this stage there is much cave collapse in the remaining upstanding relief; collapse dolines and gorges result. Corrosion plains with scattered residual hills are the endpoint (figure 86(d)). Poljes are regarded as extraneous tectonic features which may introduce older forms into younger stages. Grund's amalgam of forms from diverse specific contexts would be criticized by those who favour climatic control as bringing together elements from mid-latitude and tropical karst forms which have their own rationale of development. Those who favour structural control would regard it as implying a particular geological structure, but Grund is not specific about this.

The scheme of Cvijić (1918; cf. Sanders 1921) is perhaps the best known and is based solely on Dinaric karst features. The structural conditions are specified as of a thick limestone mass sandwiched between impervious formations (figure 87). As the impervious cover is stripped off, the limestone inherits a normal surface drainage and a valley system develops (figure 87(a)). Solution opens up joints for readier infiltration of rain and engulfment of surface streams so that underground drainage takes over (b). Dolines form and there may also be tectonic poljes. At maximal karst development, dolines have taken over on interfluves as well as in valleys. Elaborate cave systems feed risings around the karst margin and poljes (c). Thereafter the karst is destroyed, with normal valleys reappearing; steepheads recess karst margins and poljes are planed afresh at lower levels, leaving some hums. Dolines and uvalas are breached by streams. Finally the impervious basement is exposed widely and only scattered hums remain of karst (figure 87(d)).

Partly because it does not claim universality, this scheme has been less

234

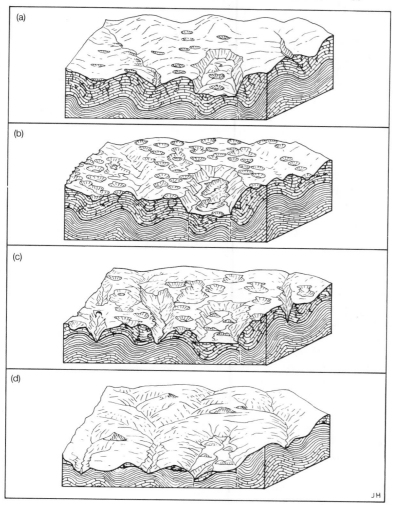

Figure 87 The karst cycle according to Cvijić (1918).

criticized, though it has been suggested that the impervious cover may not have enough opportunity to develop normal drainage through early development of subjacent dolines. It was restated by Gèze (1965), who elaborated the speleological aspects with free surface stream caves dominating the old-age stage after phreatic cave systems become most elaborate at maturity. However, Gèze did think that there would usually be interference with this cycle by tectonic and climatic factors. For the warm temperate karst of the King Country, NZ, where impervious beds survive over parts of the limestone, Williams (1982a) has deduced an

235

evolution that in several ways represents an elaboration of the Cvijić scheme.

Grund's scheme assumes that, with geology suitable for holokarst, karst processes will dominate landform evolution from the start, whereas in Cvijić's cycle, a fluvial landscape is impressed on the limestone mass by inheritance from overlying non-karst rocks. However, it takes time to develop underground circulation even on pure limestone with a favourable density of planes of weakness, so a fluviokarst may be the first stage, as, for example, H. Lehmann (1936) supposed for the Gunung Sewu in its tropical humid environment. Ford (1980) thinks that the factor of insufficient lapse of time for full karst to have eliminated this inevitable initial fluviokarst may have a wider climatic reach, certainly to include some Canadian karst forms. Steep relief has long been recognized as favouring fluvial action and retarding characteristic karst development (Grund 1910).

The converse idea is that of 'karst capital' of P. George (in Birot 1966), conceived in relation to Languedoc karsts in southern France. In polycyclic relief, an earlier phase of denudation may have reached a high degree of planation and so a later phase of rejuvenation inherits little or no surface relief which might help it on its course. On the other hand, downward-looping parts of cave systems may survive from one phase to another despite planation, hastening the later karst development. This concept is closely related to the two-cycle theory of cave development of W. M. Davis (1930).

A later cyclic scheme to be propounded was that by Jennings and Sweeting (1963) for the limestone ranges of north-western Australia outlined in chapter 9. Here all stages in the evolution of a karst are abundantly exemplified. A Tertiary planation surface survives on the karst from great expanses to small patches, with the only residuals rising above it developed on impervious inliers. Around the margins of these remnants, soil stripping and small-scale solution dissection along planes of weakness both expose the truncation of structures by the old surface and mark the beginning of the new cycle. There follow stages of giant grikeland, box-valley systems and pedimented tower karst. Finally, all remnants of projecting relief are removed, leaving gentle domes of pediment, the new surface of erosion.

It is possible that this modern pediplain is replacing a planation surface of different nature and that palaeokarst features are now coming to light that complicate this straightforward history (Jennings 1982a). Nevertheless, even these latter findings do not impugn the reality of that sequence of landform development. Jennings and Sweeting (1963) interpreted it in terms of the present short season of intense rainfall and long dry season, and Jennings (1981b) disputes the assertion of Brook and Ford (1978) that the high-latitude Nahanni karst possesses the same style. Nevertheless, this is not to deny their view that both karst areas are dependent for

236

much of their character on the highly compacted and massively jointed nature of the limestones found in both.

Climatic Change

Jennings and Sweeting (1963) recognized a major difficulty facing their climato-morphogenic interpretation of the karst of the limestone ranges; it is a karst style of great vigour suggesting active erosion, yet the precipitation is meagre (450–630 mm). This conflict made acceptance of their view impossible for some, as witness discussion by Birot (1966: 115–19). Birot favours inheritance from a former period of more humid tropical climate, as did Tricart and da Silva (1960) for the Bom Jesus de Lapa karst in similar tropical savanna climate in Brazil. Given the uncertainties about the relations between climate and karst discussed in the last chapter, it savours of circular argument to adopt such an explanation without independent evidence of an appropriate climatic history. Little is, in fact, known. Fixed deserts dunes lapping up against one of the most inland of the limestone ranges probably were mobilized during the last Glacial Maximum, and 200 km to the south–east Lake Gregory was very much larger for a period prior to 30 000 BP. Nevertheless, prolonged tropical humid climate must as yet be conservatively attributed to the Middle Miocene and earlier, and it is not certain that the cycle of erosion concerned goes back to that time. If it does, the subsequent seasonal but intense rainfall may have served to keep inherited forms sharp and fresh.

In central Europe, sedimentary evidence of climatic change is available to match postulates of inheritance of karst styles which are thought not to correspond with the present climate. The *Kuppenalb* of the Suabian Jura of southern Germany resembles tropical conekarst (Büdel 1951), and it is marked off on the south by a Middle Miocene marine cliff, with marine organism borings, which is now being exhumed. Even more like tropical conekarst is the western side of the Baljanica Mountains in Yugoslavia (Gavrilović 1969), where there is partial burial of the closed depressions between the domes, with sands, clays and lignites containing plant remains indicative of a subtropical to tropical humid climate. In the Moravian karst, Czechoslovakia, a more tower-like and older karst with pediments was buried partially to begin with by its own weathering products including lateritic materials, then more fully later by Upper Cretaceous marine sediments (Panoš 1964; Bosak 1981). The Late Jurassic and Early Cretaceous climate is regarded as having been tropical humid here. The Franconian Alb (Pfeffer 1981) provides a linking history between those of the Suabian Jura and those of Moravia. Here a karst of steep tropical residuals was partly buried by Upper Cretaceous marine sands and then in the Lower Tertiary the projecting hills were subdued in their form. Subsequently their buried parts have been re-exposed to some degree.

Considerations of climatic change arise also in eastern Asia. In the lower parts of this region, the various kinds of tropical karst are regarded as being in adjustment with present processes, but there is no doubt that they have a long history, as Glazek (1966) demonstrates for Vietnam; Gellert (1962) describes Mio-Pliocene lavas and sediments overlying some of the plains in tower karst in Guangxi. North-westwards into higher country in Guizhou and Yunnan, similar types of karst are found in a cooler climate, and the question of inheritance from warmer Tertiary climate presents itself. This is linked to the question of uplift (Silar 1965), which arises even more markedly in connection with Tibet. There, karst towers have been found at the elevation of 5200 m (Zhang 1980). Whether they represent a full development of karst of tropical style is not apparent from published photographs. Nevertheless, there is no doubt from palynological evidence from both sides of the Himalayas that much of the elevation of these high mountain ranges and of the Tibet Plateau came late and the exclusion of the humid and warm air of the south–west Monsoon from that part of inner Asia may not have happened until well into the Pleistocene.

Since the lateral solutional undercutting thought responsible for corrosional plains in the tropics has also been proposed for the formation of Yugoslavian poljes, it has been suggested by some that the latter are relict from a Pliocene subtropical humid climate (Roglić 1964a; Rathjens 1954). Furthermore, Melik (1955) proposed that cold periods in the Pleistocene had the effect of slowing down polje development so that the Tertiary forms survived. In these periods slopes became more active; frost wedging increased solifluction and landslips moved masses of regolith downslope, and rivers alluviated polje floors more abundantly. Thick layers of gravel, sands and clays accumulated and some of the underground passages were obstructed. Some high-lying poljes are filled to the level of the lowest col, and there has been no extension of their floors since that event (Rathjens 1960). According to Roglić (1964b) aggradation of glaciofluvial and periglacial fluvial deposits has led to the enlargement, even the creation, of polje floors in many Yugoslav instances, and in a few cases the associated blocking of ponors led to Pleistocene lake clay accumulation. Gams (1969), however, maintains that the effects of the cold periods were not solely constructional; increased amounts of runoff from melting snow and ice, accentuated by frozen ground, were directed against marginal limestones, and poljes enlarged in this way also.

The aggradational side of glacial and periglacial regimes exhibits contradictory kinds of intervention, as the dicussion of poljes above indicates. The heavy loads of glacial meltwater streams and summer flows in periglacial conditions block up previously formed streamsinks and temporarily restore surface drainage during cold periods in other kinds of karst also. This is true of the fluviokarst south of the Mount Field plateau in Tasmania which was glaciated in the last Glacial (Goede 1973). Periglacial conditions also promoted slope instability and mass movements; at Cooleman Plain, NSW, one instance of such temporary restoration of surface drainage was caused by a mudflow filling up a small blind valley to threshold level (Jennings 1982c). On the other hand, the decanting of water laterally from glaciofluvial and periglacial–fluvial fans into limestone divides is thought to have promoted cave formation in cold climate times in northern Tasmania (Jennings and Sweeting 1959). Glazek *et al.* (1977) describe a range of proglacial caves from Poland including some similar in style to the Tasmanian examples.

Intervals of cold climate affect karst in many other ways. Glacial erosion may strip weathering mantles and remove most preglacial solutional microforms, leaving pavements only scored by a mesh of the lower parts of former grikes. Where beds and ground are horizontal, these form large, level platforms; there are inclined pavements where dip and slope coincide. Pavement staircases (*Schichttreppenkarst*, Bögli 1964b) appear where slope exceeds the dip, but where the reverse is the case it is the edges of the beds that form the treads and the bedding planes the sloping risers (*Schichtrippenkarst*, Bögli 1964b). All are structural forms cleared free by ice action.

But glacial and karst erosion are not always in opposition. The alternation of glacials and interglacials may accentuate landforms. Thus, just as karst solution can produce large closed basins, so does the succession of extending and compressive flow along a glacier. So glacial cirque basins and glacial trough basins may be exaggerated in this way and the initiation may be by karst processes preglacially. This is thought to be true in the Picos de Europa in Spain (Miotke 1968), in the Italian Dolomites and on Durmitor in Yugoslavia (Nicod 1976a and b), and in the Owen Range, NZ (Jennings 1982d). In the classification of Ford (1979), these are *glaciokarstic* and *mixed* features. Other cirque basins in karst are only *karstiglacial*; the forms are thought to be virtually entirely glacial but karst drainage characteristics have been superimposed, either in underground drainage of the glacial lake occupying the basins or by preventing the closed depression from forming a lake at all, as at the head of the Val du Lauzon in the French Alps.

The variety of conflicting effects of glaciation upon karst is by no means exhausted by the instances given here; see Ford (1983a).

Karst land forms in semi-arid and arid climates have commonly led to ideas of past wetter climates when their surface features were eroded and caves were carved out. According to Waltham and Ede (1973), the surface karst of Kuh-e-Parau in the arid Zagros Mountains of Iran is being destroyed now by frost action and conditions are static in the 750 m deep Ghar Parau. The karst development is attributed to a former wetter climate as yet not dateable. A similar history was claimed earlier for the semi-arid Guadalupe Range of New Mexico and north–western Texas, where the Carlsbad Caverns and other caves were attributed to a wetter Pliocene by Bretz (1949) and Horberg (1949). They are unrelated to present topography and were thought to have formed by phreatic action beneath a planation surface, subsequently veneered by Pliocene gravels. Later, Moore (1960b) recognized three levels of dynamic phreatic action related to dissection of the plateau following uplift and developing in Late Pliocene and Early Pleistocene time, when the climate was still regarded as wetter than at present. Coarse fluvial sediments belonging to a late phase of cave development are incompatible with present hydrology.

However, all those earlier ideas are being disfavoured now in the preference given to hypotheses of solution by sulphuric acid, produced in various ways – from the mixing of vadose water with gypsum brines from evaporites to the east (Palmer et al. 1977a); from vadose water removing gypsum from overlying formations; from rising thermal water rich in H_2S (Egemeier 1981; D. G. Davis 1980); from sulphuric acid-rich water rising from oil and gas fields (Hill 1981). Much less water would be needed with this strong acid as the corrosive agent.

The scattered, large caves of the Nullarbor Plain have been linked not only to Pleistocene sea level oscillations but also to wetter phases in its history. Although the lowest sea levels were formerly inferred to be times of greater water availability, this is now not thought to be the case for the last Glacial maximum, at least from pollen evidence in caves (Martin 1973). Nevertheless, there is evidence from the Nullarbor Plain of phases of increased wetness, on the surface in the form of river courses extending through the present dunefield to the north out into the now riverless plain for some distance, and underground by way of former abundant calcite speleothems, now scarcely forming at all. However, it has not yet proved possible to date these events.

In southern Africa, cave deposits have yielded much evidence inter-preted in terms of wetter and drier past climates, though a few examples illustrate that there can be no simple universal interpretation. Thus early work by King (1951) rested on alternation of red sand and speleothem deposition in certain Transvaal caves. The red sands incorporated well sorted and rounded quartz grains and minor mineral constituents foreign to their neighbourhood; these were interpreted as aeolian components from drier phases. Within the eastern margin of the Kalahari in Botswana in a drier climate, red aeolian sands and calcite deposits form a repeated succession in Drotsky's Cave just as dune spreads and calcretes do in the valley outside (Cooke 1975). Some of these events, again interpreted as drier in the time of aeolian action and wetter for the carbonate precipitation, are beyond the range of radiocarbon (Cooke and Verhagen 1977).

In other Transvaal caves than those studied by King, the periods of speleothem formation alternate with the inwash of red earth, and the latter is regarded as registering the wetter phases here (Marker and Brook 1970). The discussion on the significance of flowstone in chapter 8 indicates that these different interpretations of the significance of the calcite phases are not necessarily incompatible.

Tectonic Movements and Changes of Base Level

Some of the effects of tectonic movements and eustasy on coastal karst have already been outlined in chapter 11; here the response to these factors will be approached more broadly. Perforce the effects of negative movements of base level will be given attention because positive movements lead to aggradation, burial and fixation of forms, so that knowledge is more difficult to obtain and *a priori* there may be less about which to obtain information. Thus, it was mining for gold that revealed the presence beneath the Canadian lead at Gulgon, NSW, of completely filled limestone caves; they lay beneath 25 m of river gravels of Tertiary age. In the Bau area of Sarawak, also, mining has revealed caves buried in this way with sediment (Crabtree and Friederich 1982).

Local disruption of karst by faulting is illustrated in the 300 m fault scarp on the western side of Mt Hoyo in eastern Zaire (Ollier and Harrop 1963). Here phreatic caves open high in the face of this cliff, with some modification near their entrances by vadose action. These caves originated before this early Pleistocene faulting and survived a spasm of violent tectonism.

In young orogenic belts, the possibility of significant warping during the development of caves is real, and this leads Brook (1976) to argue, from the vertical dispositions of caves (including Selminum Tel) behind the stupendous Hindenburg Wall in the central mountain chain of New Guinea, that the range has been uplifted greatly and tilted backwards during its formation, giving older caves gradients away from their former outflows. However, Gillieson (1985) opposes this interpretation, explaining the relationships by a lowering of the outlet springs, to which there was rising under pressure. The springs moved downdip at the contact with underlying, impervious but weak rocks as a transverse anticline in front of the Wall was removed during the course of cave evolution.

The historical factor that has been most widely studied in karst is rejuvenation as a result of negative movement of base level, and inland it is of little moment whether this is caused by epeirogenic uplift or eustatic fall in sea level. Warwick (1960) has stressed the importance of the effects of successive phases of rejuvenation in British karst forms. In particular, he has drawn attention to rapid lowering of water levels underground near rejuvenation heads in limestone valleys causing engulfment of rivers and cave formation (figure 88). This is all the more favoured where nickpoints pass up incised meanders, shortcuts developing especially through meander spurs; the classic study of the Grotte de Han by Broek *et al.* (1910) on the Lesse River in Belgium remains a model of this kind of event. At London Bridge, NSW, the detail of the abandoned caves on the underground cutoff appears to demand the retreat of a waterfall or rapids round the meander during their formation (Jennings *et al.* 1976).

Since there is always the tendency for underground water to find lower routes through the karst rocks, a sequence of cave passages or caves may relate to a single negative movement of base level. However, if the caves

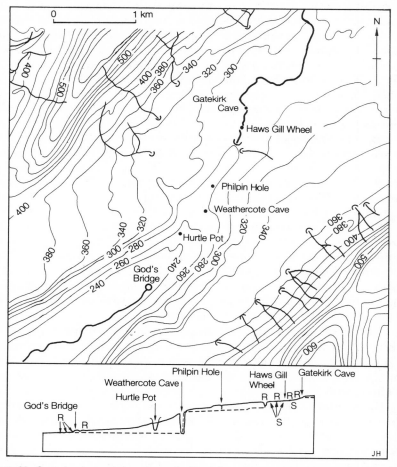

Figure 88 Cave development at a rejuvenation head, River Greta, Craven, England, after Warwick (1960): R, resurgence; S, streamsink.

exhibit strong quasi-horizontality, cutting through structures and relating to surface features such as straths and other terraces, it follows that they are the consequence of successive waves of rejuvenation reaching the karst whatever the events at the coast. This is eminently the case with the Demanovska Caves in the Slovakian Carpathians (Droppa 1966), in which nine levels in steeply dipping limestone ranging up to 140 m above the river possess gradients between about 0.5 to 2 per cent (figure 89). The lowest active level relates to the present floodplain in the Demanovska Valley, whereas the second and third levels correlate with two terraces belonging to the late and early parts, respectively, of the Riss Glacial stage. Relationships of higher cave levels to terraces in neighbouring valleys are the basis for thinking that they belong to earlier glacial stages still and the highest to the end of the Pliocene.

Where the rocks themselves are nearly horizontal, interpretation of similar cave sequences is inevitably more debatable, as in the case of the great Flint Ridge–Mammoth Caves system of Kentucky, where there are six major levels of development. Many have regarded them as purely a reflection of stratigraphic control; however, more than usually precise levelling for cave surveys, both of cave passages and of the various beds in which they occur, by A. N. and M. V. Palmer has shown that the passages do transect the structures overall. Therefore correlation with the flight of terraces in the Green River valley, to which all cave levels except one fall gently, is meaningful. The Green River is tributary to the Ohio River, the valley of which was invaded by the Laurentide Icesheet, permitting terrace correlation with Pleistocene glacial history. This takes the history of the system right back from the present to the end of the Pliocene. This has been confirmed by palaeomagnetic stratigraphy by Schmidt (1982) of fine sediments flooded back into the cave from the Green River (see chapter 8).

Denudation chronology in karst is favoured by the greater perfection of corrosion plains, compared with those formed by other terrestrial agencies, and by their greater immunity from destruction through much deflection of water underground. The relict karst margin plains of the Dinaric karst have long attracted attention (Krebs 1929; Kayser 1934) because of their high degree of perfection and the sharp breaks they make with the high plateaus. These plains occur along both the inland margins and along the Adriatic coast, e.g. the Karlovac–Sluin, Kistanje and Cetina plains. Rivers, such as the Krka and Cikola in the case of the Kistanje plain, meander in trenches through the surfaces. Hums rise from them and dolines occur especially near the river gorges. Morawetz (1967) compares these plains at 200–300 m above sea level with the lower Neretva Valley (chapter 6) practically at sea level, and argues they were fashioned in a similar way prior to a negative movement of base level which then raised them high above water rest levels and began their protracted slow destruction. However, it has been suggested that the

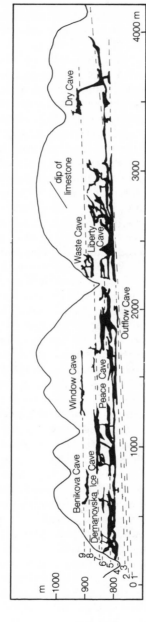

Figure 89 Demanovska Caves, Carpathians, Czechoslovakia, after Droppa (1966).

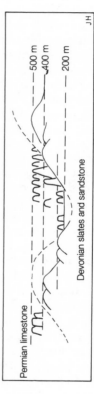

Figure 90 Tower karst in three storeys near Guilin, Guangxi, China, after Gellert (1962).

Holocene glacio-eustatic sea level recovery has led to alluviation of the lower Neretva, and that this has favoured its present phase of lateral extension. This argument may be mistaken, because in eustatic terms the Holocene sea level has only returned to approximately the same level as the last Interglacial.

Cyrenaica is made up almost entirely of Palaeocene to Miocene limestones and has a winter rainfall of 300–700 mm on its northern side, but this declines to 50 mm on its southern slope to the Sahara. The summit area consists of an erosion surface of uncertain origin (Pfeffer 1975) and northwards there is a sequence of erosional scarps and concave pediments, crossed by steep-sided wadis with intermittent flows. Closed depressions are few though there are two large shallow basins, thought to be tectonic basins, on the main pediment, which is regarded as Pliocene in age. Post-Pliocene movement also warped up these surfaces along an axis in the middle of their east–west extension. Quaternary eustatic terraces near the coast are modified by pedimentation. The dominance of pediments is attributed to the prevalence of a warm, dry climate during the formation of the whole relief below the summit surface, with the wadis cut at the transition from these phases of areal erosion in dry conditions to wet phases, when some dolines were created and some more developed soils were formed also. Karst is regarded as subordinate, though Pfeffer does not enquire to what extent solution contributes to pediment formation here, an important role being claimed for it in the limestone ranges in north-western Australia by Jennings and Sweeting (1963). At least the presence of the limestones must have contributed to the preservation of the well defined erosional forms.

Even in the fields of residual hills that prevail in many karst areas in the humid tropics, accordance of summit levels has been claimed as evidence of planation surfaces from which the karst relief has been carved. Gellert (1962) considered that there were three storeys of limestone towers near Baisha south-east of Guilin, in eastern Guangxi, China, which were inherited from three corrosion plain stages separated by uplift and rejuvenation (figure 90). Plate 45, taken in western Guangxi province, shows two storeys of towers around the floor of a polje. High up in individual towers are foot caves and through-caves also witnessing this storeying. The important finds of the large primate, *Gigantopithecus*, came from an abandoned river cave opening 90 m up the cliffed side of a karst tower near Liuzhou in the same province of China. According to Kozarski (1962–3), the Chinese geomorphologist Czen Szu-phen maintains that the whole development has taken place since the Late Cretaceous, but his attempts to date the later levels are no longer acceptable because they depend in part on the interpretation of gravels involved as glaciofluvial, which Kozarski and others have demonstrated to be wrong. In part of the northern Guizhou Plateau, Song *et al.* (1983)

Plate 45 Tower karst in Guilin, Southern China. Photo by M.M. Sweeting.

consider that there are four erosion levels, variously represented by gentle plateau surface, karst hill accordance and major valley floors.

Accordance of summits in the American Appalachian Mountains, in limestone as in other rocks, has been interpreted in an opposing manner by Hack (1960), who thought it the product of dynamic equilibrium in the landscape. With river channel incision and maintenance of character-istic slope angles being accompanied by a matching lowering of ridge crests, the whole landscape in a given lithology is lowered without the loss of a roughly common height for the summits and ridges. It is difficult to see how this concept can be applied to the Chinese regions described above, where more than one level of summit accordance is involved which do not appear to be related to lithology.

However, Aubert (1969) implicitly embraces the dynamic equilibrium concept in his reinterpretation of the karst of the Swiss Jura, where the high plateaus were previously thought to be relics of a Tertiary peneplain. Instead, there is persistent planation of anticlines because of the lateral action of surface corrosion rather than vertical, action which is hindered by marly interbeds. Dolines accumulate fines on their floors which thus become insulated from further, action which is then directed laterally. There has been continuous surface ablation attenuating the anticlines.

Regional Individuality in Karst

Over the last score of years, many geomorphologists have sought to push the nomothetic aspects of the discipline to the forefront. This search for 'laws' of general applicability has greatly enhanced their capacity to attack practical problems of environmental management. Nevertheless, it will be wise ever to be conscious of the idiographic variety of context in which such 'laws' reveal themselves. The artificiality of separate discussion of the operation of individual factors differentiating karst in this and previous chapters has been made patent by inevitable cross-reference. The reality is generally that of complex evolution, as may be illustrated by reference to four major types of British karst. They have much in common, all being plateau country of moderate height in compact, well jointed Carboniferous limestone, all part of Hercynian orogenic structures but subjected to Tertiary epeirogenic uplift, all experiencing cool temperate maritime climate. But each possesses its own character because of differences within those broad limits and varying Pleistocene histories.

In Clare, Ireland, with gentle south-south-east dips and a lack of faulting, the limestone plateau declines and drains southwards, surmounted by gentle hills of overlying Namurian shales and sandstone. The shales were breached in the late Tertiary when large depressions were initiated (Williams 1970). Though these developed further in warm Pleistocene intervals, their catchments were gradually removed by glacial stripping of the shales and they ceased to develop, though one, the Carran depression, became a polje (Sweeting 1953). The whole karst was swept by an ice sheet in the last Glacial stage and probably there were earlier invasions as well; and under structural guidance ice erosion fashioned what is mainly a stepped pavement karst. Williams thus interprets accordances of hill tops, bevelled spurs and river nickpoints which Sweeting (1955) had earlier regarded as late Tertiary erosion surface remnants. Some closed depressions are simply hollows in glacial till covering the limestone. Dry valleys are generally very shallow and many are cut through the glacial till. There has been some fresh solutional micro-sculpture of the glacial pavements in the Holocene.

Most of the extensive cave systems are active branchwork caves at shallow depth, dominantly due to vadose action; abandoned passages are limited. Commonly, the caves follow the line of the young dry valleys and are attributed to the Late Glacial and Holocene (Ollier and Tratman 1969). Comparatively few caves appear to be older than the last glaciation of the area; such a one is Poll-an-Ionain, which is largely abandoned by streams and contains varved clays. Vigo Cave is unrelated to the present local topography. Ollier and Tratman mention obvious possible causes for this youthfulness of Clare caves, namely glacial erosion removing most of the older ones and glacial deposition burying them, but they are doubtful about these arguments. Whatever the true explanation, it does seem to be a case where underground and surface karst manifestations are out of step in development. The converse relationship has also been described in the Jura, where Aubert (1969)

247

maintains that prolonged cave development has had little effect on the surface, with a great rarity of collapse dolines.

The Craven karst (Waltham and Sweeting 1974) has a higher limestone plateau, more deeply and more sharply crossed by valleys that drain against the gentle dip and expose inliers of impervious basement, with bolder residuals of the younger Yoredale Beds with their cycles of sandstone, shale and limestone rising above. There has been renewed movement along old faultlines, in part accounting for rejuvenated relief and drainage. Much limestone was exposed prior to Pleistocene glaciation, which, however, stripped more areas of shale cover. Glacial erratics are found so high as to indicate complete submergence by ice. Ice erosion not only stripped soil and loosened rock to create large expanses of pavement but deepened and widened valleys into glacial troughs. Sweeting (1950) described two phases of valley rejuvenation below a Tertiary erosion surface truncating structure at the plateau level (see figure 91). The earlier, and major, 'Dales' phase of rejuvenation is now recognized to owe much to glacial erosion (Waltham 1970). Dry valleys were left high and dry by both phases of valley deepening. The largest closed depressions are found in the east, which was uncovered from shale earliest, but they can only be likened to uvalas modified by glacial action. Many smaller depressions perforate glacial till of intermediate thickness; subsidence of till has produced these conical dolines known locally as 'shakeholes'. Most solution microforms are rounded solution runnels and grikes of subsoil origin, which have lost their soil or litter cover through forest clearance, though some later modification by direct rain solution is to be seen.

The caves of Craven are much more elaborate than those of Clare with much multi-level development common (Waltham and Sweeting 1974); the Ease Gill Caverns comprise the longest single system, with over 80 km of passage. Various phases of erosion and deposition are present in individual caves and the deposits include vast bodies of gravels, interpreted as glaciofluvial, so histories are in general much longer than in Clare. Nearly horizontal rocks, vertical jointing and much faulting provide pronounced structural control, making level passages and

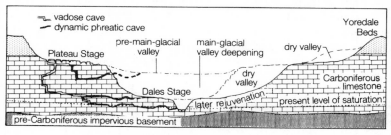

Figure 91 The denudation chronology of Craven, England, based on Sweeting (1950) and Waltham (1970).

vertical shafts dominant. Decipherment of history is often difficult as a result, especially with phreatic passages looping as much as 60 m below rest levels and former resurgences. Waltham stresses that, although vadose development often modifies earlier phreatic passages, the two commonly accompany one another along a system. It is generally possible, however, to recognize a contrast between high-level, pre-main glaciation cave systems antedating the major valley deepening and widening (the 'Dales Stage') and low-level, post-main-glaciation systems, which have themselves been affected by later rejuvenation draining parts of the phreatic passages belonging to these systems. Cold periods are regarded as mainly depositional events. It is not easy in this area to be sure of the chronology of the main glaciation, but speleothem dating suggests that it is prior to 400 000 BP (Atkinson et al. 1978). Later glacial stages had much less effect though glaciers were present.

Even when the limestones of the Peak District were accumulating, it formed a submarine massif with a rim of reefs and lagoons giving much facies variation (T. D. Ford 1977). Interbedded tuffs and lavas ('toad-stones') on the eastern side and dolomitization add to the lithological complexity. Nor is it a simple tectonic dome, but rather reflects the interference pattern of three trends of folding.

Overlying Carboniferous and later marine formations were entirely stripped in the Tertiary, and in Miocene–Early Pliocene times a braided river system laid its deposits over a subdued surface near sea level. These survive now in filled dolines, probably of 'solution-shuffle' type, which were tapped by at least one ancient cave, Golconda. Superimposed allogenic rivers have cut deep, steep-sided valleys across the plateau to which it was subsequently elevated. Prominent and elaborate dry valley systems, including gorge-like ones, mainly began as surface drainage superimposed from overlying shales. They hang above the major valleys, which have flights of terrace remnants regarded as of climatic origin. Some valleys went dry in the course of the successive valley deepenings.

It is not known how these terraces relate to the glacial history. The Peak was overswept by two earlier glaciations though it largely escaped the last. However, most of the tills have been removed and little glacial erosion has been recognized. It is a covered karst, largely by loess, often with residual soil material mixed by gelifluction. Together with other periglacial effects these are more in evidence than the results of glaciation. Dolomite tors, cemented screes and landslides of limestone on dipping tuff beds are among them. More dry valleys were created by periglacial phases of frozen ground and meltwater, desiccated on climatic amelioration. The few occurrences of solutional microforms are of subsoil origin.

Much mineralization along faults led to a long history of mining; the mines and especially the 'soughs', adits driven from valley bottoms to drain them, have altered underground drainage relationships but also have revealed caves with no natural entrances and emptied phreatic passages for easier entry. It seems that the apparent poverty of much of the Peak in caves may be due to blockages by glacial and periglacial deposits. However, most of the big cave systems lie at the northern end where the shale–limestone contact lies high, and here are the most streamsinks. Halts in valley erosion and in retreat of the shale margin find counterparts in cave levels. Also toadstones and interbedded shales perch water bodies, leading to cave formation, as do reef limestones and mineral veins. Old, possibly Pliocene, nothephreatic cavities in the mineral veins were incorporated in later cave development. At water rest levels dynamic phreatic passages trend along the strike, with short lifting passages in the dip, though where the dip is steep caves run down it to the strike passages. From speleothem dating, cave enlargement is attributed mainly to interglacial periods while there was much introduction of sediment into them during glacials (Ford et al. 1983).

The Mendip Hills (Ford and Stanton 1968; Smith and Drew 1975) are a compact plateau, overlooked by Devonian sandstone monadnocks along the cores of four periclines in echelon, from which the Carboniferous limestone dips steeply. Tight Hercynian folding was renewed by broad doming in the Miocene, and the main plateau level is regarded as a Pliocene erosion surface. However, there are older exhumed sub-Triassic features, such as some marginal valleys that were formerly filled with Triassic dolomitic conglomerate, which also filled some caves. A Jurassic unconformity appears to have survived in parts through coincidence with the Pliocene surface. Deep residual soils cover the limestone plateau.

This karst practically escaped glaciation but suffered permafrost and gelifluction several times. Integrated dry valley patterns over the plateau, mainly the product of initial surface drainage as underground drainage was created, were nevertheless reactivated in the cold periods of frozen ground. There are also a few gorges cutting back into the plateau margin. Some are in part along exhumed sub-Triassic valleys, e.g. Burrington Combe, and others, e.g. Ebbor Gorge, are due partly to cave destruction; but in the main they are due mainly to surface valley rejuvenation during the cold periods. Dolines, generally found along the dry valleys, are due mainly to surface solution, compounded with some shuffling-down of blocks loosened by bedding plane and joint enlargement, and they may owe a lot to windows in the permafrost – taliks. At the heads of the valley systems right on the plateau surface are large, shallow closed depressions with flat clay floors; they are due to surface solution and were occupied by small lakes, probably during the last Glacial.

Although there are buried cave remnants from the Triassic, this early karst development has not been shown to have influenced the main cave development in Mendip from mid-Pleistocene time onwards. Drew (in Smith and Drew 1975) finds the variety of cave development so great from one outflow spring catchment area to another as to preclude much generalization. Thus, the extreme west is influenced by the absence of a sandstone inlier and the eastern end by late removal of overlying bedrocks. There are great local variations in the number and extent of caves, in the relative importance of phreatic and vadose excavation in inflow systems, and in the presence or not of different levels of development. Early phreatic phases in the inflow systems are succeeded by alternating phases of vadose incision and aggradation. These complex histories are interpreted by most in terms of periods of rejuvenation (usually neglecting glacio-eustatic oscillations in base level) and of the alternation of cold and warmer climates, with their effects on stream volumes and loads. Ford (1964b) related different levels in the inflow G. B. Cave with different outflow caves, abandoned and active, in Cheddar Gorge, though Drew suggests the possibility of unification of passages close behind the resurgences, which would demolish this correlation. Whichever view is correct, it does not appear to vitiate the implications of speleothem dating in G. B. Cave (Atkinson *et al.* 1978) that the upper levels of that cave are older than 360 000 BP and that Cheddar Gorge has been deepened some 70 m since that time.

Even though they have so much in common in factors controlling their geomorphology, these four types of karst have undeniable marked individualities. This underlines the great difficulties facing those who try to define systematic karst types on the total basis of structure, climato-geomorphic processes and historical evolution, though Birot (1954) attempted this for the Alpine and Hercynian belts of Europe and Zhang (1980) for the greater variety of Chinese karst. Stringfield and Le Grand (1969a) have invoked 'hydrogeologic uniqueness' for particular limestone areas. This situation seems likely to perpetuate two leading characteristics in those who study karst and caves: strong regional loyalty, and a tempering global freemasonry bonded by the attraction of the underground.

References

Abel, O. and Kyrle, G. (eds) (1931), *Die Drachenhöhle bei Mixnitz*. Spel. Mon. Bds. 7, 8 and 9, Vienna.

Alpine Karst Symposium (1979), *Bull. Nat. Spel. Soc., 41*, 51–104.

Ambert, P. (1981), Les travertins de Millau: recherches préliminaires. *Ass. Française Karstologie Mém., 3*, 9–14.

Atkinson, T.C., (1977), Carbon dioxide in the atmosphere of the unsaturated zone: an important control of groundwater hardness in limestones. *J. Hydrol., 35*, 111–23.

Atkinson, T.C. (1983), Growth mechanisms of speleothems in Castleguard Cave, Columbia Icefields, Alberta, Canada. *Arctic Alp. Res., 15*, 523–36.

Atkinson, T.C. Harmon, R.S., Smart P.L. and Waltham, A.C. (1978), Palaeoclimatic and geomorphic implications of ^{230}Th/^{234}U dates on speleothems in Britain. *Nature, 272*, 24–8.

Atkinson, T.C. and Smith, D.I. (1974), Rapid groundwater flow in fissures in the Chalk: An example from south Hampshire. *Q.J. Engng Geol., 7*, 197–205.

Atkinson, T.C. and Smith, D.I. (1976), The erosion of limestones: p. 151–77 in *The Science of Speleology* (ed. T.D. Ford and C.H.D. Cullingford), Academic Press, London.

Atkinson, T.C., Smith, D.I., Lavis, J.J. and Whitaker, R.J. (1973), Experiments in tracing underground waters in limestones. *J. Hydrol., 19*, 323–49.

Aub, C.F. (1969), The nature of cockpits and other depressions in the karst of Jamaica. *Proc. 5th Int. Cong. Speleol., M15*, 1–7.

Aubert, D. (1966), Structure, activité et évolution d'une doline. *Bull. Soc. Neuchateloise Sci. Nat., 89*, 113–20.

Aubert, D. (1969), Phénomènes et formes du karst jurassien. *Eclogae Geol. Helv., 62*, 325–99.

Back, W., Hanshaw, B.B. and van Driel, J.N. (1984), Role of groundwater in shaping the eastern coastline of the Yucatan peninsula, Mexico: pp. 281–93 in *Groundwater as a Geomorphic Agent* (ed. R.G. LaFleur), Allen & Unwin, Boston.

Backshall, D.G., Barnett, J., Davies, P.J., Duncan, D.C., Harvey, N., Hopley, D., Isdale, P.J., Jennings, J.N., Moss, R. (1979) Drowned dolines – the blue holes of the Pompey Reefs, Great Barrier Reef. *BMR J. Aust. Geol. Geophys., 4*, 99–109.

Bakalowicz, M. (1981), Les eaux d'infiltration dans l'aquifère karstique. *Proc. 8th Int. Cong. Speleol., 2*, 710–12.

Balazs, D. (1973), Relief types of tropical karst areas: p. 16–32 in *Symposium on Karst-morphogenesis* (ed. L. Jakucs), Attila Jozsef University, Szeged.

Balch, E.S. (1900), *Glacières or Freezing Caverns*, Allen, Lane & Scott, Philadelphia.

Balchin, W.G. and Lewis, W.V. (1938), The chalk water table south-east of Cambridge: pp. 20–4 in *The Cambridge Region* (ed. H.C. Darby), Cambridge University Press.

Barrett, P. (1963), The development of Kairimu Cave, Marakopa District, South West Auckland. *New Zealand J. Geol. Geophys.*, 6, 288–98.

Barrett, P. (1964), Residual seams and cementation in Oligocene shell calcarenites, Te Kuiti Group. *J. Sed. Pet.*, 34, 524–31.

Bassett, J. (1976), Hydrology and geochemistry of the Upper Lost River drainage basin, Indiana. *Bull. Nat. Spel. Soc.*, 38, 79–87.

Bastian, L. (1964), Morphology and development of caves in the Southwest of Western Australia. *Helictite*, 2, 105–18.

Bathurst, R.G.C. (1975), *Carbonate-sediments and their Diagenesis* (2nd ed.), Elsevier, Amsterdam.

Beck, J. (1975), The caves of the Foolow–Eyam–Stoney Middleton area, Derbyshire and their genesis. *Trans. Br. Cave Res. Ass*, 2, 1–11.

Bird, E.C.F. (1984), *Coasts* (3rd ed.), Basil Blackwell, Oxford.

Birot, P. (1954), Problèmes de morphologie karstique. *Ann. Géogr.*, 63, 161–92.

Birot, P. (1966), *Le Relief calcaire*. Centre de Documentation Universitaire, Paris.

Bleahu, M.D. (1972), Karst of Rumania: pp. 341–53 in *Important Karst Regions of the Northern Hemisphere* (ed. M. Herak and V.T. Stringfield, Elsevier, Amsterdam.

Bögli, A. (1956), Grundformen von Karsthöhlenquerschnitten. *Stalactite*, 6, 56–62.

Bögli, A. (1960), Kalklösung und Karrenbildung. *Z. Geomorph., supplementary issue*, 2, 4–21.

Bögli, A. (1961a), Karrentische, ein Beitrag zur Karstmorphologie. *Z. Geomorph.*, 5, 185–93.

Bögli, A. (1961b), Der Höhlenlehm. *Mem. Rass. Spel. Ital.*, 5, 11–29.

Bögli, A. (1964a), Mischungskorrosion – ein Beitrag zur Verkarstungsproblem. *Erdkunde*, 18, 83–92.

Bögli, A. (1964b), Un exemple de complexe glacio-karstique. Le Schichttreppenkarst. *Rev. Belge. Géogr.*, 88, 63–82.

Bögli, A. (1969), Neue Anschauungen uber die Rolle von Schichtfugen und Kluften in der karsthydrographischen Entwicklung. *Geol. Rund.*, 58, 395–408.

Bögli, A. (1978), *Karsthydrographie und physische Spelaologie*. Springer, Berlin.

Bosak, P. (1981), The Lower Cretaceous paleokarst in the Moravian Karst (Czechoslovakia). *Proc. 8th Int. Cong. Spel.*, 1, 164–6.

Brain, C.K. (1958), *The Transvaal Ape-man-bearing Cave Deposits*. Transvaal Museum Memoir, 11.

Bramwell, D. (1977), Archaeology and palaeontology: pp. 263–91 in *Limestones and Caves of the Peak District* (ed. T.D. Ford), Geoabstracts, Norwich.

Bray, L.G. (1975), Recent chemical work in the Ogof Ffynnon Ddu system: Further oxidation studies. *Trans. Br. Cave Res. Ass.*, 2, 127–32.

Bretz, J.H. (1942), Vadose and phreatic features of limestone caverns. *J. Geol.*, 50, 675–811.

Bretz, J.H. (1949), Carlsbad Caverns and other caves of the Guadalupe Block, New Mexico. *J. Geol.*, 57, 447–63.

References

Bretz, J.H. (1950), Origin of filled-sink structures and circle deposits of Missouri. *Bull. Geol. Soc. Amer., 61,* 789–834.

Bretz, J.H. (1960), Bermuda: A partially drowned, late mature, Pleistocene karst. *Bull. Geol. Soc. Amer., 71,* 1729–54.

Broek, E. van den, Martel, E.A. and Rahir, E. (1910), *Les cavernes et les rivières souterraines de la Belgique . . .,* Lamartin, Bruxelles.

Brook, D. (1976), The karst and cave development of Selminum Tel. *Trans. Br. Cave Res. Ass., 3,* 183–91.

Brook, G.A. (1983), Application of LANDSAT imagery to flood studies in the remote Nahanni Karst, Northwest Territories, Canada. *J. Hydrol., 61,* 305–24.

Brook, G.A. and Ford, O.C. (1976), The Nahanni North Karst: A question mark , on the validity of the morphoclimatic concept of karst development. *Proc. 6th Int. Cong. Speleol., 2,* 43–57.

Brook, G.A. and Ford, D.C. (1978), The origin of labyrinth and tower karst and the climatic conditions necessary for their development. *Nature, 275,* 493–6.

Brown, E.H. (1969), Jointing, aspect and orientation of scarp-face dry valleys, near Ivinghoe, Buckinghamshire. *Trans. Inst. Brit. Geogr., 48,* 61–74.

Büdel, J. (1951), Fossiler Tropenkarst in der Schwäbischen Alb und den Ostalpen; und seine Stellung in der klimatischen Schichtstufen der Karstentwicklung. *Erdkunde, 5,* 168–70.

Bull, P.A. (1977), Cave boulder chokes and doline relationships. *Proc. 7th. Int. Cong. Speleol.,* 93–6.

Bull, P.A. (1978), A study of stream gravels from a cave: Agen Allwedd, South Wales. *Z. Geomorph., 22,* 275–96.

Bull, P.A. (1981), Some fine-grained sedimentation phenomena in caves. *Earth Surf. Proc., 6,* 11–22.

Bull, P.A. (1983), Chemical sedimentation in caves: pp. 301–19 in *Chemical Sediments and Geomorphology* (ed. A.S. Goudie and K. Pye), Academic Press, London.

Bull, P.A. and Laverty, M. (1982), Observations on phytokarst. *Z. Geomorph. 26,* 393–416.

Bunting, B.T. (1961), The role of seepage moisture in soil formation, slope development and stream initiation. *Amer. J. Sci., 259,* 503–18.

Burdon, D.J. and Safadi, C. (1963), Ras-el-ain: The great karst spring of Mesopotamia. *J. Hydrol., 1,* 58–95.

Burke, A.R. and Bird, P.F. (1966), A new mechanism for the formation of vertical shafts in Carboniferous limestone. *Nature, 210,* 831–2.

Burnaby, T.P. (1950), The tubular chalk stacks at Sheringham. *Proc. Geol. Ass., 61,* 226–41.

Burns, K.L. (1964), *Geological Survey Explanatory Report Devonport.* Tasmania Department of Mines, Hobart.

Cabrol, P. (1978), *Contribution à l'étude du concrétionnement carbonate des grottes du sud de la France. Morphologie, genèse, diagenèse,* CERGA, Montpellier.

Carson, M.A. and Kirkby, M.J. (1972), *Hillslope Form and Process,* Cambridge University Press, London.

Casanova, J. (1981), Morphologie et biolithogenèse des barrages de travertins. *Ass. Française Karstologie Mém., 3,* 45–54.

Caumartin, V. and Renault, P. (1958), La corrosion biochimique dans un reseau karstique et la genèse du mondmilch. *Notes biospél., 13,* 87–109.

Cavaillé, A. (1962), Le système karstique et l'évolution des grottes. *Spelunca. Mem.*, *2*, 9–28.

Chandler, R.H. (1909), On some dry chalk valley features. *Geol. Mag.*, *6*, 538–9.

Chappell, J. (1974), Geology of coral terraces, Huon Peninsula, New Guinea: A study of Quaternary tectonic movements and sea level changes. *Bull. Geol. Soc. Amer.*, *85*, 553–70.

Chardonnet, J. (1948), Les calenques provençales, origine et divers types. *Ann. Geogr.*, *57*, 289–97.

Charity, R.A.P. and Christopher, N.S.J. (1977), The Ogof Ffynnon Ddu system, South Wales, in relation to the structure of the Carboniferous Limestone. *Proc. 7th Int. Cong. Speleol.*, 108–10.

Chilingar, C.V., Bissell, H.J. and Fairbridge, R.W. (eds) (1967), *Carbonate Rocks. Origin, Occurrence and Classification*, Elsevier, Amsterdam.

Chinese Academy of Geological Sciences (1976), *Karst in China*, Shanghai People's Publishing House.

Chorley, R.J. (1978), The hillslope hydrological cycle: pp. 1–42 in *Hillslope Hydrology* (ed. M.J. Kirkby), John Wiley, London.

Christopher, N. (1975), The use of saturation index and potassium/sodium ratios as indicators of speleological potential, with special reference to Derbyshire. *Trans. Br. Cave Res. Ass.*, *2*, 29–34.

Christopher, N., Beck, J.S. and Mellors, P. (1977), Hydrology – water in the limestone: pp. 185–230 in *Limestones and Caves of the Peak District* (ed. T.D. Ford), Geoabstracts, Norwich.

Clausen, E.N. (1970), Badland caves of Wyoming. *Bull. Nat. Spel. Soc.*, *32*, 59–69.

Cleland, H.F. (1910), North American natural bridges, with a discussion of their origin. *Bull. Geol. Soc. Amer.*, *21*, 313–38.

Coase, A. and Judson, D. (1977), Dan yr Ogof and its associated caves. *Trans. Br. Cave Res. Ass.*, *4*, 245–344.

Coates, D.F. (1967), *Rock Mechanics Principles*. Mines Branch Monograph no. 874, Ottawa.

Coleman, A.M. and Balchin, W.G.V. (1959), The origin and development of surface depressions in the Mendip Hills. *Proc. Geol. Ass.*, *70*, 291–309.

Collier, C.R. and Flint, R.F. (1974), Fluvial sedimentation in Mammoth Cave, Kentucky. *U.S. Geol. Surv. Prof. Pap.*, no. 475–D, pp. 141–3.

Collingridge, B.R. (1969), Geomorphology of the area: pp. 42–58 in *The Caves of North-West Clare, Ireland* (ed. E.K. Tratman), David and Charles, Newton Abbot, Devon.

Conrad, G., Gèze, B. and Paloc, H. (1967), Observations sur des phénomènes karstiques et pseudo-karstiques du Sahara. *Rev. Géogr. Phys. Géol. Dyn.*, *9*, 357–70.

Cook, P.J., Colwell, J.B., Firman, J.B., Lindsay, J.M., Schwebel, D.A., von der Borch, C.C. (1977), The late Cainozoic sequence of southeast South Australia and Pleistocene sea level changes. *BMR J. Aust. Geol. Geophys.*, *2*, 81–8.

Cooke, H.J. (1975), The palaeoclimatic significance of caves and adjacent landforms in western Ngamiland, Botswana. *Geogr. J.*, *141*, 430–4.

Cooke, H.J. and Verhagen, B. Th. (1977), The dating of cave development – an example from Botswana. *Proc. 7th Int. Cong. Speleol.*, 122–3.

Corbel, J. (1952), A comparison between the karst of the Mediterranean Region and of North Western Europe. *Trans. Cave Res. Grp Gt Br.*, *2*, 1–26.

References

Corbel, J. (1957), *Les karsts du Nord-Ouest de l'Europe*. Institut des Études Rhodaniennes de l'Université de Lyon, 12.

Corbel, J. (1958), Karsts du Yucatan et de la Floride. *Bull. Ass. Géogr. Français*, pp. 2–14.

Corbel, J. (1959), Erosion en terrain calcaire. *Ann. Géogr., 68*, 97–120.

Corbel, J. (1960), Nouvelles recherches sur les karsts arctiques Scandinaves. *Z. Geomorph., supplementary issue, 2*, 74–80.

Corbel, J. (1963), Marmites de géant et microformes karstiques. *Norois, 38*, 123–32.

Corbel, J. (1964), Les karsts des régions polaires. *Rev. Belge. Géogr., 88*, 83–103.

Crabtree, S. and Friederich, H. (1982), The caves of the Bau district, Sarawak. *Cave Science, 9*, 83–93.

Cramer, H. (1941), Die Systematik der Karstdolinen. *Neues Jb. Miner. Geol. Palaont., 85*, 293–382.

Crawford, N. (1984), Karst landform development along the Cumberland Plateau escarpment of Tennessee: pp. 294–339 in *Groundwater as a Geomorphic Agent* (ed. R.S. LaFleur), Allen & Unwin, Boston.

Crowther, J. (1978), The Gunong Gajah–Tempurong massif, Perak, and its associated cave system, Gua Tempurong. *Malayan Nature Journal, 30*, 1–13.

Crowther, J. (1979), Limestone solution on exposed rock outcrops in west Malaysia: p. 31–50 in *Geographical Approaches to Fluvial Processes* (ed. A.F. Pitty), Geoabstracts, Norwich.

Crowther, J. (1982a), A technique for sampling soil air: Some results and methodological investigations. *Trans. Br. Cave Res. Ass., 9*, 47–54.

Crowther, J. (1982b), Ecological observations in a tropical karst terrain, West Malaysia. Variations in topography, soils and vegetation. *J. Biogeog., 9*, 65–78.

Crowther, J. (1983), Hydrology of autogenic percolation systems in some tropical karst outcrops, west Malaysia. *J. Hydrol., 60*, 227–42.

Curl, R.L. (1966), Caves as a measure of karst. *J. Geol., 74*, 798–830.

Curl, R.L. (1972), Minimum diameter stalactites. *Bull. Nat. Spel. Soc., 34*, 129–36.

Curl. R.L. (1973), Minimum diameter stalagmites. *Bull. Nat. Spel. Soc., 35*, 1–9.

Curl, R.L. (1974), Deducing flow velocity in cave conduits from scallops. *Bull. Nat. Spel. Soc., 36*, 1–5.

Cvijić J. (1893), Das Karstphänomen. *Geogr. Abh., 5*, 217–329.

Cvijić, J. (1918), L'hydrographie souterraine et l'évolution morphologique du karst. *Rev. Géogr. Alp., 6*, 375–426.

Cvijić, J. (1925), Types morphologiques du terrains calcaires. Le holokarst Le merokarst. Types karstiques de transition. *C.R. Acad. Sci., 180*, 592–4, 757–3, 1038–40.

Cvijić, J. (1960), *La géographie des terrains calcaires*. Acad. serbe. Sci. Arts Mon., no. 141. Belgrade.

Daneš, J.V. (1908), Geomorphologische Studien im Karstgebiete Jamaikas. *9th Int. Geog. Congr., 2*, 178–82.

Daneš, J.V. (1910), Die Karstphänomene im Goenoeng Sewoe auf Java. *Tijdschr. K. ned. aardr. Genoot., 27*, 247–60.

Dannin, A. and Garty, J. (1983), Distribution of cyanobacteria and lichens on hillsides in the Negev Highlands and their impact on biogenic weathering. *Z. Geomorph., 27*, 423–44.

References

Davies, C.W. (1977), Breakout domes in South Wales caves. *Proceedings 7th International Speleological Congress*, Sheffield, 136–9.

Davies, W.E. (1951), Mechanics of cave breakdown. *Bull. Nat. Spel. Soc., 13*, 36–43.

Davies, W.E. (1960), Origin of caves in folded limestone. *Bull. Nat. Spel. Soc., 22*, 5–18.

Davis, D.G. (1980), Cave development in the Guadalupe Mountains: a critical review of recent hypotheses. *Bull. Nat. Spel. Soc., 42*, 42–8.

Davis, S.N. (1966), Initiation of groundwater flow in jointed limestone. *Bull. Nat. Spel. Soc., 28*, 111–19.

Davis, W.M. (1930), Origin of limestone caverns. *Bull. Geol. Soc. Amer., 41*, 475–628.

Day, M. (1976), The morphology and hydrology of some Jamaican karst depressions. *Earth Surf. Proc., 1*, 111–29.

Day, M. (1978), Morphology and distribution of residual limestone hills (mogotes) in the karst of northern Puerto Rico. *Bull. Geol. Soc. Amer., 89*, 426–32.

Day, M. (1979), The hydrology of polygonal karst depressions in northern Jamaica. *Z. Geomorph., supplementary issue, 32*, 25–34.

Day, M. (1980), Rock hardness: field assessment and geomorphic importance. *Professional Geographer, 32*, 72–81.

Day, M. (1982), The influence of some material properties on the development of tropical karst terrain. *Trans. Br. Cave Res. Ass., 9*, 27–37.

Day, M. and Goudie, A. (1977), Field assessment of rock hardness using the Schmidt Hammer. *British Geomorphological Research Group Technical Bulletin, 18*, 19–29.

Deike, G.H. (1960), Origin and geologic relations of Breathing Cave, Virginia. *Bul. Nat. Spel. Soc., 22*, 30–42.

Deike, G.H. (1967), The development of caverns in the Mammoth Cave region: unpublished PhD thesis, Pennsylvania State University.

Deike, G.H. and White, W.B. (1969), Sinuosity in limestone solution conduits. *Amer. J. Sci., 267*, 230–41.

Deike, R.G. (1969), Relation of jointing to the orientation of solution cavities in the limestone of Central Pennsylvania. *Amer. J. Sci., 267*, 1230–48.

Dill, R.F. (1977), The Blue Holes – geologically significant submerged sink holes and caves off British Honduras and Andros, Bahama Islands. *Proc. 3rd Int. Coral Reef Symp. Miami Florida*, 2 Geology, 238–42. Miami, Florida.

Doornkamp, J.C., Brunsden, D. and Jones, D. (1980), *Geology, Geomorphology and Pedology of Bahrain*, Geoabstracts, Norwich.

Doran, E. (1955), Landforms of the southeast Bahamas. *Univ. Texas Pub.*, no. 5509, pp. 1–38.

Douglas, I. (1968), Some hydrologic factors in the denudation of limestone terrains. *Z. Geomorph., 12*, 241–55.

Drake, J. and Ford, D.C. (1972), The analysis of growth patterns of two generation populations; the example of karst sink holes. *Can. Geog., 16*, 381–4.

Drew, D.P. (1970), Limestone solution within the east Mendip area, Somerset. *Trans. Cave Res. Grp Gt Br., 12*, 259–70.

Drew, D.P. (1975), The limestone hydrology of the Mendip Hills: pp. 171–213 in *Limestones and Caves of the Mendip Hills* (ed. D.I. Smith and D.P. Drew), David and Charles, Newton Abbot, Devon.

References

Drew, D.P. (1983), Accelerated soil erosion in a karst area: The Burren, western Ireland. *J. Hydrol.,* 61, 113–26.

Drew, D.P. and Cohen, J.M. (1978), Geomorphology and sediments of Aillwee Cave, Co. Clare, Ireland. *Proc. Univ. Brist. Spel. Soc.,* 15, 227–40.

Dreybrodt, W. (1981a), The kinetics of calcite precipitation from thin films of calcareous solutions and the growth of speleothems: Revisited. *Chem. Geol.,* 32, 237–45.

Dreybrodt, W. (1981b), Mixing corrosion in $CaCO_3$ $-CO_2$ $-H_2O$ systems and its role in the karstification of limestone areas. *Chem. Geol.,* 32, 221–36.

Droppa, A. (1966), The correlation of some horizontal caves with river terraces. *Studies in Speleology,* 1, 186–92.

Dunham, R.J. (1962), Classification of carbonate rocks according to depositional texture. *Amer. Ass. Petrol. Geol. Mem.,* 1, 108–21.

Dunkerley, D.L. (1979), The morphology and development of Rillenkarren. *Z. Geomorph.,* 23, 332–48.

Dunkerley, D.L. (1980), The study of the evolution of slope form over long periods of time: A review of methodologies and some observational data from Papua New Guinea. *Z. Geomorph.,* 24, 52–67.

Dunkerley, D.L. (1983), Lithology and microtopography in the Chillagoe Karst, Queensland, Australia. *Z. Geomorph.,* 27, 191–204.

Eavis, A.J. (ed.) (1981), *Caves of Mulu '80',* Royal Geographical Society, London.

Egemeier, S.J. (1981), Cavern development by thermal waters. *Bull. Nat. Spel. Soc.,* 43, 31–51.

Ek, C. (1961), Conduits souterrains en relation avec les terrasses fluviales. *Ann. Soc. Géol. Belg.,* 84, 313–40.

Ek, C. (1964), Notes sur les eaux de fonte des glaciers de la Haute Maurienne. *Rev. Belge. Géogr.,* 88, 127–56.

Ek, C. (1970), Carte géologique de la Grotte de Remouchamps (Belgique) Notice explicative. *Ann. Soc. Géol. Belg.,* 93, 287–92.

Emig, W.H. (1917), *Travertine Deposits of Oklahoma.* Oklahoma Geological Survey Bulletins, no. 29.

Ewers, R.O. (1966), Bedding plane anastomoses and their relation to cavern passages. *Bull. Nat. Spel. Soc.,* 28, 133–40.

Fagg, C.C. (1954), The coombes and embayments of the Chalk escarpment. *Proc. Croydon Nat. Hist. Sci. Soc.,* 12, 117–31.

Farr, M. (1980), *The Darkness Beckons,* Diadem Books Ltd, London.

Fermor, J. (1972), The dry valleys of Barbados. *Trans. Inst. Brit. Geogr.,* 57, 153–66.

Fish, J.E. (1977), Karst hydrology and geomorphology of the Sierra de El Abra and the Valles–San huis Potosi region, Mexico: unpublished PhD thesis, McMaster University.

Flathe, H. and Pfeiffer, D. (1965), Grundzuge der Morphologie, Geologie und Hydrogeologie im Karstgebiet Gunung Sewu/Java (Indonesien), *Geol. Jb.,* 83, 533–62.

Flemming, N.C. (1983), Survival of submerged Lithic and Bronze Age artifact sites: A review of case histories: pp. 135–73 in *Quaternary Coastlines and Marine Archaeology* (ed. P.M. Masters and N.C. Flemming), Academic Press, London.

Flenley, J.R. (1979), The late Quaternary vegetational history of the equatorial mountains. *Progress in Physical Geography,* 3, 488–509.

Flint, D.E., Corwin, G., Dings, M.C., Fuller, W., MacNeil, F.S., Saplis, R.A. (1953), Limestone walls of Okinawa. *Bull. Geol. Soc. Amer.*, *64*, 1247–60.

Folk, R.L. (1959), Practical petrographic classification of limestones. *Bull. Am. Ass. Petrol. Geol.*, *43*, 1–38.

Folk, R.L., Roberts, H.H. and Moore, C.H. (1973), Black phytokarst from Hell, Cayman Islands, British West Indies. *Bull. Geol. Soc. Amer.*, *84*, 2351–60.

Ford, D.C.(1964a), Origin of closed depressions in the central Mendip Hills, Somerset, England: pp. 105–6 in *Abstracts of Papers, 20th Int. Geogr. Cong.*, London.

Ford, D.C. (1964b), On the geomorphic history of G.B. Cave, Charterhouse-on-Mendip, Somerset. *Proc. Univ. Bristol Spel. Soc.*, *10*, 149–88.

Ford, D.C. (1965a), Stream potholes as indicators of erosion phases in limestone caves. *Bull. Nat. Spel. Soc.*, *27*, 27–32.

Ford, D.C. (1965b), The origin of limestone caverns: A model from the central Mendip Hills, England. *Bull. Nat. Spel. Soc.*, *27*, 109–32.

Ford, D.C. (1971), Geologic structure and a new explanation of limestone cavern genesis. *Trans. Cave Res. Grp Gt Br.*, *13*, 81–94.

Ford, D.C. (1979), A review of alpine karst in the southern Rocky Mountains of Canada. *Bull. Nat. Spel. Soc.*, *41*, 53–65.

Ford, D.C. (1980), Threshold and limit effects in karst geomorphology: pp. 345–62 in *Thresholds in Geomorphology* (ed. D.R. Coates and J.D. Vilek), Allen & Unwin, London.

Ford, D.C. (1983a), Effects of glaciations upon karst aquifers in Canada. *J. Hydrol.*, *61*, 149–58.

Ford, D.C. (ed.) (1983b), Castleguard Cave and Karst, Columbia Icefields area, Rocky Mountains of Canada: A symposium. *Arctic Alp. Res.*, *15*, 425–554.

Ford, D.C. (1984), Karst groundwater activity and landform genesis in modern permafrost regions in Canada: pp. 340–50 in *Groundwater as a Geomorphic Agent* (ed. R.G. LaFleur), Allen & Unwin, London.

Ford, D.C. and Drake, J.J. (1982), Spatial and temporal variations in karst solution rates: The structure of variability: pp. 147–70 in *Space and Time in Geomorphology* (ed. C.E. Thorn), Allen & Unwin, London.

Ford, D.C. and Ewers, R.O. (1978), The development of cave systems in dimensions of length and depth. *Can. J. Earth Sci.*, *15*, 1783–98.

Ford, D.C., Schwarcz, H.P., Drake, J.J., Gascoyne, M., Harmon, R.S., Latham, A.G. (1981), Estimates of the age of the existing relief within the southern Rocky Mountains of Canada. *Arctic Alp. Res.*, *13*, 1–10.

Ford, D.C. and Stanton, W.L. (1968), The geomorphology of the south–central Mendip Hills. *Proc. Geol. Ass.*, *79*, 401–28.

Ford, T.D. (ed.) (1977), *Limestone and Caves of the Peak District*, Geoabstracts, Norwich.

Ford, T.D. (1978), Chillagoe – a tower karst in decay. *Trans. Br. Cave Res. Ass.*, *5*, 61–84.

Ford, T.D. and Burek, C.V. (1976), Anomalous limestone gorges in Derbyshire. *Mercian Geologist*, *6*, 59–66.

Ford, T.D., Gascoyne, M. and Beck, J.S. (1983), Speleothem dates and Pleistocene chronology in the Peak District of Derbyshire. *Cave Science*, *10*, 103–15.

Ford, T. and Worley, N.E. (1977), Mineral veins and cave development. *Proc. 7th Int. Cong. Speleol.*, 192–3.

References

Frank, R.M. (1971), Cave sediments as palaeoenvironmental indicators, and the sedimentary sequence in Koonalda Cave: pp. 94–104 in *Aboriginal Man and his Environment in Australia* (ed. D.J. Mulvaney and J. Golson), Australian National University Press, Canberra.

Frank, R.M. (1973), Sedimentary and morphological development of the Boremore Caves, New South Wales, 2. *Helictite, 2,* 27–44.

Frank, R. (1975a), Late Quaternary climatic change: Evidence from cave sediments in central eastern New South Wales. *Aust. Geogr. Stud., 13,* 154–68.

Frank, R. (1975b), The significance of speleothems to Quaternary environment: A review of selected literature. *Reading Geographer, 4,* 51–61.

Frank, R. and Jennings, J.N. (1978), Development of a subterranean meander cutoff: The Abercrombie Caves, New South Wales. *Helictite, 16,* 71–85.

Franke, H.W. and Geyh, M.A. (1976), Zur Datierung von Versturzereignissen. *Proc. 6th Int. Cong. Speleol., 3,* 95–100.

Friederich, H. and Smart, P.L. (1981), Dye tracer studies of the unsaturated-zone discharge of the Carboniferous Limestone aquifer of the Mendip Hills, England. *Proc. 8th Int. Cong. Speleol., 1,* 283–6.

Gams, I. (1962), Slepe doline slovenije v primerjalni metodi [Blind valleys in comparative method]. *Zbornik v. kongresa geografov FLRJ v Ljubljani.*

Gams, I. (1963), Der Einfluss der Schichtenlage auf die Richtung der Höhlengänge und auf die Querschnitte in den längsten Höhlen Sloweniens. *Proc. 3rd Int. Cong. Speleol., 2,* 215–19.

Gams, I. (1965), Types of accelerated corrosion: pp. 133–9 in *Problems of the Speleological research* (ed. O. Stelcl), Academia, Prague.

Gams, I. (1966), Faktorji in dinamika Korozije na karbonatnih Kameninah Slovenskeya dinarskega in alpskegan krasa [Factors and dynamics of corrosion of the carbonate rocks in the Dinaric and alpine karst of Slovenia (Yugoslavia)]. *Geografski Vestnik, 38,* 11–68.

Gams, I. (1968), Über die Faktoren, die die Intensität der Sintersedimentation bestimmen. *Proc. 4th Int. Cong. Speleol., 3,* 107–15.

Gams, I. (1969), Some morphological charateristics of the Dinaric karst. *Geogr. J., 135,* 563–72.

Gams, I. (1971), Podtalne Kraske Oblike [Subsoil karst forms]. *Geografski Vestnik, 43,* 27–45.

Gams, I. (ed.) (1973), *Slovenska Kraska Terminologa,* Zveza Geografiskih Ljubljana Institucij Jugoslavije.

Gams, I. (1974), *Kras Zgodovinski Naravoslovniin Geografski Oris,* Izdala Slovenska matica, Ljubljana.

Gams, I. (1978), The polje: The problem of definition. *Z. Geomorph., 22,* 170–81.

Gams, I. (1979), Retention water in karst areas: Its role in influencing total water hardness and denudation rate: pp. 7–16 in *Actes du Symposium Internationale sur l'Érosion Karstique,* U.I.S.

Gams, I. (1981a), Comparative research of limestone solution by means of standard tablets (Second preliminary report of the Commission of Karst Denudation ISU). *Proc. 8th Int. Cong. Speleol., 1,* 273–5.

Gams, I. (1981b), Contribution to morphometry of stalagmites. *Proc. 8th Int. Cong. Speleol., 1,* 276–7.

Gardner, R.A.M. (1983), Aeolianite: p. 265–300 in *Chemical Sediments and Geomorphology* (ed. A.S. Goudie and K. Pye), Academic Press, London.

Gascoyne, M., Benjamin, G.J., Schwarcz, H.P., and Ford, D.C. (1979), Sea-level lowering during the Illinoian Glaciation: Evidence from a Bahama 'Blue Hole'. *Science, 205,* 806–8.

Gascoyne, M., Currant, A.P. and Lord, T.C. (1981), Ipswichian fauna of Victoria Cave and the marine palaeoclimatic record. *Nature, 294,* 652–4.

Gascoyne, M., Ford, D.C. and Schwarcz, H.P. (1981), Late Pleistocene chronology and paleoclimate of Vancouver Island determined from cave deposits. *Can. J. Earth Sci., 18,* 1643–52.

Gautier, E.F. (1914–15), Le Rocher de Sel de Djelfa. *Ann. Géogr., 23–4,* 245–60.

Gavazzi, A. (1904), Die Seen des Karstes. *Abh. K. K. Geogr. Ges. Wien., 5.*

Gavrilović, D. (1969), Kegelkarst–Elemente im Relief des Gebirges Beljanica, Jugoslavien: pp. 159–66 in *Problems of the Karst Denudation* (ed. O. Stelcl), Institute of Geography, Brno.

Gellert, J. (1962), Der Tropenkarst in Sudchina im Rahmen der Gebirgsformung des Landes. *Verh. dt. Geogr. Tags, 33,* 376–84.

Gerstenhauer, A. (1960), Der tropische Kegelkarst in Tabasco (Mexico). *Z. Geomorph., supplementary issue, 2,* 22–48.

Gèze, B. (1949), Les gouffres à phosphate du Quercy. *Ann. Spéléol., 4,* 89–107.

Gèze, B. (1953), La genèse des gouffres. *Proc. 1st Int. Cong. Spéléol., 2,* 11–23.

Gèze, B. (1958), Sur quelques caractères fondamentaux des circulations karstiques. *Ann. Spéléol., 13,* 5–22.

Gèze, B. (1965), *La spéléologie scientifique,* Seuil, Paril.

Gillieson, D. (1985), Geomorphic development of limestone caves in the Highlands of Papua New Guinea. *Z. Geomorph., 29,* 51–70.

Gillieson, D. and Mountain, M.J. (1983), Environmental history of Nombe rock-shelter, Papua New Guinea Highlands. *Archaeology in Oceania, 18,* 53–62.

Gines, A., Gines, J. and Pomar, L. (1981), Phreatic speleothems in coastal caves of Majorca (Spain) as indicators of Mediterranean Pleistocene paleolevels. *Proc. 8th Int. Cong. Speleol., 2,* 533–6.

Glazek, J. (1966), On the karst phenomena in North Vietnam. *Bull. Acad. Polonaise Sci., 14,* 45–50.

Glazek, J., Lindner, L. and Wysoczanski-Minkowicz, T. (1977), Geologiczna interpretaya stanowiska fauny staro plejstocenskiez Kozi Grzbiet w Gorach Swietokryskich [Old Pleistocene cave deposits with fauna at Kozi Grzbiet (Holy Cross Mts, Central Poland) – a geological interpretation]. *Kras i Speleologia, 1,* 13–28.

Glazek, J., Rudnicki, J. and Szynkiewicz, A. (1977), Proglacial caves – a special genetic type of cave in glaciated areas. *Proc. 7th Int. Cong. Speleol.,* 215–17.

Glennie, E.A. (1948), Some points relating to Ogof Ffynnon Ddu. *Trans. Cave Res. Grp Gt Br., 1,* 13–25.

Glennie, E.A. (1950), Further notes on Ogof Ffynnon Ddu. *Trans. Cave Res. Grp Gt Br., 1,* (3), 1–47.

Glennie, E.A. (1958), Nameless streams: Proposed new terms. *Cave Res. Grp Gt Br. Newsletter,* 72–7, 22–3.

Glew, J.R. and Ford, D.C. (1980), A simulation study of the development of Rillenkarren. *Earth Surf. Proc., 5,* 25–36.

Goede, A. (1973), Hydrological observations at the Junee resurgence and a brief regional description of the Junee area, Tasmania. *Helictite, 11,* 3–24.

Goede, A. (1983), Holocene climatic change – evidence from a Tasmanian speleothem. *International Symposium on the Late Cainozoic Palaeoclimates*

References

of the Southern Hemisphere (29 August–2 September 1983, Swaziland), Balkema, Rotterdam.

Goede, A. and Harmon, R.S. (1983), Radiometric dating of Tasmanian speleothems – evidence of cave evolution and climatic change. *J. Geol. Soc. Aust., 30,* 89–100.

Goldie, H.S. (1973), The limestone pavements of Craven. *Trans. Cave Res. Gp Gt Br., 15,* 175–90.

Goldie, H.S. (1978), Morphometry of limestone pavements of Farleton Knott (Cumbria, England). *Trans. Br. Cave Res. Ass., 8,* 207–24.

Goodchild, J.G. (1875), Glacial erosion. *Geol. Mag., 12,* 232–8, 356–62.

Goodchild, M.S., and Ford, D.C. (1971), Analysis of scallop patterns by simulation under controlled conditions. *J. Geol., 79,* 52–62.

Goran, C. (1978), Le karst du plateau de Mehedinti. *Tran. Inst. Spel. Emile · Racovitza, 17,* 165–83.

Gospodarić, R. (1974), [Fluvial sediments in Krizna Jama]. *Acta Carsologica, VI/25,* 327–66.

Goudie, A. (ed.) (1981), *Geomorphological Techniques,* Allen & Unwin, London.

Goudie, A. (1983a), Calcrete: pp. 93–131 in *Chemical Sediments and Geomorphology* (ed. A.S. Goudie and K. Pye), Academic Press, London.

Goudie, A. (1983b). *Environmental change,* Clarendon Press, Oxford.

Green, H.S. (ed.) (1984), *Pontnewydd Cave.* National Museum of Wales, Cardiff.

Gregg, W.J. (1974), Structural control of cavern development in Howe Caverns, Schoharie County, New York. *Bull. Nat. Spel. Soc., 36,* 1–6.

Gregory, J.W. (1911), Constructive waterfalls. *Scot. Geog. Mag., 27,* 537–46.

Grimes, K.G. (1975), Pseudokarst: Definition and types. *Proc. 10th Bienn. Conf. Aust. Spel. Fed.,* pp. 6–10.

Grodzicki, J. (1985), Genesis of the Nullarbor Plain caves in southern Australia. *Z. Geomorph., 29,* 37–49.

Groom, G.E. and Coleman, A. (1958), *The Geomorphology and Speleogenesis of the Dachstein Caves.* Cave Research Group of Great Britain, Occasional Paper no. 2.

Grund, A. (1903), Die Karsthydrographie. *Geogr. Abh., 7,* 1–200.

Grund, A. (1910), Das Karstphänomen. *Geol. Charakterbilder, 3.*

Grund, A. (1914), Der geographische Zyklus im Karst. *Z. Ges. Erdk. Berl.,* pp. 621–40.

Guangxi Chuang Autonomous Region Geological Bureau (1976), *On the Underground River System of the Tisu Karst Area, Tu-an County, Kwangsi.* Beijing, China.

Guilcher, A. (1953), Essai sur la zonation et la distribution des formes littorales de dissolution du calcaire. *Ann. Géogr., 72,* 161–79.

Guilcher, A. (1958), Coastal corrosion forms in limestone around the Bay of Biscay. *Scot. Geog. Mag., 35,* 137–49.

Gunn, J. (1981), Hydrological processes in karst depressions. *Z. Geomorph., 25,* 313–31.

Gunn, J. (1982), Magnitude and frequency proporties of dissolved solids transport. *Z. Geomorph., 26,* 505–11.

Gunn, J. (1983), Point-recharge of limestone aquifers – a model from New Zealand karst. *J. Hydrol., 61,* 19–29.

Gušić, B. (1973), Über die Entwaldung unseres Karstes. *Proc. 4th Int. Cong. Speleol.*, 1–2, 93–117.

Hack, J.T. (1960), Interpretation of erosional topography in humid temperate regions. *Amer. J. Sci.*, 238A, 80–97.

Hall, R.D. (1976), Investigations of sinkhole stratigraphy and hydrology, south–central Indiana. *Bull. Nat. Spel. Soc.*, 38, 88–92.

Hallet, B. (1976), Deposits formed by subglacial precipitation of $CaCO_3$. *Bull. Geol. Soc. Amer.*, 87, 1003–15.

Halliday, W.R. (1957), *The Origin of the Limestone Caves of the Sierra Nevada of California*. Bulletin of the Western Speleological Survey, Miscellaneous Series, no. 3.

Halliday, W.R. (1960), Changing concepts of speleogenesis. *Bull. Nat. Spel. Soc.*, 22, 23–9.

Halliwell, R.A., Ternan, J.L. and Pitty, A.F. (1974), Introduction to the karst hydrology of north-west Yorkshire: pp. 106–14 in *Limestone and Caves of North-west England* (ed. A.C. Waltham and M.M. Sweeting), David and Charles, Newton Abbot, Devon.

Halstead, L.B. and Nicoll, P.G. (1971), Fossilized caves of Mendip. *Studies in Speleology*, 2, 93–102.

Hancock, P.L. (1968), Joints and faults: The morphological aspects of their origin. *Proc. Geol. Ass.*, 79, 146–51.

Harmon, R.S. and Atkinson, T.C. (1981), The mineralogy of Castleguard Cave. *Proc. 8th Int. Cong. Speleol.*, 428–32.

Harmon, R.S., Schwarcz, H.P. and Ford, D.C. (1978), Late Pleistocene sea level history of Bermuda. *Quat. Res.*, 9, 205–18.

Harmon, R.S., Thompson, P., Schwarcz, H.P. and Ford, D.C. (1978), Late Pleistocene paleoclimates of North America as inferred from stable isotope studies of speleothems. *Quat. Res.*, 9, 54–70.

Harmon, R.S., Mittener, R.M., Kriausakul, N., Land L.S., Schwarcz, H.P., Garrett, P., Larson, G.J., Vacher, H.L. and Rowe, M. (1983), U-series and amino acid racemization geochronology of Bermuda: Implications for eustatic sea-level fluctuation over the past 250 000 years. *Palaeogeography, Palaeoclimatology and Palaeoecology*, 44, 41–70.

Harrison, J.V. (1930), The geology of some salt plugs in Laristan (Southern Persia). *Q.J. Geol. Soc. Lond.*, 86, 463–520.

Haserodt, K. (1969), Beobachtungen zur Karstdenudation am Kluftkarren in glazialüberformten alpinen Bereichen: pp. 123–38 in *Problems of the Karst Denudation* (ed. O. Stelcl), Institute of Geography, Brno.

Heinemann, U., Klaaden, K., Pfeffer, K.H. (1977), Neue Aspekte zum Phänomen der Rillenkarren. *Abh. Karst Höhlenkunde. Reihe A-Speläologie*, 15, 56–80.

Hendy, C.H. (1970), The use of C-14 in the study of cave processes: pp. 419–43 in *Radiocarbon Variations and Absolute Chronology, Nobel Symposium 12* (ed. I.U. Olsson), Almquist and Wiksell, Stockholm.

Hendy, C.H. and Wilson, A.T. (1968), Palaeoclimatic data from speleothems. *Nature*, 219, 48–51.

Hess, J.W. and Harmon, R.S. (1981), Geochronology of speleothems from the Flint Ridge – Mammoth Cave System. *Proc. 8th Int. Cong. Speleol.*, 2, 433–6.

Hey, R.W. (1963), Pleistocene screes in Cyrenaica (Libya). *Eiszeitalter und Gegenwart*, 14: 77–84.

Hill, C.A. (1976), *Cave Minerals*, National Speleological Society, Huntsville, Alabama.

K

References

Hill, C.A. (1981), Speleogenesis of Carlsbad Caverns and other caves of the Guadelupe Mountains. *Proc. 8th Int. Cong. Speleol.*, 1, 143–4.

Hills, E.S. (1971), A study of cliffy coastal profiles based on examples in Victoria, Australia: 2. *Geomorph.*, 15, 137–80.

Hodgkin, E.P. (1970), Geomorphology and biological erosion of limestone coasts in Malaysia. *Bull. Geol. Soc. Malaysia*, 3, 27–51.

Holmes, J.W. and Colville, J.S. (1970a), Grassland hydrology in a karstic region of southern Australia. *J. Hydrol.*, 10, 38–58.

Holmes, J.W. and Colville, J.S. (1970b), Forest hydrology in a karstic region of southern Australia. *J. Hydrol.*, 10, 59–74.

Hooper, J.H.D. (1958), Bat erosion as a factor in cave formation. *Nature*, 182, 1464.

Hopley, D. (1982), *The Geomorphology of the Great Barrier Reef*, John Wiley, New York.

Hopley, D. and Mackay, M.G. (1978), An investigation of morphological zonation of beach rock erosional features. *Earth Surf. Proc.*, 3, 363–77.

Horberg, L. (1949), Geomorphic history of the Carlsbad Caverns area, New Mexico. *J. Geol.*, 57, 464–76.

Howard, A.D. (1963), The development of karst features. *Bull. Nat. Spel. Soc.*, 25, 45–65.

Howard, A.D. (1964), Process of limestone cavern development. *Int. J. Spel.*, 1, 47–60.

Howard, A.D. (1968), Stratigraphic and structural controls on landform development in the central Kentucky karst. *Bull. Nat. Spel. Soc.*, 30, 95–114.

Hughes, P.J. (1978), Weathering in sandstone shelters in the Sydney Basin and the survival of rock art: pp. 36–41 in *Conservation of Rock Art*, Inst. Cons. Cult. Mat., Canberra.

Hundt, R. (1950), *Erdfalltektonik*, Knapp, Halle.

Hunt, G. (1970), The origin and development of Mullamullang Cave, Nullarbor Plain, Western Australia. *Helictite*, 8, 3–22.

Iliffe, T.M. (1981), The submarine caves of Bermuda. *Proc. 8th Int. Cong. Speleol.* 1, 161–3.

Ineson, J. (1962), A hydrogeological study of the permeability of the Chalk. *J. Inst. Water Eng.*, 16, 449–63.

Ireland, P. (1979), Geomorphological variations of case-hardening in Puerto Rico. *Z. Geomorph.*, supplementary issue, 32, 9–20.

Jacobson, G. and Hill, P. (1980), Hydrogeology of a raised coral atoll – Niue Island, South Pacific Ocean. *BMR J. Aust. Geol. Geophys.*, 5, 271–8.

Jaeger, J.C. and Cook, N.G.W. (1969), *Fundamentals of Rock Mechanics*, Methuen, London.

James, J.M. (1977), Carbon dioxide in the cave atmosphere. *Trans. Br. Cave Res, Ass.*, 4, 417–29.

James, J.M. (1980), Water chemistry of the Atea Kananda and the related drainage area. *Helictite*, 18, 8–24.

James, J.M. and Dyson, H.J. (eds) (1980), *Caves and Karst in the Muller Range*, Speleological Research Council, Sydney.

Jennings, J.N. (1963), Geomorphology of the Dip Cave, Wee Jasper, New South Wales, *Helictite, 1*, 43–58.

Jennings, J.N. (1964), Geomorphology of Punchbowl and Signature Caves, Wee Jasper, New South Wales, *Helictite, 2*, 57–80.

Jennings, J.N. (1965), The Big Hole near Braidwood, New South Wales. *J. Proc. Roy. Soc. N.S.W.*, 98, 215–19.
264

References

Jennings, J.N. (1967), Some karst areas of Australia: pp. 256–92 in *Landform Studies from Australia and New Guinea* (ed. J.N. Jennings and J.A. Mabbutt), Australian National University Press, Canberra.

Jennings, J.N. (1968), Syngenetic karst in Australia: pp. 41–110 in *Contributions to the Study of Karst*, Dept of Geography Publication no. G/5, Australian National University.

Jennings, J.N. (1969), Karst of the seasonally humid tropics in Australia: pp. 149–58 in *Problems of the Karst Denudation* (ed. O. Stelcl), Institute of Geography, Brno, Czechoslovakia.

Jennings, J.N. (1972), Observations at the Blue Waterholes, March 1965–April 1969, and limestone solution on Cooleman Plain, N.S.W. *Helictite, 10*, 3–46.

Jennings, J.N. (1975), Doline morphometry as a morphogenetic tool: New Zealand examples. *New Zealand Geog., 31*, 6–28.

Jennings, J.N. (1976), A test of the importance of cliff-foot caves in tower karst development. *Z. Geomorph.*, supplementary issue, 26, 92–7.

Jennings, J.N. (1977), Caves around Canberra: pp. 79–95 in *Proc. 11th Bienn. Conf. Aust. Spel. Fed. Canberra 1976*.

Jennings, J.N. (1978a), Genetic varieties in A-tents and related features. *Aust. Geogr. Stud., 14*, 34–38.

Jennings, J.N. (1978b), Limestone solution on bare karst and covered karst compared. *Trans. Br. Cave Res. Ass., 5*, 215–20.

Jennings, J.N. (1981a), Further results from limestone tablet experiments at Cooleman Plain. *Aust. Geogr. Stud., 19*, 224–7.

Jennings, J.N. (1981b), Morphoclimatic control – a tale of piss and wind or a case of the baby out with the bathwater? *Proc. 8th Int. Cong. Speleol., 1*, 367–8.

Jennings, J.N. (1982a), Principles and problems of reconstructing karst history. *Helictite, 20*, 37–52.

Jennings, J.N. (1982b), Karst of northeastern Queensland reconsidered. *Tower Karst Chillagoe Caving Club*, Occasional Paper no. 4, pp. 13–52.

Jennings, J.N. (1982c), Quaternary complications in fluviokarst at Cooleman Plain, N.S.W. *Aust. Geogr. Stud., 15*, 137–47.

Jennings, J.N. (1982d), Limestone mountains transformed by ice. *Geog. Mag., 54*, 268–76.

Jennings, J.N. (1983a), Sandstone pseudokarst or karst? pp. 21–30 in *Aspects of Australian Sandstone Landscapes* (ed. R.W. Young and G.C. Nanson), Australia and New Zealand Geomorphological Group Special Publication no. 1.

Jennings, J.N. (1983b), The disregarded karst of the arid and semiarid domain. *Karstologia, 1*, 61–73.

Jennings, J.N. and Bao, H. (1980), Determining doline origins: A case study. *Helictite, 18*, 3–7.

Jennings, J.N., Bao, H. and Spate, A.P. (1980), Equilibrium versus events in river behaviour and blind valleys at Yarrangobilly, New South Wales. *Helictite, 18*, 39–54.

Jennings, J.N. and Bik, M.T. (1962), Karst morphology in Australian New Guinea. *Nature, 194*, 1036–8.

Jennings, J.N., Brush, J.B., Nicoll, R.S. and Spate, A.P. (1976), Karst stream self-capture at London Bridge, Burra Creek, N.S.W. *Aust. Geogr., 13*, 238–49.

Jennings, J.N., James, J.M. and Montgomery, N.R. (1982), The origin and evolution of the caves. *Syd. Spel. Soc. Occ. Pap., 8*, 83–104.

References

Jennings, J.N. and Sweeting, M.M. (1959), Underground breach of a divide, *Aust. J. Sci., 21*, 261−2.

Jennings, J.N. and Sweeting M.M. (1963), The Limestone Ranges of the Fitzroy Basin Western Australia. *Bonner. Geogr. Abh., 32*.

Jennings, J.N. and Sweeting, M.M. (1966), Old Napier Downs Cave, West Kimberley, W.A. *Helictite, 42*, 25−32.

Johnson, D. (1932), Rock fans of arid regions. *Amer. J. Sci., 223*, 389−416.

Jones, R.J. (1965), Aspects of the biological weathering of limestone pavement. *Proc. Geol. Ass., 76*, 421−33.

Jordan, G.F. (1954), Large sinkholes in Straits of Florida. *Bull. Amer. Ass. Petrol. Geol., 38*, 1810−17.

Jordan, R.H. (1950), An interpretation of Floridian karst. *J. Geol., 58*, 261−8.

Karanjac, J. and Gunay, G. (1980), Dumanli Spring, Turkey − the largest karstic spring in the world? *J. Hydrol., 45*, 219−31.

Kastning, E.H. Jr (1984), Hydrogeomorphic evolution of karsted plateaus in response to regional rectonism:.pp. 351−82 in *Groundwater as a Geomorphic Agent* (ed. R.G. LaFleur), Allen & Unwin, Boston.

Katzer, F. (1909), *Karst und Karsthydrographie.* Zur Kunde der Balkanhalbinsel, vol. 8, Sarajevo.

Kavalieris, I. and Martini, J. (1976), Structural control of some western Transvaal caves *S. Afr. J. Sci., 72*, 308−9.

Kayser, K. (1934), Morphologische Studien in Westmontenegro II: Rumpftreppe Cetinje, Formenschatz der Karstabtragung. *Z. Ges. Erdk. Berlin*, pp. 26−49, 81−102.

Kemmerly, P.R. (1976), Definitive doline characteristics in the Clarksville quadrangle, Tennessee. *Bull. Geol. Soc. Amer., 87*, 42−6.

Kemmerly, P.R. and Towe, S.K. (1978), Karst depressions in a time context. *Earth Surf. Proc., 35*, 355−62.

Kerney, M.P., Brown, E.H. and Chandler, T.J. (1964), The Late-glacial and Postglacial history of the Chalk escarpment near Brook, Kent. *Phil. Trans. Roy. Soc. B., 248*, 135−204.

King, L. (1951), The geology of the Makapan and other caves. *Trans. R. Soc. S. Afr., 33*, 121−51.

King-Webster, W.A. and Kenny, J.S. (1958), Bat erosion as a factor in cave formation. *Nature, 181*, 1813.

Kirk, R.M. (1977), Rates and forms of erosion on intertidal platforms at Kaikoura Peninsula, New Zealand. *New Zealand J. Geol. Geophys., 20*, 571−613.

Kirkaldy, J.F. (1950), Solution of the Chalk in the Mimms valley, Herts. *Proc. Geol. Ass., 61*, 219−24.

Klaer, W. (1957), Karstkegel, Karstinselberge, und Poljeboden, am Beispiel Jezeropoljes. *Pet. Mitt., 101*, 108−11.

Kozarski, S. (1962−3), Sub-tropical needle karst between Kweiling and Yangshue, Kwangsi Chuang Autonomous Region, China. *Bull. Soc. Amis. Sci. Lett. Poznan*, B, *18*, 139−56.

Krebs, N. (1929), Ebenheiten und Inselberge im Karst. *Z. Ges. Erdk. Berl.*, pp. 81−94.

Krejci-Graf, K. (1935), Felsen aus Salz in Rumanien. *Natur Volk., 65*, 116−20.

Krumbein, W.E. (1969), Über den Einfluss der Mikroflora auf die exogene Dynamik (Verwitterung und Krustenbildung). *Geol. Rund., 58*, 333−63.

Kukla, J. and Lozek, V. (1958), K problematice vyzkumu jeskynnich vyplni. *Cslky Kras, 11,* 19–59.

Kunaver, J. (1976), On quantity, effects and measuring of the karst denudation in western Julian Alps – Kannin Mountains: pp. 117–226 in *Karst Processes and Relevant Landforms* (ed. I. Gams), University of Ljubljana.

Kunsky, J. (1958), *Karst et grottes* (trans. Heintz), Bur. Rech. Geol. Geophys. Min., Paris.

Kyrle, G. (1923), *Grundriss der theoretischer Speläologie.* Österreichische Staatsdruckerei, Vienna.

Lamarche, V.C. (1967), Spheroidal weathering of thermally metamorphosed limestone and dolomite, White Mountains, California. *U. S. Geol. Surv. Prof. Pap., 575–C,* 32–7.

Lasserre, G. (1954), Notes sur le karst de Guadeloupe. *Erdkunde, 8,* 115.

Latham, A.G., Schwarcz, A.P., Ford, D.C. and Pearce, G.W. (1979), Palaeomagnetism of stalagmite deposits. *Nature, 280,* 383–5.

Lauritzen, S.E. (1981), Statistical symmetry analysis of scallops. *Bull. Nat. Spel. Soc., 43,* 52–5.

Lauritzen, S-E., Ive, A. and Wilkinson, B. (1983), Mean annual runoff and the scallop flow regime in a subarctic environment. *Cave Science, 10,* 97–102.

Lavalle, P. (1968), Karst morphology in south central Kentucky. *Geogr. Ann., 50,* 94–108.

Leach, A.L. (1933), The geology and scenery of Tenby and the south Pembrokeshire coast. *Proc. Geol. Ass., 44,* 187–226.

Lehmann, H. (1936), *Morphologische Studien auf Java,* Engelhorn, Stuttgart.

Lehmann, H. (1959), Studien über Poljen in den venezianischen Voralpen und im Hochapennin. *Erdkunde, 12,* 258–89

Lehmann, H. (1960), La terminologie classique du karst sous l'aspect critique de la morphologie climatique moderne. *Revue Géogr. Lyon.,* pp. 1–6.

Lehmann, H., Krömmelbein, K. and Lötschert, W. (1956), Karstmorphologiche, geologische und botanische Studien in der Sierra de los Organos auf Cuba. *Erdkunde, 10,* 185–204.

Lehmann, H., Roglic, J., Rathjens, C., Lasserre, G., Harrassowitz, H., Corbel, J., Birot, P. (1954), Das Karstphänomen in den verschiedenen Klimazonen. *Erdkunde, 8,* 112–22.

Lehmann, O. (1927), Das Tote Gebirge als Hochkarst. *Mitt. Geogr. Ges. Wien., 70,* 201–42.

Lehmann, O. (1932), *Die Hydrographie des Karstes,* Deuticke, Leipzig.

Leighton, M.W. and Pendexter, C. (1962), Carbonate rock types. *Amer. Ass. Petrol. Geol. Mem., 1,* 33–61.

Lewis, I.D. (1979), The Nullarbor Plain – and the world's longest cave dive. *Caving International, 3,* 3–10.

Ley, R.G. (1979), The development of marine karren along the Bristol Channel coastline. *Z. Geomorph.,* supplementary issue, *32,* 75–89.

Löffler, E. (1974), Piping and pseudokarst features in the tropical lowlands of New Guinea. *Erdkunde, 28,* 13–18.

Löffler, E. (1977), *Geomorphology of Papua New Guinea.* Australian National University Press, Canberra.

Löffler, E. (1978), Karst features in igneous rocks in Papua New Guinea: pp. 238–49 in *Landform Evolution in Australia* (ed. J.L. Davies and M.A.J. Williams), Australian National University Press, Canberra.

References

Logan, B.W., Rezak, R. and Ginsburg, R.N. (1964), Classification and environmental significance of algal stromatolites. *J. Geol.*, 72, 68–83.

Logan, B.W. and Semeniuk, V. (1976), *Dynamic Metamorphism, Processes and Products in Devonian Carbonate Rocks, Canning Basin, Western Australia.* Geological Society of Australia Special Publications, no. 6.

Louis, H. (1956), Die Entstehung der Poljen und ihre Stellung in der Karstabtragung auf Grund von Beobachtungen in Taurus. *Erdkunde, 10,* 33–53.

Lowry, D.C. (1967), The origin of Easter Cave doline, Western Australia. *Aust. Geogr. Stud., 10,* 4, 300–2.

Lowry, D.C. and Jennings, J.N. (1974), The Nullarbor karst Australia. *Z. Geomorph., 18,* 35–81.

Lozek, V. (1965), The formation of rock shelters and foam sinters in the high limestone Carpathians: pp. 73–84 in *Problems of the Speleological Research* (ed. O. Stelcl), Academia, Prague.

Lozek, V. and Skrivanek, F. (1965), The significance of fissures and their fills for dating of karst processes. *Cesky. Kras., 17,* 7–22.

Lozinski, W. von (1907), Die Karsterscheinungen in Galazisch–Podolien. *Jb. geol. Reichsamst. Wien.*, pp. 683–726.

Lundberg, J. (1977a), Analysis of the form of Rillenkarren from the tower karst of Chillagoe, North Queensland, Australia. *Proc. 7th Int. Cong. Speleol.*, pp. 294–6.

Lundberg, J. (1977b), Karren of the littoral zone, Burren district, Co. Clare, Ireland. *Proc. 7th Int. Cong. Speleol.*, pp. 291–3.

McConnell, H. and Horn, J.M. (1972), Probabilities of surface karst: pp.111–33 in *Spatial Analysis in Geomorphology* (ed. R. Chorley), Methuen, London.

McDonald, R.C. (1975), Observations on hillslope erosion in tower karst topography of Belize. *Bull. Geol. Soc. Amer., 86,* 255–6.

McDonald, R.C. (1976), Limestone morphology in South Sulawesi, Indonesia. *Z. Geomorph.*, supplementary issue, 26, 79–91.

McDonald, R.C. (1979), Tower karst geomorphology in Belize. *Z. Geomorph.* supplementary issue,32, 35–45.

Maclay, R.W. and Small, T.A. (1983), Hydrostratigraphic subdivisions and fault barriers of the Edwards Aquifer, south-central Texas, USA. *J. Hydrol., 61,* 127–46.

McLean, R.F. (1974), Geologic significance of bioerosion of beachrock: pp. 401–8 in *Proceedings of the 2nd International Coral Reef Symposium, Great Barrier Reef Committee, Brisbane, December 1974.*

Magaldi, D. and Sauro, U. (1982), Landforms and soil evolution in some karstic areas of the Lessini Mountains and Monte Baldo (Verona, Northern Italy). *Geogr. Fis. Dinam. Quat., 5,* 82–101.

Maire, R. (1981), Synthèse hydrogéologique et karstologique. *Spelunca Suppl., 3,* 23–30.

Maire, R. (1982), Recherches hydrogéomorphologiques et spéléologiques sur le bassin-versant du Saint Georges et le réseau du BU56 (−1338m) (Navarre et Pyrénées Atlantiques). *Rev. Géog. Alp., 70,* 215–25.

Malott, C.A. (1932), Lost River at Wesley Chapel Gulf, Orange County, Indiana. *Proc. Indiana Acad. Sci., 41,* 285–316.

Malott, C.A. (1937), Invasion theory of cavern development. *Proc. Geol. Soc. Amer.*, p. 323.

Malott, C.A. (1952), The swallow holes of Lost River, Orange County, Indiana. *Proc. Indiana Acad. Sci.,* 61, 187–231.

Mangin, A. (1974–5), Contribution à l'étude hydrodynamique des aquifères. *Ann. Spéléol.,* 29, 283–332; 29, 495–601; 30, 121–4.

Marker, M.E. (1976), Cenotes: a class of enclosed karst hollows. *Z. Geomorph.* supplementary issue, 26, 104–23.

Marker, M.E. and Brook, G.A. (1970), *Echo Cave: A tentative Quaternary Chronology for the Eastern Transvaal.* Department of Geography and Environmental Studies, University of Witwatersand, Occasional Papers no. 3.

Martel, É. (1910), La théorie de la 'Grundwasser' et les eaux souterraines du karst. *Géographie,* 21, 126–30.

Martel, É. (1921), *Nouveau traité des eaux souterraines,* Doin, Paris.

Martin, H.A. (1973), Palynology and historical ecology of some cave excavations in the Australian Nullarbor. *Aust. J. Bot.,* 21, 283–316.

Martin, J. (1981), *Le moyen Atlas Central Étude gémorphologique,* Serv. Géol. Maroc, Rabat.

Martini, J. (1981a), The control of karst development with reference to the formation of caves in poorly soluble rocks in the eastern Transvaal, South Africa. *Proc. 8th Int. Cong. Speleol.,* 1, 4–5.

Martini, J. (1981b), Early Proterozoic paleokarst of the Transvaal, South Africa. *Proc. 8th Int. Cong. Speleol.,* 1, 6–8.

Maucci, W. (1960), La speleogenesi nel Carso Triestino. *Bull. Soc. Adr. Sc. Nat.,* 51, 233–54.

Maximovich, G.A. (1963), *Osnovi Karstovedenya* [Principles of Karst Science]. Institute of Karstology and Speleology, Perm.

Mazur, E. and Jakal, J. (1976), Basic principles of the typological division of karst in the Western Carpathians. *Proc. 6th Int. Cong. Speleol.,* 2, 237–48.

Melik, A. (1955), *Kraska polja Slovenije v Pleistocenu,* Slovenska Akad. Znanosti in Umetnosti 7. Inst. Geog. 3 (Ljubljana).

Milanović, P.T. (1979), *Hidrogeologija Karsta 1. Metode Istrazulivanja,* Hidroetcktrane na Trebisnjici, Trebinje.

Miller, T. (1983), Hydrology and hydrochemistry of the Caves Branch karst, Belize. *J. Hydrol.,* 61, 83–8.

Miller, V.C. (1953), *A Quantitative Geomorphic Study of Drainage Basin Characteristics in the Clinch Mountain Area Virginia and Tennessee,* Department of Geology, Columbia University Technical Report no. 3, New York.

Mills, L.D.J. and Waltham, A.C. (1981), Geomorphology of the Matienzo caves. *Trans. Br. Cave Res. Ass.,* 8, 68–84.

Miotke, F.D. (1968), Karstmorphologische Studien in der glazial – überformten Höhenstufe der 'Picos de Europa', Nordspanien. *Jb. geogr. Gesell. Hannover Sonderheft,* 4.

Miotke, F.D. (1973), The subsidence of the surface between mogotes in Puerto Rico east of Arecibo. *Caves and Karst,* 15 (1), 1–12.

Miotke, F.D. (1974), Carbon dioxide and the soil atmosphere. *Abh. Karst und Höhlenkunde,* A. Spel., 9, 1–49.

Miserez, J.J. (1976), Complements to the water geochemistry of the karstic system of the Ljubljanica River: p. 82–92 in *Underground Water Tracing Investigations in Slovenia 1972–1975* (ed. R. Gospodarić and P. Habič). Institute of Karst Research, SAZU, Postojna.

References

Mistardis, G. (1968), Investigations upon influences of sea level fluctuations on underground karstification in some coastal regions of south Greece. *Proc. 4th Int. Cong. Speleol.*, 3, 335–40.

Mitchell, C.W. and Willimott, D. (1974), Dayas of the Morocco Sahara and other arid regions. *Geographical Journal*, 140, 441–53.

Moneymaker, B. (1941), Sub-river solution cavities in the Tennessee Valley. *J. Geol.*, 49, 74–86.

Monroe, W.H. (1966), Formation of tropical karst topography by limestone solution and reprecipitation. *Carrib. J. Sci.*, 6, 1–7.

Monroe, W.H. (1968), The karst features of northern Puerto Rico. *Bull. Nat. Spel. Soc.*, 30, 75–86.

Monroe, W.H. (1969), Evidence of subterranean sheet solution under weathered, detrital cover in Puerto Rico: pp. 111–21 in *Problems of the Karst Denudation* (ed. O. Stelcl), Brno.

Montoriol-Pous, J. (1971), Estudio de una captura karstico-marina en la isla de Cabrua (Balearas). *Acta Geological Hispanica*, 6, 89–91.

Moore, G.W. (1960a), Introduction to the origin of limestone caves. *Bull. Nat. Spel. Soc.*, 22, 1, 3–4.

Moore, G.W. (1960b), Geology of Carlsbad Caverns, New Mexico. *Guide Book, Nat. Spel. Soc.*, 1, 10–18.

Moore, G.W. (1962), The growth of stalactites. *Bull. Nat. Spel. Soc.*, 24, 95–106.

Morawetz, S. (1967), Zur Frage der Karstebenheiten. *Z. Geomorph.*, 11, 1–13.

Murray, P., Goede, A. and Bada, J.L. (1980), Pleistocene human occupation at Beginners Luck Cave, Florentine Valley, Tasmania. *Archaeol. Phys. Anthropol. Oceania*, 15, 142–52.

Myers, J.O. (1948), The formation of Yorkshire caves and potholes. *Trans. Cave Res. Grp Gt Br.*, 1(1), 26–9.

Newson, M.D. (1971), The role of abrasion in cavern development. *Trans. Cave Res. Grp Gt Br.*, 13, 101–7.

Nicod, J. (1972), *Pays et Paysages du Calcaire*, Presses Universitaires, Paris.

Nicod, J. (1976a), Corrosion du type crypto-karstique dans les karsts Méditerranéens: pp. 171–80 in *Karst Processes and Relevant Landforms* (ed. I. Gams), Department of Geography, Ljubjlana University.

Nicod, J. (1976b), Les Dolomites de la Brenta (Italie) karst haut-alpin typique et le problème des cuvettes glacio-karstiques. *Z. Geomorph.*, supplementary issue, 26, 35–57.

Nir, D. (1964), Les marges méridionales du phénomène karstique en Israel. *Rev. Geogr. Alp.*, 52, 533–41.

Obert, L. and Duvall, W.I. (1967), *Rock Mechanics and the Design of Structure in Rock*, John Wiley, New York.

Ollier, C.D. (1963), The origin of limestone caves. *Helictite*, 1(2), 8–12.

Ollier, C.D. (1975), Coral island geomorphology – the Trobriand Islands. *Z. Geomorph.*, 19, 164–90.

Ollier, C.D. and Harrop, J.F. (1963), The caves of Mont Hayo, Belgian Congo. *Bull. Nat. Spel. Soc.*, 25, 73–8.

Ollier, C.D., Tratman, E.K. (1969), Geomorphology of the caves: pp. 59–95 in *The Caves of North-west Clare Ireland* (ed. E.K. Tratman), David and Charles, Newton Abbot, Devon.

Ongley, E.D. (1968), An analysis of the meandering tendency of Serpentine Cave, NSW *J. Hydrol.*, 6, 15–32.

Palmer, A.N. (1972), Dynamics of a sinking stream system: Onesquethaw Cave, New York. *Bull. Nat. Spel. Soc., 34*, 89–110.

Palmer, A.N. (1975), The origin of maze caves. *Bull. Nat. Spel. Soc., 37*, 56–76.

Palmer, A.N. (1981), *A Geological Guide to Mammoth Cave National Park*, Zephyrus Teaneck, NJ.

Palmer, A.N. (1984), Geomorphic interpretation of karst features: pp. 173–209 in *Groundwater as a Geomorphic Agent* (ed. R.G. LaFleur), Allen & Unwin, Boston.

Palmer, A.N., Palmer, M.V. and Powell, R.L. (1981), *Guidebook to the Indiana Excursion 1981* Int. Cong. Speleol.

Palmer, A.N., Palmer, M.V. and Queen, J.M. (1977a), Speleogenesis in the Guadalupe Mountains, New Mexico: Gypsum replacement of carbonate by brine mixing. *Proc. 7th Int. Cong. Speleol.*, 333–6.

Palmer, A.N., Palmer, M.V. and Queen, J.M. (1977b), Geology and origin of caves of Bermuda. *Proc. 7th Int. Cong. Speleol.* 366–9.

Palmer, M.V. and Palmer, A.N. (1975), Landform development in the Mitchell Plain of southern Indiana: Origin of a partially karsted plain. *Z. Geomorph. 19*, 1–39.

Palmquist, R. (1979), Geologic controls on doline characteristics in mantled karst. *Z. Geomorph.*, supplementary issue, *32*, 90–106.

Palmquist, R., Madenford, G.A. and Van Driel, J.N. (1976), Doline densities in northeastern Iowa. *Bull. Nat. Spel. Soc., 38*, 59–67.

Panoš, V. (1964), Die Urkarst in Ostflügel der Böhmischen Masse. *Z. Geomorph., 8*, 105–62.

Panoš, V. (1976), Some notes on the coastal karst development: pp. 181–7 in *Karst Processes and Relevant Landforms* (ed. I. Gams), Department of Geography, Ljubljana University.

Panoš, V. and Stelcl, O. (1968), Physiographic and geologic control in development of Cuban mogotes. *Z. Geomorph., 12*, 117–65.

Pardé, M. (1965), *Influences de la perméabilité sur le régime des rivières. Colloquium Geographicum*, vol. 7. Dummlers, Bonn.

Parker, G.G. (1964), Piping: A geomorphic agent in landform development of the drylands. *Int. Ass. Sci. Hydrol. Pub., 65*, 103–13.

Paskoff, R. and Sanlaville, P. (1978), Observations géomorphologiques sur les côtes de l'archipel maltais. *Z. Geomorph., 22*, 310–28.

Penck, A. (1924), Das unterirdische Karstphänomen: pp. 175–97 in *Zbornik Radova Posvecen Jovanu Cvijicu* (ed. P. Vujevic), Belgrade.

Pengelly, W. (1864), The introduction of cavern accumulations. *Rep. Trans. Devonshire Ass., 3*, 31–41.

Peterson, J.A. (1982), Limestone pedestals and denudation estimates from Mt Jaya, Irian Jaya. *Aust. Geogr. Stud., 15*, 170–3.

Pevalek, I. (1935), Der Travertin und die Plitvice Seen. *Verh. int. Verein. theor. angew. Limnol., 7*, 165–81.

Pfeffer, K-H. (1969), Charakter der Verwitterungsresiduen im tropischen Kegelkarst und ihre Beziehung zum Formenschatz. *Geol. Rund., 58*, 408–26.

Pfeffer, K-H. (1973), Flachenbildung in den Kalkgebieten: pp. 111–32 in *Neue Ergebnisse der Karstforschung in den Tropen und in Mittelmeerraum* (ed. A. Semmei), Geogr. Zeit. Beiheft.

Pfeffer, K-H. (1975), *Zur Genese von Oberflächenformen im Gebieten mit flachlagernden Carbonategesteinen*, Steiner, Wiesbaden.

References

Pfeffer, K-H. (1981), Relikte tropischer Karstformen auf der Frankischen Alb im Pegnitzgebiet. *Sonderveroff. Geol. Inst. Univ. Köln, 41*, 155–72.

Picknett, R.G. (1972), The pH of calcite solution with and without magnesium carbonate present, and the implications concerning rejuvenated aggressiveness. *Trans. Cave Res. Grp Gt Br., 14*, 141–50.

Picknett, R.G. (1976), The chemistry of cave waters: pp. 213–48 in *The Science of Speleology* (ed. T.D. Ford and C.H.D. Cullingford), Academic Press, London.

Picknett, R.G. and Stenner, R.D. (1978), Enhanced calcite solubility in dilute magnesium carbonate solutions. *Trans. Br. Cave Res. Ass., 5*, 47–54.

Pierre, S. and Pierre, D.S. (1980), Caves of Velfjord, south Nordland, Norway, with particular reference to Sirijordgrotten. *Trans. Br. Cave Res. Ass., 7*, 70–82.

Pinchemel, P. (1954), *Les Plaines de Craie*, Colin, Paris.

Pisarowicz, J.A. and Maslyn, R.M. (1981), Empirical confirmation of Curl's (1974) flow velocity calculations. *Proc. 8th Int. Cong. Speleol., 2*, 772–4.

Pitman, J.I. (1978), Carbonate chemistry of groundwater from tropical tower karst in South Thailand. *Water Resources Research, 14*, 961–7.

Pitty, A.F. (1966), *An Approach to the Study of Karst Water*, University of Hull Occasional Papers in Geography, no. 5.

Pitty, A.F. (1968a), Calcium carbonate content of karst water in relation to flow-through time. *Nature, 217*, 939–40.

Pitty, A.F. (1968b), The scale and significance of solutional loss from the limestone tract of the southern Pennines. *Proc. Geol. Ass., 79*, 153–77.

Pitty, A.F. (1971), *Introduction to Geomorphology*, Methuen, London.

Pitty, A.F. (1974), Karst water studies in and around Ingleborough Cavern: pp. 127–39 in *Limestones and Caves of North-west England* (ed. A.C. Waltham and M.M. Sweeting), David and Charles, Newton Abbot, Devon.

Playford, P.E. and Lowry, D.C. (1966), Devonian Reef complexes of the Canning Basin, Western Australia. *Geol. Surv. W. Aust. Bull., 118*, 1–150.

Pluhar, A. and Ford, D.C. (1970), Dolomite karren of the Niagara escarpment, Ontario, Canada. *Z. Geomorph., 14*, 392–410.

Plummer, L.N. and Wigley, J.M.L. (1976), The dissolution of calcite in CO_2–saturated solutions at 25°C and 1 atm. total pressure. *Geochim. Cosmochim. Acta, 40*, 191–202.

Plummer, L.N., Wigley, T.M.L. and Parkhurst, D.L. (1978), The kinetics of calcite dissolution in CO_2–water systems at 5° to 60°C and 0.0 to 1.0 atm CO_2. *Amer. J. Sci., 278*, 179–216.

Pohl, E.R. (1955), *Vertical Shafts in Limestone Caves*. National Speleological Society Occasional Paper, no. 2.

Popov, I.V., Gvozdetskiy, N.A., Chikishev, A.G. and Kudelin, B.I. (1972), Karst of the USSR: pp. 355–416 in *Karst Important Karst Regions of the Northern Hemisphere* (ed. M. Herak and V.T. Stringfield), Elsevier, Amsterdam.

Powell, R.L. (1977), Joint patterns and solution channel evolution in Indiana: pp. 255–69 in *Proc. 12th Int. Cong. Karst Hydrogeology* (ed. J.S. Tolson and F.L. Doyle), University of Alabama, Huntsville.

Price, H.J. (1959), Mechanics of jointing rocks. *Geol. Mag., 96*, 149–67.

Priesnitz, K. von (1969), Über die Vergleichbarkeit von Lösungsformen auf Chlorid-, Sulfat- und Karbonatgestein – Überlegungen zur Fragen der Nomenklatur und Methodik der Karstmorphologie. *Geol. Rund., 58*, 427–38.

References

Prinz, W. (1908), Les cristallisations des grottes de Belgique, *Nouv. Mém. Soc. Belge. Géol., de Paléontologie et Hydrologie*, 4.

Purdy, E.G. (1974), Reef configuration: Cause and effect. *Soc. Econ. Pal. Min. Spec. Pub.,* 18, 9–76.

Quinlan, J.F. (1972), Karst-related mineral deposits and possible criteria for the recognition of paleokarsts. *Proc. 24th Int. Cong. Geol. Montreal,* 6, 156–68.

Quinlan, J.F. (1976), *Hydrology of the Turnhole Spring Groundwater Basin and Vicinity, Kentucky,* Western Kentucky University, Bowling Green.

Quinlan, J.F., Ewers, R.O., Ray, J.A., Powell, R.L. and Krothe, N.C. (1983) Groundwater hydrology and geomorphology of the Mammoth Cave region, Kentucky, and the Mitchell Plain, Indiana: pp. 1–85 in *Field trips in midwestern geology: Bloomington, Ind.,* 2 (ed. R.H. Shaver and J.A. Sundermann), Geol. Soc: America and Indiana Geol Survey.

Rathjens, C. (1954), Zur Frage der Karstrandebene im dinarischen Karst. *Erdkunde,* 8, 114–15.

Rathjens, C. (1960), Beobachtungen am hochgelegenen Poljen im südlichen Dinarischen Karst. *Z. Geomorph.,* 4, 141–51.

Rauch, H.W. and White, W.B. (1970), Lithologic controls on the development of solution porosity in carbonate aquifers. *Water Resources Research,* 6, 1175–92.

Reams, M.W. (1968), Cave sediments and the geomorphic history of the Ozarks. Unpublished PhD thesis, Washington University, St Louis, Miss.

Reid, C. (1887), On the origin of dry chalk valleys and of coombe rock. *Q.J. Geol. Soc. Lond.,* 43, 364–73.

Renault, P. (1958), Éléments de spéléomorphologie karstique. *Ann. Spéléol.,* 13, 23–48.

Renault, P. (1959), Le karst Kouilou (Moyen Congo, Gabon). *Rev. Géogr. Lyon,* 305–14.

Renault, P. (1967–8), Contribution à l'étude des actions mécaniques et sedimentologiques dans la spéléogenèse. *Ann. Spéléol.,* 22, 5–21; 209–67; 23, 259–307, 529–96.

Renault, P. (1970), *La formation des cavernes.* Presses Universitaires de France, Paris.

Richardson, D.T. (1974), Karst waters in the Alum Pot area: pp. 140–8 in *Limestones and Caves of Northwest England* (ed. A.C. Waltham and M.M. Sweeting), David and Charles, Newton Abbot, Devon.

Richter, E. (1907) Beitrag zur Landeskunde Bosniens u.d. Herzegovina, *Wiss. Mitt and Bosnia & Herzegovina (Wien)* 10, 102–8.

Rogers, R.M. (1981), Soil pipe caves in the Death Valley region, California. *Proc. 8th Int. Cong. Speleol.,* 2, 547–8.

Roglić, J. (1939), Morphologie der Poljen von Kupres und Vukovsko. *Z. Ges. Erdk. Berlin,* pp. 291–316.

Roglić, J. (1940), Geomorphologische Studien von Duvanjsko (Polje von Duvno) in Bosnien. *Mitt. Geog. Ges. Wien,* 83, 152–76.

Roglić, J. (1960), Das Verhältnis der Flusserosion zum Karstprozess. *Z. Geomorph.,* 4, 116–28.

Roglić, J. (1964a), Karst valleys in the Dinaric Karst. *Erdkunde,* 18, 113–16.

Roglić, J. (1964b), Les poljes du karst dinarique et les modifications climatiques du Quaternaire. *Rev. Belge Géogr.,* 88, 105–25.

Roglić, J. (1965), The delimitations and morphological types of the Dinaric Karst. *Nase Jama,* 7, 12–20.

References

Roglić, J. (1967), A contribution to the knowledge of the seabottom relief at the Adriatic coast. *Juglòslavenska Akademija Znanostii Umjetnosti, 22,* 39–54.

Rossi, G. (1976), Karsts et dissolution des calcaires en milieu tropical. *Z. Geomorph.* supplementary issue, *26,* 124–52.

Rudnicki, J. (1980), Kras wybrzezy morskich – rozwoj procesow krasowych w strefie oddzialywania wod slonych i slodkich (na przykladzie Apulii, poludniowe Wlochy [Subsurface karst processes in coastal areas(based on example of Apulia, southern Italy]. *Studia Geologica Polonica* no. 65.

Ryder, P.F. (1975), Phreatic network caves in the Swaledale area, Yorkshire. *Trans. Br. Cave Ass., 2,* 177–92.

Sanders, E.M. (1921), The cycle of erosion in a karst region (after Cvijić). *Geogr. Rev., 11,* 593–604.

Sawicki, L.R. von (1909), Ein Beitrag zum geographischen Zyklus im Karst. *Geogr. Z., 15,* 185–204, 259–81.

Schmid, E. (1958), *Höhlenforschung und Sedimentanalyse. Ein Beitrag zur Datierung des alpinen Paläolithikums.* Schr. Inst. Ur-und Frühgeschichte Schweiz, no. 13.

Schmidt, V.A. (1982), Magnetostratigraphy of sediments in Mammoth Cave, Kentucky. *Science, 217,* 827–9.

Schmidt, V.A., Jennings, J.N. and Bao, H. (1984), Dating cave sediments at Wee Jasper, New South Wales, by magnetostratigraphy. *Aust. J. Earth Sci., 31,* 361–70.

Schofield, J.C. (1959), The geology and hydrology of Niue Island, South Pacific. *New Zealand Geol. Surv. Bull., 62.*

Schroeder, J. (1979), Development de cavités d'origine méchanique dans un karst froid (Nahanni, T.N.D., Canada). *Ann. Soc. Géol. Belg., 102,* 59–67.

Schroeder, J. and Ford, D.C. (1983), Clastic sediments in Castleguard Cave, Columbia Icefields, Alberta, Canada. *Arctic Alp. Res., 15,* 451–61.

Siffre, M. (1961), Niveau de base et formes karstiques submergées. *Ann. Spéléol., 16,* 87–92.

Siffre, A. and Siffre, M. (1961), Le façonnement des alluvions karstiques. *Ann. Spéléol., 16,* 73–80.

Silar, J. (1965), Development of tower karst of China and north Vietnam. *Bull. Nat. Spel. Soc., 27,* 35–46.

Sinclair, I.G.L. (1967), Bauxite genesis in Jamaica: New evidence from trace element distribution. *Econ. Geol., 62,* 482–6.

Smart, C.C. and Brown, M.C. (1981), Some results of application of hydraulic geometry to vadose stream passages. *Proc. 8th Int. Cong. Speleol., 2,* 724–6.

Smart, P. (1981), Surface geomorphology: pp. 43–4 in *Caves of Mulu '80* (ed. A.J. Eavis), Royal Geographical Society, London.

Smith, B.J. (1978), The origin and geomorphic implications of cliff foot recess and tafoni on limestone hamadas in the northwest Sahara. *Z. Geomorph.,22,* 21–43.

Smith, D.I. (1969), The solution erosion of limestone in an arctic morphogenetic region: pp. 99–110 in *Problems of the Karst Denudation* (ed. O. Stelcl), Institute of Geography, Brno.

Smith, D.I. (1971), The residual hypothesis for the formation of Jamaican bauxite – a consideration of the rate of limestone erosion. *J. Geol. Soc. Jamaica, 11,* 3–12.

Smith, D.I. (1975), The erosion of limestones on Mendip: pp. 135–70 in *Limestones and Caves of the Mendip Hills* (ed. D.I. Smith and D.P. Drew), David and Charles, Newton Abbot, Devon.

Smith, D.I. and Atkinson, T.C. (1977), Underground flow in cavernous limestones with special reference to the Malham area. *Field Studies, 4.* 597–616.

Smith, D.I., Atkinson, T.C. and Drew, D.P. (1976), The hydrology of limestone terrains: pp 179–212 in *The Science of Speleology* (ed. T.D. Ford and C.H.D. Cullingford), Academic Press, London.

Smith, D.I. and Drew, D.P. (1975), *Limestones and Caves of the Mendip Hills,* David and Charles, Newton Abbot, Devon.

Smith, D.I., Drew, D.P. and Atkinson, T.C. (1972), Hypotheses of karst landform development in Jamaica. *Trans. Cave Res. Grp Gt Br., 14,* 159–73.

Smith, D.I., High, C. and Nicholson, F.H. (1969), Limestone solution and the caves: pp. 96–123 in *The Caves of North-West Clare, Ireland* (ed. E.K. Tratman), David and Charles, Newton Abbot, Devon.

Smith, D.I. and Mead, D.G. (1962), The solution of limestone. *Proc. Univ. Brist. Spel. Soc., 9,* 188–211.

Smyk, B. and Drzal, M. (1964), Research on the influence of micro-organisms on the development of karst phenomena. *Geographia Polonica, 2,* 57–60.

Society of Economic Geologists (1971), A paleoaquifer and its relation to economic mineral deposits. The Lower Ordovician Kingsport Formation and Mascot Dolomite – a symposium. *Econ. Geol., 66,* 695–810.

Song, L., Zhang, Y., Fang, J. and Gu, Z. (1983), Karst development and the distribution of karst drainage systems in Dejiang, Guizhou Province, China, *J. Hydrol., 61,* 3–17.

Sparks, B.W. (1961), *Geomorphology.* Longman, London.

Sparks, B.W. and Lewis, W.V. (1957), Escarpment dry valleys near Pegsdon, Hertfordshire. *Proc. Geol. Ass., 68,* 26–38.

Spate, A.P., Gillieson, D.S., Jennings, J.N. and Davey, A.G. (1983a), Preliminary note on a sand from a Nullarbor Plain Cave: paper presented at Australian Speleology Federation Conference, January 1983.

Spate, A.P., Greenaway, M., Jennings, J.N. and Smith, D.I. (1983b), The micro-erosion meter: Use and limitations: paper presented at Institute of Australian Geography Conference, January 1983.

Stelcl, O. (1976), Geomorphological characteristics of the karst regions in the Czech. Socialist Republic. *Proc. 6th Int. Cong. Speleol., 11,* 373–80.

Stenner, R.D. (1970), Preliminary results of an application of the procedure for the measurement of aggressiveness of water to calcium carbonate. *Trans. Cave Res. Grp Gt Br., 12,* 283–9.

Stitt, R.R. (1977), Human impact on caves: pp. 36–42 in *National Cave Management Proceedings* (ed. T. Aley and D. Rhodes), Speleobooks, Albuquerque.

Stringfield, V.T. and LeGrand, H.E. (1969a), Relation of sea water to fresh water in carbonate rocks in coastal areas with special reference to Florida, USA and Cephalonia (Kephallinia), Greece. *J. Hydrol., 9,* 387–404.

Stringfield, V.T. and LeGrand, H.E. (1969b), Hydrology of carbonate rock terrains – a review with special reference to the United States. *J. Hydrol., 8,* 349–417.

Sunartadirdja, M.A. and Lehmann, H. (1960), Der tropische Karst von Maros und Nord-Bone in SW-Celebes (Sulawesi). *Z. Geomorph.* supplementary issue, *2,* 49–65.

Sweeting, M.M. (1950), Erosion cycles and limestone caverns in the Ingleborough District of Yorkshire. *Geogr. J., 115,* 63–78.

References

Sweeting, M.M. (1953), The enclosed depression of Carran, County Clare. *Irish Geography*, 2, 218–24.

Sweeting, M.M. (1955), Landforms in north-West County Clare, Ireland. *Trans. Inst. Br. Geog.*, 21, 33–49.

Sweeting, M.M. (1958), The karstlands of Jamaica. *Geogr. J.*, 124, 184–99.

Sweeting, M.M. (1966), The weathering of limestones. With particular reference to the Carboniferous Limestones of northern England: pp. 177–210 in *Essays in Geomorphology* (ed. G.H. Dury), Heinemann, London.

Sweeting, M.M. (1972a) *Karst Landforms*, Macmillan, London.

Sweeting, M.M. (1972b), Karst of Great Britain: pp. 417–43 in *Karst Important Karst Regions of the Northern Hemisphere* (ed. M. Herak and V.T. Stringfield), Elsevier, Amsterdam.

Sweeting, M.M. (1973), Karst landforms and limestones. *S. Afr. Geogr. J.*, 55, 81–8.

Sweeting, M.M. (1978), Some observations on New Zealand limestone areas: pp. 250–8 in *Landform Evolution in Australia* (ed. J.L. Davies and M.A.J. Williams), Australian National University Press, Canberra.

Swinnerton, A.C. (1929), The caves of Bermuda. *Geol. Mag.*, 66, 79–84.

Swinnerton, A.C. (1932), Origin of limestone caverns. *Bull. Geol. Soc. Amer.*, 43, 662–93.

Szczerban, E. and Urbani, F. (1974), Carsos de Venezuala. 4: Formas carsicas en areniscas precambricas del Territorio Federal·Amazonas y Estado Bolivar. *Bol. Soc. Venezolana Ispel.*, 5(1), 27–54.

Thomas, M.F. (1966), Some geomorphological implications of deep weathering patterns in crystalline rocks in Nigeria. *Trans. Inst. Br. Geogr.*, 40, 173–93.

Thomas, T.M. (1974), The South Wales interstratal karst. *Trans. Brit. Cave Res. Ass.*, 1, 131–52.

Thorp, J. (1934), The asymmetry of the Pepino Hills of Puerto Rico in relation to the Trade Winds. *J. Geol.*, 42, 537–45.

Thorpe, P.M., Otlet, R.L. and Sweeting, M.M. (1980), Hydrological implications from C-14 profiling on UK tufa. *Radiocarbon*, 22, 897–908.

Thrailkill, J. (1968), Chemical and hydrologic factors in the excavation of limestone caves. *Bull. Geol. Soc. Amer.*, 79, 19–45.

Thrailkill, J. (1976), Carbonate equilibria in karst waters: pp. 745–71, vol. 2, in *Karst Hydrology and Water Resources* (ed. V. Yevjevich).

Tratman, E.K., Donovan, D.T. and Campbell, J.B. (1971), The Hyaena Den (Wookey Hole), Mendip Hills, Somerset. *Proc. Univ. Brist. Spel. Soc.*, 12, 245–79.

Tricart, J. (1968), Notes géomorphologiques sur la karstification en Barbade (Antilles). *Mém. Domcus. Cent. docum. cartogr. géogr.*, 4, 329–34.

Tricart, J. and da Silva, T.C. (1960), Un exemple d'évolution karstique en milieu tropical sec: le morne de Bom-Jesus da Lapa (Bahia, Brésil). *Z. Geomorph.*, 4, 1, 29–42.

Trimmel, H. (1951), Morphologische und genetische Studien in der Salzofenhöhle. *Hohle*, 2, 2–7.

Trimmel, H. (ed.) (1965), Speläologisches Fachwörterbuch. *Proc. 3rd Int. Cong. Speleol, Wien, IV, sektion 3–4*.

Trimmel, H. (1968), *Höhlenkunde*. Vieweg, Brunswick.

Trombe, F. (1952), *Traité de Spéléologie*, Payot, Paris.

Trudgill, S.T. (1976a), The marine erosion of limestones on Aldabra Atoll, Indian Ocean. *Z. Geomorph.*, supplementary issue, 26, 164–200.

Trudgill, S.T. (1976b), The subaerial and subsoil erosion of limestones on

Aldabra Atoll, Indian Ocean. *Z. Geomorph.*, supplementary issue, *26*, 201–10.

Trudgill, S.T. (1977), A comparison of tropical and temperate marine karst erosion. *Proc. 7th Int. Cong. Speleol.*, 404–5.

Trudgill, S., High, C.J. and Hanna, F.K. (1981), Improvements to the micro-erosion meter. *Brit. Geom. Res. Grp Tech. Bull.*, *29*, 3–17.

Twidale, C.R. (1964), Effect of variations in rate of sediment accumulation on a bedrock slope at Fromm's Landing, South Australia. *Z. Geomorph.*, supplementary issue, *5*, 177–91

Twidale, C.R. (1984), Role of subterranean water in landform development in tropical and subtropical regions: pp. 91–134 in *Groundwater as a Geomorphic Agent* (ed. R.G. LaFleur), Allen & Unwin, Boston.

Twidale, C.R. and Bourne, J.A. (1975), The subsurface initiation of some minor granite landforms. *J. Geol. Soc. Aust.*, *22*, 477–84.

Varnes, D.J. (1958), Landslide types and processes: pp. 20–47 in *Landslides and Engineering Practice* (ed. E.B. Eckel), Highway Research Board Special Report 29.

Vasseur, P. (1974), The overhangs, tunnels and dark reef galleries of Tuléar (Madagascar), and their sessile invertebrate communities. *Proc. 2nd Int. Coral Reef Symp.*, *2*, 143–59.

Verstappen, H.T. (1960a), Some observations on karst development in the Malay Archipelago. *J. Trop. Geogr.*, *14*, 1–10.

Verstappen, H.T. (1960b), On the geomorphology of raised coral reefs and its tectonic significance. *Z. Geomorph.*, *4*, 1–28.

Viles, H.A. (1984), Progress report: Biokarst. *Progress in Physical Geography, 8*, 523–43.

Viles, H.A. and Trudgill, S.T. (1984), Long term measurements of micro-erosion meter sites, Aldabra Atoll, Indian Ocean. *Earth Surf. Proc. Landforms, 9*, 89–94.

Vincent, P.J. (1983), The morphology and morphometry of some arctic Trittkarren. *Z. Geomorph.*, *27*, 205–22.

Vincent, W.B. (1974), Environmental influences of the glacières of the Pryor Mountains, Montana. *Bull. Nat. Spel. Soc.*, *36*, 15–21.

Walker, D. (1956), Studies in the Quaternary of the Malay Peninsula. I: Alluvial deposits of Perak and changes in the relative levels of land and sea. *Fed. Mus. J., 1*, 19–34.

Wall, J.R.D. and Wilford, G.E. (1966), Two small-scale solution features of limestone outcrops in Sarawak, Malaysia. *Z. Geomorph.*, *10*, 90–4.

Walsh, P.T., Boulter, M.C., Ijtaba, M. and Urbani, D.M. (1972), The preservation of the Neogene Brassington Formation of the southern Pennines and its bearing on the evolution of Upland Britain. *Q. J. Geol. Soc. Lond, 128*, 579–659.

Waltham, A.C. (1970), Cave development in the limestone of the Ingleborough district. *Geogr. J., 136*, 574–84.

Waltham, A.C. (1971), Controlling factors in the development of caves. *Trans. Cave Res. Grp Gt Br., 13*, 73–80.

Waltham, A.C. (1972), Geological environment of cave development. *International Geography 1972, 2*, 1328–30.

Waltham, A.C. (1977), Cave development at the base of the limestone in Yorkshire. *Proc. 7th Int. Cong. Speleol.*, 421–3.

Waltham, A.C. (1978), The caves and karst of Astraka, Greece. *Trans. Br. Cave Res. Ass., 5*, 1–12.

References

Waltham, A.C. and Ede, D.P. (1973), The karst of Kuh-E-Parau, Iran. *Trans. Cave Res. Grp. Gt Br.*, 15(1), 27–40.

Waltham, A.C. and Sweeting, M.M. (eds) (1974), *The Limestone and Caves of North-west England*, David and Charles, Newton Abbot, Devon.

Waltz, J.P. (1969), Groundwater: pp. 259–67 in *Water, Earth and Man* (ed. R.J. Chorley), Methuen, London.

Warwick, G.T. (1950), The reef limestone caves of the Dove and Manifold Valleys. *Cave Res. Grp Gt Br. Newsl.*, 31, 2–6.

Warwick, G.T. (1953), Polycyclic swallow holes in the Manifold Valley, Staffordshire, England. *Proc. 1st Int. Cong. Speleol.*, 2, 59–68.

Warwick, G.T. (1960), The effect of knick point recession on the watertable and associated features in limestone regions, with special reference to England and Wales. *Z. Geomorph.* supplementary issue, 2, 92–7.

Warwick, G.T. (1964), Dry valleys in the southern Pennines, England. *Erdkunde*, 18, 116–23.

Warwick, G.T. (1968), Some primitive features in British caves. *Proc. 4th Int. Cong. Spel.*, 3, 239–52.

Warwick, G.T. (1971), Caves and the ice age. *Trans. Cave Res. Grp Gt Br.*, 13, 123–30.

Wentworth, C.K. (1939), Marine bench-forming processes. II: Solution benching. *J. Geomorph.*, 11, 3–25.

Weyman, D.R. (1975), *Runoff Processes and Streamflow*, Clarendon Press, Oxford.

White, E.L. (1977), Sustained flow in small Appalachian watersheds underlain by carbonate rocks. *J. Hydrol.*, 32, 71–86.

White, E.L. and Reich, B.M. (1970), Behaviour of annual floods in limestone basins in Pennsylvania. *J. Hydrol.*, 10, 193–8.

White, E.L. and White, W.B. (1969), Processes of cavern breakdown. *Bull. Nat. Spel. Soc.*, 30, 115–29.

White, E.L. and White, W.B. (1979), Quantitative morphology of landforms in carbonate rock basins in the Appalachian Highlands. *Bull. Geol. Soc. Amer.*, 90, 385–96.

White E.L. and White, W.B. (1983), Karst landforms and drainage basin evolution in the Obey River Basin, north-central Tennessee, USA. *J. Hydrol.*, 61, 69–82.

White, W.B. (1960), Terminations of passages in Appalachian caves as evidence for a shallow phreatic origin. *Bull. Nat. Spel. Soc.*, 22, 43–53.

White, W.B. (1963), Cavern and karst development in the Swago Creek area, West Virginia, USA. *Proc. 3rd Int. Cong. Spel.*, 2, 279–85.

White, W.B. (1969), Conceptual models for carbonate aquifers. *Groundwater*, 7, 15–21.

White, W.B. (1976), Cave minerals and speleothems: pp. 267–327 in *The Science of Speleology* (ed. T.D. Ford and C.H.D. Cullingford), Academic Press, London.

White, W.B. (1984), Rate processes: Chemical kinetics and karst landform development: pp. 227–48 in *Groundwater as a Geomorphic Agent* (ed. R.G. LaFleur), Allen & Unwin, London.

White, W.B., Jefferson, G.L. and Haman, J.F. (1966), Quartzite karst in southeastern Venezuela. *Int. J. Speleol.*, 2, 309–14.

Wigley, T.M.L. (1967), Non-steady flow through a porous medium and cave breathing. *J. Geophys. Res.*, 72, 3199–205.

Wigley, T.M.L., Drake, J.J., Quinlan, J.F. and Ford, D.C. (1973), Geomorphology and geochemistry of a gypsum karst near Canal Flats, British Columbia. *Can. J. Earth Sci.*, 10, 113–29.

Wilford, G.E. (1964), The geology of Sarawak and Sabah Caves. *Bull. Geol. Surv. Borneo Region, Malaysia*, 6.

Wilford, G.E. and Wall, J.R.D. (1965), Karst topography in Sarawak. *J. Trop. Geogr.*, 21, 44–70.

Williams, P.W. (1966a), Morphometric analysis of temperate karst landforms. *Irish Speleol.*, 1, 23–31.

Williams, P.W. (1966b), Limestone pavements with special reference to western Ireland. *Trans. Inst. Br. Geogr.*, 40, 155–72.

Williams, P.W. (1968), An evaluation of the rate and distribution of limestone solution in the River Fergus basin, Western Ireland: pp. 1–40 in *Contributions to the Study of Karst*, Australian National University Department of Geography, Publication no. G/5.

Williams, P.W. (1970), Limestone morphology in Ireland: pp. 105–24 in *Irish Geographical Studies* (ed. R. Glasscock and N. Stephens), Queen's University Press, Belfast.

Williams, P.W. (1972a), Morphometric analysis of polygonal karst in New Guinea. *Bull. Geol. Soc. Amer.*, 83, 761–96.

Williams, P.W. (1972b), The analysis of spatial characteristics of karst terrains: pp. 136–63 in *Spatial Analysis in Geomorphology* (ed. R.J. Chorley), Methuen, London.

Williams, P.W. (1977), Hydrology of the Waikoropupu Springs: A major tidal karst resurgence in northwest Nelson (New Zealand.) *J. Hydrol.*, 35, 73–92.

Williams, P.W. (1978), Interpretations of Australasian karst: pp. 259–88 in *Landform Evolution in Australasia* (ed. J.L. Davies and M.A.J. Williams) Australian National University Press, Canberra.

Williams, P.W. (1982a), Karst in New Zealand: pp. 105–26 in *Landforms of New Zealand* (ed. J.M. Soons and M.J. Selby), Longman Paul, Auckland.

Williams, P.W. (1982b), Speleothem dates, Quaternary terraces and uplift rates in New Zealand. *Nature*, 298, 257–60.

Williams, P.W. (1983), The role of the subcutaneous zone in karst hydrology, *J. Hydrology*, 61, 45–67.

Williams, P.W. and Dowling, R.K. (1979), Solution of marble in karst of the Pikikiruna Range, northern Nelson, New Zealand. *Earth Surf. Proc.*, 4, 15–36.

Wissmann, H. von (1954), Der Karst der humiden heissen und sommerheissen Gebiete Ostasiens. *Erdkunde*, 8, 122–9.

Wissmann, H. von (1957), Karsterscheinungen in Hadramaut. Ein Beitrag zur Morphologie der semiariden und ariden Tropen. *Pet. Mitt. Erg.*, 262, 259–68.

Wolfe, T.E. (1972a), A classification of cave sediments. *International Geography* 1972, 2, 1332–3.

Wolfe, T.E. (1972b), Fluvial cave sediments: A description and interpretation. *International Geography* 1972, 1, 74–6.

Woodward, H.P. (1936), Natural Bridge and Natural Tunnel Virginia. *J. Geol.*, 44, 604–16.

Würm, A. (1953), Der Salzberg bei Djelfa im Sahara-Atlas. *Natur Volk.*, 83, 141–7.

Yaalon, D.H. and Singer, S. (1974), Vertical variation in strength and porosity of calcrete (nari) on chalk, Shefela, Israel and interpretation of its origin. *J. Sed. Pet.*, 44, 1016–23.

References

Yuan, D. (1981), *A Brief Introduction to China's Research in Karst*, Institute of Karst Geology, Guilin.

Yuan, D. *et al.* (1979), *[Method of Hydrogeological Research in Karst terrains]* (in Chinese). Geological Press, Beijing.

Zhang, Z. (1979), Old formations in a young republic. *Geog. Mag.*, *52*, 89–91.

Zhang, Z. (1980), Karst types in China. *Geo. Journal*, *4*, 541–70.

Zötl, J. (1957), Neue Ergebnisse der Karsthydrologie. *Erdkunde*, *11*, 107–17.

Zötl, J. (1965), Tasks and results of karst hydrology: pp. 141–5 in *Problems of the Speleological Research* (ed. O. Stelcl), Academia, Prague.

Zötl, J. (1974), *Karsthydrologeologie*, Springer, Vienna.

Zotov, V.D. (1941), Potholing of limestone by development of solution cups *J. Geomorphology*, *4*, 71–3.

Index of Authors

Author Index

Index of Subjects

The following abbreviations have been used:
Au = Australia
Fr = French; France
Ger = German; Germany
Ire = Ireland
NG = New Guinea
NZ = New Zealand
US = United States
UK = United Kingdom; Britain
Yug = Yugoslavia

Subject Index

Niue Island, 223
North Branch (Au), 44
Norway, 77, 193, 194, 201
notch (nip), 218, 219, 220
solution, 79–80
nothephreatic solution, 141–4, 190
Novigrad Bay (Yug), 227
Nullarbor Plain (Au), 30–3, 71
caves, 153, 155, 166, 170, 176, 196, 240
climate, 195–6, 232
coastal features, 217, 232
drainage, 35, 40, 68

Oawra (Malta), 225
Ochtinska Aragonite Cave (Czechoslovakia), 137, 144
Ogof Ffynnon Ddu Cave (Wales), 24–5, 154, 187
Okinawa (Japan), 210
Onesquethaw Cave (US), 152, 187
oolites, 12
oozes, 11–12
Oparara River (NZ), 92
Orangeville Rise (US), 63
Organos karst, 203
orogeny, 179, 241
Ourthe River cave (Belgium), 148
outflow, 208
points, 148
overland flow, 35, 37–8
Owen Range (NZ), 74–5, 239
Ice Cave, 163
Owenterbolea (Ire), 51
oxygen isotope ratio, 174–5
Ozark Caves (US), 166

packstone, 12
Padirac cave (Fr), 136
palaeoenvironmental history of cave deposits, 173–6
palaeokarst, 7
palaeomagnetism, 172–3
Palmer River (Au), 73, 181
pans, solution, 79, 84
Papua New Guinea see New Guinea
paragenetic cave, 144
partly-covered karst, 78–80
Paturau (NZ), 224
pavement, limestone, 80, 84
pavement staircases, 239
Pazinski River (Yug), 98–9
Peak District (UK), 6, 17, 249
caves, 43, 58, 68, 152, 155–7, 169, 249–50
drainage, 43, 58, 68
geological history, 187
surface forms, 100, 113, 183
surface weathering, 71

pellets, 12
percolation spring, 62
percolines, 26
perennial spring, 49–50
periglacial see under glaciation
Perlis (Malaysia), 213
permeability, 15–18, 64, 187
phreas, 65
phreatic action, 144–9, 248
phreatic solution, 51
phytokarst, black, 73, 218, 220
Piano Cave (Au), 143
Piccanninnie Ponds (South Africa), 50
Picos de Europa (Spain), 239
Pine Creek (US), 106
pinnacles, 201–2
pipes, 26–7, 82, 107, 111–12, 148, 183, 222
pitting, 220
Pivka, River (Yug), 42
plains, karst, 133–4, 201
planes of weakness, 16
Planima Polje (Yug), 126
plants see vegetation
plasticity of rocks, 31
plateau outliers, 214
platforms, shore, 217–21
Plitvice Lakes (Yug), 103, 105
plunge pools and swirlholes, 139, 150
Podolia (USSR), 2
Poland, 171, 172, 193
poljes, 65–6, 113, 124–9, 131
and climate, 192, 199, 207, 214
drowned, 227
floods, 66
and historical geomorphology, 234, 238
Poll-an-Ionain cave (Ire), 247
polygonal karst, 201, 214
pond sediments, 165–8
ponding, 153
ponors, 124, 127
Poole's Cavern (UK), 155
pools, 48
Popovo Polje (Yug), 125, 127
porosity, 15–16, 35, 181–2, 207
Porta di Prada (Italy), 92
posas, 51
positive feedback, roots and solution pipes, 82
Postojna Cave (Yug), 42, 159, 188
Poulacapple (Ire), 53
Poulnagallum caves (Ire), 156
precipitation see deposition; solution and precipitation; rainfall
pressure solution, 12–13
Prices Falls (US), 106
processes, karst, 19–33

cave weathering, 32–3
collapse, 28–32
piping, 26–7
solution and precipitation, 19–26
subsidence, 27–8
pseudokarst, 2–5
Puerto Rico, 17, 179, 193, 203–4, 209–11
Punchbowl cave (Au), 137, 148, 153, 172
Putrid Pit (Au), 139
Pyrenees, caves in, 157–8

quartz, 4–5
Quercy caves (Fr), 171

radiocarbon dating, 171
rain solution runnels, 77
rainfall, 35, 71, 191–4, 200, 209, 214
lack of see arid
see also drainage; solution
rainpit, 73–4
Rak River (Yug), 92, 93
ramparts, 210, 229
Ras el'Ain River (Syria), 58, 60–1
Rasa River (Yug), 98–9
reciprocating spring, 47
reculées (Fr), 97
Redhurst Swallet (UK), 43
reefs, 10–11, 12, 179–80, 219
emerged biogenic, 210, 222–4
knolls, 7, 183
modern, 228–30
Regenrinnenkarren (Ger), 77
regimes of rivers, 40–2
regimes of springs, 58–64
regional effects of geology, 177–80
rejuvenation, 94, 100, 103, 241–3, 248
reprecipitation, 24–5
residual hills, 127, 201–5, 207, 209
historical geomorphology of, 234, 245–6
rest levels, 67
resurgences, 46–7, 55, 97
return flow, 35
Reynold's Number, 65
'Richter slopes of denudation', 91
Rieseneishöhle cave (Austria), 163
Rillenkarren (Ger), 75
Rillensteine (Ger), 197–8
rimstone dams, 162
Rinnenkarren (Ger), 78
ripples, 74–5, 77
rise pits', 48
'rising', 48

290